LOW TEMPERATURE RESEARCH STATION
DOWNING STREET
CAMBRIDGE

———

LIBRARY

Date received...

Accession No.   Classification No.

130   544.42

FREEZE-DRYING

[DRYING BY SUBLIMATION]

By

EARL W. FLOSDORF

*Formerly Assistant Professor of Bacteriology,
School of Medicine, University of Pennsylvania*

F. J. Stokes Machine Co.

Philadelphia

REINHOLD PUBLISHING CORPORATION

330 West Forty-second St., New York 18, U. S. A.

1949

PRINTED IN THE UNITED STATES OF AMERICA BY
KINGSPORT PRESS, KINGSPORT, TENN.

TO

Francis J. Stokes

PREFACE

DURING the past ten years, freeze-drying has increased more than one hundredfold in industrial use and more than that in research and other laboratory uses. As one result there have been over 300 scientific and engineering publications during this time. The purpose of this book is to bring together all of this technical knowledge as well as much heretofore unwritten "know-how."

The book is directed to those conducting freeze-drying in research and other laboratory and industrial work in microbiological, serological, immunological, histological, chemical, pharmaceutical, engineering and related fields. It is hoped that this presentation may in some measure serve as a stimulus to further research on freeze-drying per se as well as to suggest new uses and applications. This includes the human and veterinary medical fields and such industrial applications as food. The task has not been easy because of the varied interests of workers in the field, these being found in medical schools, departments of public health, hospitals, engineering schools and industry. Basic principles, procedures and applications have received most attention. Laboratory and industrial equipment have been described in general with detail limited to representative types, many modifications of the several basic types having been described in scientific literature but frequently differing in minor detail only.

There is of necessity some repetition in order to avoid extensive cross referring by readers interested solely in one aspect of the subject, e. g., food field, engineering or laboratory research. Probably few will read the book from cover to cover.

To all workers in the field and particularly to former colleagues and co-workers, and to my present associates, I am indebted. It has not been possible to recall the origin of all material but I have tried to give due credit in the text, and in the bibliographies, to everyone concerned. A supplemental bibliography at the end of the book lists the works which are not shown in chapter bibliographies nor specifically mentioned in the text. Titles of the bibliographical references have been given to provide brief indication of the subject-matter.

Particular gratitude is due to my wife, who, as a bacteriologist, made many helpful suggestions, especially in the years when the work was in its infancy, and finally for her help in the preparation of the manuscript for this book. Acknowledgment is made of the suggestion of Professor W. B. Meldrum, of Haverford College, that I undertake the writing of this book. Appreciation is due Professor T. K. Sherwood, of Massachusetts Institute of Technology, for supplying me with the results of his studies with penicillin. My thanks are due to many who have been directly or indirectly responsible for photographs, whose source is individually acknowledged, and particularly to Dr. R. I. N. Greaves, of the British Medical Research Council, and to Dr. Ralph W. G. Wyckoff, of our National Institute of Health. Extreme gratitude is due to Mr. Francis J. Stokes who early gave his unselfish aid and encouragement in the development of freeze-drying, first as a tool for medical research and finally as a means for full-scale industrial processing of some of our life-saving medicinals.

E. W. FLOSDORF

Forest Grove, Pennsylvania
January 3, 1949

CONTENTS

CHAPTER 1: INTRODUCTION

FOR the past few years the drying of products while in the frozen state has been termed "drying by sublimation." The common laboratory expression "freeze-drying" well describes the process. Although it is now widely used in commercial operation, a little over ten years ago it was scarcely more than a laboratory curiosity. Since then it has been carried from what was not even a good laboratory stage of development to a point at which it could be used industrially on a large scale. During the war industrial applications expanded widely in the drug and pharmaceutical fields, and the method is now being tried commercially with foods.

The desiccation of blood plasma from the frozen state as part of the program of the American Red Cross for the armed forces of the United States provided the first spectacular and extensive use of freeze-drying. When the problem of stabilizing penicillin solution arose during 1942 and 1943, little attention was paid to it because it was thought that as a result of experience with blood plasma drying by sublimation had been shown to be fully workable in large-scale operation. The lack of attention in some measure was a mistake; problems of handling penicillin were of a different and of a somewhat more difficult nature than in the case of blood plasma, because of the large number of small-volume containers to be charged into the dryers without melting of the penicillin. The situation did serve to demonstrate the position which the process had reached in the industrial production of pharmaceuticals. Blood plasma equipment was readily adapted to the freeze-drying of penicillin.

Before drying by sublimation the product is frozen; the ice is

then sublimed rapidly under high vacuum. With many materials
the solids contained originally are left in shape and the over-all
volume corresponds closely to that of the original frozen product.
Blood plasma is typical of such products, showing little over-all
reduction in volume after drying from the frozen state. The advantages of drying while frozen will be set forth in detail in the
next chapter. At this point, it suffices to point out two of the major
advantages: (1) the properties of labile substances are unchanged
during drying, with consequent prolonged preservation of desired
characteristics during the storage period which follows; (2) the
solubility of products dried in this way is remarkably fast and complete. As a result the life of commercial labile products can be
greatly extended.

As has been pointed out,[1] low-temperature evaporation of water
under vacuum to produce freezing, followed by sublimation of the
ice is old—so old, in fact, that William Hyde Wollaston was apolo-
getic in exhibiting it before the Royal Society of London in 1813.
Wollaston's demonstration, nevertheless, is of more than historical
interest because of the simplicity and clarity with which it demon-
states the relation of vapor pressure to temperature and the cooling
effect of evaporation.

"That a fluid,[2] from which a portion is evaporated, becomes colder
in consequence of the heat absorbed by that part which assumes the
gaseous state: that fluids rise in the state of vapour at a lower temperature when the pressure of the atmosphere is removed, and consequently may be cooled to a lower degree by evaporation *in vacuo* than
in the open air, are facts too well known to need confirmation before the
Members of this Society by any new experiments.

"Nevertheless, a new mode of applying the most established principles may deserve to be recorded, if it assist the illustration of them, and
be instructive from the novelty of the view in which it exhibits a certain
class of phenomena; although no immediate use be at present proposed,
to which it can be applied with advantage.

"If an attempt were made to freeze water by evaporation, without
other means than the vacuum of an air-pump, the pump must be of the
best construction, and though the quantity of water be small, the re-
ceiver must be of large dimensions, otherwise its capacity would set too
confined a limit to the quantity of vapour that will rise, and consequently
to the degree of cold produced. . . .

"As a means of avoiding the necessity of so large a vacuum, Mr. Leslie had recourse to the ingenious expedient of employing an extensive surface of sulphuric acid, for the purpose of absorbing the vapour generated in the course of the experiment, and by that means contrived to freeze much larger quantities of water, than could otherwise have been done, and by a far less laborious process.

"But even in this method the labour is not inconsiderable, and the apparatus, though admirably adapted to the purpose for which it is designed, is large and costly. I have therefore thought the little instrument I am about to describe may possess some interest, as affording a readier and more simple mode of exhibiting so amusing and instructive an experiment.

"Let a glass tube be taken, having its internal diameter about ⅛ of an inch, with a ball at each extremity of about one inch diameter; and let the tube be bent to a right angle at the distance of half an inch from each ball. One of these balls should contain a little water (if the ball be more than half full, it will be liable to burst by the expansion of water in freezing) and the remaining cavity should be as perfect a vacuum as can readily be obtained. . . .

"When an instrument of this description has been successfully exhausted, if the ball that is empty be immersed in a freezing mixture of salt and snow, the water in the other ball, though at the distance of two or three feet, will be frozen solid in the course of a very few minutes. The vapour contained in the empty ball is condensed by the common operation of cold, and the vacuum produced by this condensation gives opportunity for a fresh quantity to arise from the opposite ball, with proportional reduction of its temperature. . . .

"The instrument, by which this is effected, may aptly be called a Cryophorus, which correctly expresses its office of frost-bearer."

The "ingenious expedient" of Professor John Leslie[3,4] consisted of a chamber containing sulfuric acid in a broad flat pan and a vessel containing water. On exhaustion of the chamber by an air-pump the water froze through loss of latent heat of vaporization; the ice gradually "wasted away" by sublimation of water-vapor to the sulfuric acid. Leslie later successfully substituted porphyritic trap rock or even parched oatmeal for sulfuric acid as desiccant; in view of later developments it is interesting that he tried anhydrous sulfate of lime without success.

It does not seem to have occurred to either Wollaston or Leslie to use sublimation for drying. It would be difficult if not impossible to trace definite connection between their experiments and developments of the present century in biological preservation. Nevertheless the phenomena they so ingeniously and amusingly exhibited unquestionably became part of the general lore of physical science.

The first clearly recorded use of sublimation for preserving is that of Shackell[5] in 1909, who applied it to biological substances.

Strumia, McGraw, and Reichel[6] credit d'Arsonval and Bordas[7] and Vansteenberghe[8] with the principles of drying by sublimation. While the apparatus of d'Arsonval and Bordas was built on the cryophorus principle and that of Vansteenberghe resembled the Leslie prototype, neither publication mentions that the material undergoing desiccation was observed to have been frozen, although the equipment they used might have lent itself, with better pumping equipment and other modifications, to drying by sublimation. The stated purpose of d'Arsonval and Bordas was to carry out ordinary distillation of liquids at a lower temperature (about $+15°C$) than that then currently or previously used.

The stability of serum in dried form, although not dried from the frozen state, was recognized by Ehrlich in the last century. Apparatus for desiccation of serum from the liquid state was described as early as 1896 by C. Martin.[9] Serum was filtered through a Chamberland candle and received in bottles kept in a water bath at $40°C$. These bottles were connected with a condensing bottle packed in ice, to which was connected a water pump. Water vapor distilling over from the serum bottles was collected in the condenser.

M. J. Rosenau,[10] as Director of the Hygienic Laboratory in Washington, undertook the establishment of an antitoxin standard for American Laboratories. He dried and ground antitoxin and preserved it in evacuated, sealed "Ehrlich tubes" with phosphorus pentoxide as a desiccant. The preparation of dried antisera or complement by modifications of Martin's method or other simple methods had been described also by Noguchi,[11] Friedberger,[12] Massol and Grysez,[13] Massol and Nowaczynski,[14] Predtetschensky,[15] and Grigorowitsch.[16]

Burrows and Cohn[17] described a modification of Martin's

method capable of drying sera in fairly large amounts. A dropping funnel was introduced into a flask in a water bath at 45 to 50°C. A side tube of the flask was connected with a condenser in iced water, which was in turn attached to a calcium chloride tower, a manometer and a vacuum pump, with which the whole apparatus was evacuated. Dried complement and antisera were further studied by Hartley, Eagleton and Okell,[18] by Tullock[19] and by Hartley.[20]

Shackell described a procedure by which biologicals might be dried, presumably while frozen. In Shackell's process the material was first thoroughly frozen in a salt-ice mixture. The frozen material was then dried *in vacuo* in a desiccator with sulfuric acid as desiccant. Complement, antisera, rabies virus, meat and blood were preserved by this method. Harris and Shackell[21] in 1911 reported the preservation of rabic brains by the method of Shackell. Hammer[22] the same year reported the preservation of bacteria by this method.

Swift[23] in 1921 described a technique of drying bacteria from the frozen state which became standard for some years in many laboratories for preserving bacterial strains with unaltered biological characteristics. An apparatus was developed by Sawyer[24] and his associates with which serum infected with yellow fever virus had been preserved so as to retain its infectivity over a period of years. Craigie[25] prepared complement dried from the frozen state.

W. J. Elser of Cornell carried on extensive work for some years with a variety of products of a biological nature. This work has been described by Elser, Thomas and Steffen.[26] Low-temperature condensation was used for removal of the water vapor. In none of this early work, including that of Shackell and Swift, was any means used for rapid application of heat to the frozen product without melting it while bringing it to a final temperature well above 0°C. In other words, there was no means of forcing rapid and complete drying to a suitable low final moisture content. In later chapters we shall discuss the implications of subsequent improvements which have resulted in better products through the development of modern methods of commercial freeze-drying.

Certain important steps in advance were taken by Reichel,

Masucci, McAlpine and Boyer.[27] A practical procedure was developed for the rapid freezing and rapid dehydration of serum in bulk under vacuum. The serum was frozen at $-78°C$ in a shell in very large "Pyrex" glass or metal bulbs, which were connected to a large spherical condenser at a distance from the containers. This condenser was immersed in a refrigerant bath of solid carbon dioxide (Dry Ice) in acetone. The serum was kept in the frozen state solely by the rapid sublimation *in vacuo* of water vapor from its surface. The outer surfaces of the bulbs were surrounded by the air of the room at ordinary or elevated temperature during the entire dehydration process for rapid heating and drying of the frozen material.[28] The final dried product was then raised to a temperature well above $0°C$ and often to $70°C$ or higher, in order to reduce the final moisture content rapidly to a minimum. This apparatus was in use for some time for the bulk preservation of serum and other biologicals in commercial amounts.

The product resulting when serum is rapidly frozen and rapidly dehydrated from the frozen state under high vacuum is a porous solid occupying essentially the same volume as the liquid serum from which it was prepared. Its content of antibodies and complement suffers no detectable loss in processing, and the rate of subsequent deterioration is reduced to a small fraction of that occurring in the liquid state. The porous product, on addition of distilled water, redissolves with remarkable ease and completeness. The term "lyophile" has been applied by Reichel[28,29] to serum so dehydrated. In this usage the ordinary colloid-chemical term lyophile (solvent-loving) is given a somewhat special connotation. The word is convenient, however, and serves to emphasize a noteworthy characteristic of the product so prepared, namely its remarkable solubility, which is a result both of the unaltered lyophilic properties of the serum proteins and of the physical structure of the porous solid.

In 1933 in the author's laboratory (Fig. 1.1) at the University of Pennsylvania (School of Medicine), the first products for actual clinical use were freeze-dried.[29] These were human convalescent and normal human serum and plasma. According to plans laid by Drs. Joseph Stokes, Jr. and Stuart Mudd for a "library" of human

Fig. 1.1. Apparatus in author's laboratory at the University of Pennsylvania (School of Medicine) used in freeze-drying convalescent and normal human serum and plasma in 1933 for the Philadelphia Serum Exchange, representing the first production of freeze-dried products for clinical use.

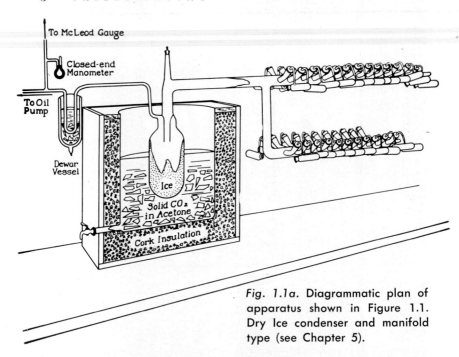

To McLeod Gauge

Closed-end
Manometer

To Oil
Pump

Dewar
Vessel

Ice

Solid CO₂
in Acetone

Cork Insulation

Fig. 1.1a. Diagrammatic plan of apparatus shown in Figure 1.1. Dry Ice condenser and manifold type (see Chapter 5).

sera, the blood was collected at the Children's Hospital by Dr. Aims C. McGuinness, and prepared and tested at the University of Pennsylvania by Dr. Harry Eagle for freeze-drying by the author. The dry products were used and distributed by the Philadelphia Serum Exchange organized at the time for the purpose, and now a going institution under the direction of Dr. McGuinness. It was not long before distribution was nation-wide.

This was the first use of freeze-dried human products and it undoubtedly accounts for their subsequent ready acceptance in the Red Cross program for human plasma for our armed forces in World War II. Hence it was freeze-drying which finally brought about the realization of an unheeded plea made by Captain Gordon R. Ward, R.A.M.C., for the use of blood plasma in place of whole blood in the treatment of shock and hemorrhage.[30] The plea was made in a letter addressed to the Editor of the *British Medical Journal* of March 3, 1918. Only a product as stable bacteriologically, immunologically and biochemically as that produced by freeze-drying could meet the military requirements of a global war, conditions varying from those of the hot, moist tropics to those of the cold arctic.

Desiccation from the frozen state finally became generally available on a practical basis in 1934 for laboratory research, for hospital production of human serum and other substances for parenteral use, for guinea-pig complement and other laboratory reagents, and for commercial production. This represented the culmination of prior work and of certain further major developments.[29] These new contributions included the establishment of proper surface relationships of frozen products for fast and complete drying without melting while exposed to heat from the atmosphere, as well as equipment for aseptic production of medical products in final market containers. The equipment consisted of a carbon dioxide condenser and a manifold for the containers with connectors arranged to maintain sterility. Later, other advances were made in equipment and manner of processing. Thus, it has been recognized only within the last 10 or 15 years that by establishing proper conditions of vacuum for removal of water vapor, and by rapidly applying heat to the frozen product (rather than keeping it in an icebox), the process can be made industrially workable and will yield excellent products.

The firm of Sharp & Dohme, Inc. very early recognized the advantages that freeze-drying could hold for industry; they installed the first market-container units[29] in 1935, when the firm took over processing human serum for the Philadelphia Serum Exchange for clinical distribution. Other products appeared on the market in 1935, and freeze-dried blood plasma in 1940. Sharp & Dohme's early pioneering efforts and full-scale experience made it possible for the U. S. military forces to begin accumulating supplies of freeze-dried human blood plasma for transfusion in 1941, nearly six months before our actual entry into World War II. The decision to proceeed with the vast plasma program was crystallized after Dr. Alexis Carrell addressed the annual meeting of the American Human Serum Association in New York City in June, 1940. Just returned from France, he described graphically the utter collapse of the system of French blood banks upon the advance of the German army just before the fall of France.

The contrast under such emergency conditions, with dried human plasma available, was set forth by Dr. I. S. Ravdin in a brochure published by the Southeastern Pennsylvania Chapter of the American Red Cross on February 9, 1942 entitled, "A Philadelphia Doctor's Story of Pearl Harbor." Dr. Ravdin said of liquid plasma that it "saved the lives of more men than it will ever be possible for you or me to tell." Ravdin went on to state, "Now, a second type of plasma which was available, and which has been made available to the armed forces and civilian aid, almost entirely through the efforts of the Red Cross, is the dry plasma. That is the same material which you have just seen, but it is dried by a method which was originally developed at the University of Pennsylvania, in the Department of Bacteriology, by Doctors Flosdorf and Mudd. This has certain advantages, in that the material can be transported over long distances and at extremes of temperature and, merely by adding sterile water, can be regenerated and given intravenously." Ravdin further quoted Mr. Alfred Castle, who was Chairman of the American Red Cross in Honolulu at the time of the raid, as follows: "We have got a problem here. We are now collecting large amounts of plasma. We can't store all of this wet plasma. We must have some mechanism for drying it. Do you know where such apparatus is to be obtained?" Ravdin said, "I told him such apparatus was made in Philadelphia and he wanted to know how much it would cost. I told him perhaps a minimum of $12,000. He said, 'Well, you just ask the Red Cross when you get back in Washington, whether they would be willing to foot the bill. If the Red Cross won't pay the bill, send the apparatus, and have it charged to me. I'll foot the bill.'" Thus we have the first graphic account of how well freeze-dried plasma could meet such an unexpected emergency situation as was experienced at Pearl Harbor and the appraisal made of the situation by those present at the scene.

As indicated above, Sharp and Dohme was in commercial production of human blood plasma and so was ready in 1941 for the Red Cross part of the program. They processed and dried the plasma prepared from blood collected by the American Red Cross for the Army and Navy. This program later was extended to centers throughout the country, processing and drying being carried out at the laboratories of Ben Venue, Cutter, Eli Lilly, Hyland, Lederle, Parke-Davis and Reichel (now Wyeth). Peak production for the entire country ultimately reached around 100,000 units per week. With the assistance and co-operation of Sharp and Dohme, Inc., F. J. Stokes Machine Company, the University of Pennsylvania, the Philadelphia Serum Exchange of the Children's Hospital, and the author, freeze-drying of human serum for transfusion prepared from blood collected by the Canadian Red Cross was started in 1940. This was done at the Connaught Laboratories of Toronto under direction of Drs. C. H. Best and D. Y. Solandt.[31] Production there soon reached about 2,000 units a week and ultimately was expanded several-fold. Full pilot production began at Cambridge, England, in 1940,[32] with a full-scale production plant for 2500 units a week beginning operation in 1943.[32] It was at this time that commercial production of penicillin was ready to get under way, and it was fortunate that the blood plasma program had so amply demonstrated the successful stage attained by the large-scale freeze-drying process.

Later methods include the successful use of regenerable chemical desiccants[33] and the direct evacuation[34] of water vapor without freezing-condenser or desiccants. Apparatus for drying by sublimation has also been described more recently by Greaves and Adair,[32,35] Hill and Pfeiffer,[36] Strumia, McGraw and Reichel,[6] Folsom,[37] and Wyckoff and Lagsdin.[38] The various methods of drying from the frozen state and the types of equipment described later by many other workers will be discussed in subsequent chapters.

One indication of the recent rapid development of freeze-drying is the number of scientific articles in the field before and after 1930. Of the references located which deal with freeze-drying and its applications, fewer than 10 are before and over 350 are after 1930. No patents were issued before 1934.

BIBLIOGRAPHY

1. Flosdorf, E. W., Hull, L. W., and Mudd, S., "Drying by Sublimation," *J. Immunol.*, 50, 21 (1945).

2. Wollaston, W. H., "On a method of freezing at a distance," *Phil. Trans. Royal Soc. London,* 103, 71–74 (1813).
3. Leslie, J., "Méthode nouvelle de produice et d'entretenir la congélation," *Ann. chim. phys.,* 78, 177–182 (1811).
4. Leslie, J., "On a new mode of artificial congelation," *Phil. Mag.,* 51, 411–421 (1818).
5. Shackell, L. F., "An improved method of desiccation, with some applications to biological problems," *Am. J. Physiol.,* 24, 325–340 (1909).
6. Strumia, M. M., McGraw, J. J., and Reichel, J., "The preparation and preservation of human plasma. IV. Drying of plasma from the frozen state by low temperature condensation," *Am. J. Clin. Path.,* 11, 480–496 (1941).
7. D'Arsonval and Bordas, F. "Les basses températures et l'analyse chimique," *Compt. rend. acad. sci.,* 142, 1058–1059 (1906).
8. Vansteenberghe, P., "Procedé de conservation du virus rabique à l'état sec," *Compt. rend. soc. biol.,* 55, 1646 (1903).
9. Martin, C., *J. Path. Bact.,* 3, 507 (1896).
10. Rosenau, M. J. Bull. No. 21, Hyg. Lab. Wash., pp. 50–54 (1905).
11. Noguchi, H., *J. Exper. Med.,* 9, 455 (1907); 11, 392 (1909).
12. Friedberger, E. *Berlin, klin. Woch.,* 44, 1299 (1907).
13. Massol, L., and Grysez, V., *Compt. rend. soc. biol.,* 68, 825 (1910).
14. Massol, L., and Nowaczynski, J., *ibid.,* 69, 430 (1910).
15. Predtetschensky, S., *Centrabl. f. Bakt.,* Abt. I, 52, 651 (1912).
16. Grigorowitsch, A., *Zentralbl. Biochem. Biophysik,* 16, 71 (1913–14).
17. Burrows, G. H., and Cohn, E. J., *J. Biol. Chem.,* 36, 587 (1918).
18. Hartley, P., Eagleton, A. J., and Okell, C. C., *J. Path. Bact.,* 26, 53 (1923).
19. Tullock, W. J., *J. Roy. Army Med. Corps,* 50, 448 (1928).
20. Hartley, P. *System of Bacteriology (London),* 6, 224, London (1931).
21. Harris, D. L., and Shackell, L. F., *J. Am. Pub. Health Assoc.,* 7, 52 (1911).
22. Hammer, B. W., *J. Med. Res.,* 24, 527 (1911).
23. Swift, H. F., *J. Exper. Med.,* 33, 69 (1921).
24. Sawyer, W. A., Lloyd, W. D. M., and Kitchen, S. F., *J. Exper. Med.,* 50, 1 (1929).
25. Craigie, J. *Brit. J. Exper. Pathol.,* 12, 75 (1931).
26. Elser, W. J., Thomas, R. A., and Steffen, G. I., *J. Immunol.,* 28, 433 (1935).
27. Reichel, J., Masucci, P., McAlpine, K. L., and Boyer, J., Unpublished work (See Ref. 28).
28. Reichel, J., U. S. Pat. Re. 20, 969 (1939).
29. Flosdorf, E. W., and Mudd, S., "Procedure and apparatus for preservation in 'Lyophile' form of serum and other biological substances." *J. Immunol.,* 29, 389 (1935).

30. Kendrick, D. B. Jr. and Newhouser, L. R., Edited by Mudd and Thalhimer. "The problems confronting the armed services concerning the use of blood substitutes," pp. 226–234 in "Blood Substitutes and Blood Transfusion," Charles C. Thomas, Springfield, Ill., 1942.

31. Best, C. H., Solandt, D. Y., and Ridoult, J. H., "The Canadian project for the preparation of dried human serum for military use," *ibid.*, 103 and 235–241, 1942.

32. Greaves, R. I. N., "The preservation of proteins by drying with special reference to the production of dried human serum and plasma for transfusion," Medical Research Council. Special Report Series No. 258, (1946).

33. Flosdorf, E. W., and Mudd, S., "An improved procedure and apparatus for preservation of sera, micro-organisms and other substances: the cryochem-process." *J. Immunol.*, 34, 469–490 (1938).

34. Flosdorf, E. W., Stokes, F. J., and Mudd, S., "The Desivac process for drying from the frozen state," *J. Am. Med. Assoc.*, 115, 1095–1097 (1940). U. S. Patent No. 2,345,548.

35. Greaves, R. I. N., and Adair, M. E., "High vacuum condensation drying of proteins from the frozen state," *J. Hyg.*, 39, 413–445 (1939).

36. Hill, J. M. and Pfeiffer, D. C., "A new and economical desiccating process particularly suitable for the preparation of concentrated plasma or serum for intravenous use: the Adtevac process," *Ann. Int. Med.*, 14, 201–214 (1940).

37. Folsom, T. R., "A method for drying clinically useful quantities of plasma and serum: the unit desiccator," pp. 49–63, "Blood Substitutes and Blood Transfusion," C. C. Thomas, Springfield, Ill., 1942.

38. Wyckoff, R. W. G. and Lagsdin, J. B., "A simple outfit for drying plasma from the frozen state," *Am. J. Clin. Path., Tech. Sec.*, 8, 10–16 (1944).

CHAPTER 2: BASIC PRINCIPLES

DRYING products from the frozen state is advantageous for numerous reasons. For any given product one or more possible objectives may be realized. Following is a summary of these objectives.

1. *Low temperature.* In many cases the sub-freezing temperature is required to avoid chemical change in labile components during drying. This applies to blood plasma and serum, to most viruses, to many bacteria and other forms of micro-organisms and to various other biologicals and pharmaceuticals.

For example, complement, a component of blood, is rapidly inactivated when stored even at temperatures around about 5°C. Guinea-pig serum is widely used as a laboratory reagent because of its high content of complement, as in the Wasserman reaction in testing for syphilis. Certain modifications of the test are particularly sensitive to complement potency, and in these the guinea-pig serum cannot be used if it is more than a few hours old. In most tests, the serum cannot be used after overnight storage under ordinary refrigeration. Drying by sublimation is the only way in which this particular component can be prepared in a dry, stable form. After completely drying in this way to a minimal moisture content, the product is stable for as long as two years at room temperature and for five years if stored at about 5°C.

Similarly, viruses are generally very delicate, in some instances even more so than guinea-pig complement. Freeze-drying of the product affords the only satisfactory means of stabilizing labile

viral vaccines. Except for frozen storage, it is also the only satisfactory means of holding live viruses while carrying out research
studies. Similarly, certain bacteria and other extracts may be handled successfully, although of course there are many types of bacteria which can readily withstand higher temperature treatment.

As applied to many commercial preparations of labile medicinals, the out-dating time is greatly extended. This lowers cost and
also enables products to be taken to out-of-the-way places otherwise beyond reach. Freeze-drying also permits low-temperature
concentration of products without continuing to complete dryness.

2. *Low volatility.* Because of the low temperature, the loss
of volatile constituents is small. Although the process takes place
in vacuum and there is some loss of volatile components into the
vacuum system, this usually is minimal. The decrease in vapor
pressure with lower temperature is greater with many substances
than with water. Toward the end of drying, when the products
reach a higher temperature, virtually all the moisture has been
removed, so that there is little or no vapor distillation of vola-
tiles. For example, the powder remaining after freeze-drying fresh
orange juice has little or no odor. Upon opening a sealed can of the
dried juice and smelling it, one is disappointed to find no odor
comparable with that of fresh juice. However, upon reconstitution
with water and aeration by shaking, an excellent aroma develops.
The reconstituted mixture then obtained is like fresh juice. This is
particularly important in application to many other foods, especially pineapple juice, grape juice, etc.

3. *No foaming.* Because a product may be frozen solid,
there is no bubbling or foaming, unless it is dried well above the
temperature at which there is eutectic separation. Changes due to
surface action are thus avoided in drying certain substances. This
is particularly true of protein material. One of the best examples
is the successful drying of blood plasma without loss in potency of
any of its constituents.

4. *Permanent dispersion.* In most cases, the solute remains
evenly dispersed without undergoing concentration as the frozen
solvent sublimes. As a result, the remaining dry residue emerges as
a highly porous framework, occupying essentially the same overall

space as the original solution. The final residue is not the fine pow
der with which the chemist is familiar; rather, it has a friable inter-
locking and sponge-like structure. This is a major factor contributing to the extremely rapid and complete solubility of freeze-dried
products. Blood plasma again offers one of the best examples of a
product which, to be useful in an emergency, must have rapid
solubility. An entire dose can be ready for transfusion within five
minutes from the time a package is available. This includes all the
operations involved, of which reconstituting with water is but one.
Gelatin provides, perhaps, one of the most spectacular of these
products. Gelatin which must be dissolved first by boiling water
may be changed to a porous solid by drying the liquid from the
frozen state. The resulting solid is then instantly soluble in *cold
water*. There are other products, such as preparations of vitamin B
complex, which go into solution only with some difficulty. The solution may then be dried by sublimation, whereupon the pharmaceutical manufacturer is able to offer an instantly soluble product
to the physician, which is also highly stable.

On the other hand, not all products have such excellent solubility after drying by sublimation. One of the best examples is
serum globulin. In the case of concentrated globulin antitoxins,
the rate of solubility may be slow, requiring many minutes for
restoration. Nevertheless, in certain cases it may be advantageous
to dry even these biologicals if distribution under hot tropical and
desert conditions is necessary. This is particularly true in the case
of antivenom preparations, where the product may be subjected
to the hot desert sun or the tropical heat of India for long periods.
The added time for dissolving is not serious in this case, and the
alternative would be no product at all.

5. *Minimal coagulation.* Since the molecules of solute and
colloidally dispersed particles are virtually "locked" in position as
solvent evaporates, the tendency for coagulation of even lyophobic
sols is minimal. This is particularly advantageous with blood
plasma from donors who have not been on complete fast sufficiently long. In the case of liquid plasma stored for a period of
time or processed in any other way, these lipoids rise to the surface
as a separate liquid phase. In the case of dried blood plasma, how-

ever, even though the lipoidal constituents do not reconstitute perfectly after drying and produce a slight degree of turbidity, there is far from complete coalescence. The particles are small enough to be safe for intravenous injection and do not cause capillary embolism. Bentonite clays and other colloidal products may be dried with excellent results.

6. *No case-hardening.* In drying from the frozen state, there is no continual mixing of solution or any other movement of solvent. The surface of the evaporating frozen ice layer gradually recedes and leaves more and more of the highly porous residue of dry solute exposed. As a result, "case-hardening" never occurs. This is one reason why a far lower content of moisture may be obtained in the final product without use of excessively high final temperature. Because of lower moisture content, a greater degree of stability is imparted to labile products than by any other method of drying.

7. *Sterility.* Bacterial growth and enzymatic changes cannot take place under the frozen conditions of drying. This is important for foods as well as for medical products used parenterally. Likewise, the final fully dried product resists bacterial growth and enzymatic action. In the case of some products, *e.g.*, streptomycin, this is an important reason for drying. It is exceedingly difficult in commercial production to be certain of complete sterility in every step. Streptomycin, for example, cannot be readily sterilized before packing in market containers, as is done with many biological products like antitoxin which may be sterilized by filtration.

In such a material, it might well be that only a few organisms would exist in an entire batch and only a few of the final containers would become contaminated. These, upon random selection for testing, might be missed. Distributed as a liquid, there would be opportunity for these organisms to multiply. During storage, these few containers would become grossly contaminated. With a dry product, however, there is no opportunity for multiplication of organisms until the product is restored for use. Since it then is used immediately (and directions should always provide for this), there can be no harm to the recipient from the few organisms which may be present in occasional containers.

8. *Oxidation.* Because of the high vacuum used, in contrast with that used in ordinary low-temperature liquid evaporation, there is insufficient oxygen for even the most readily oxidizable constituents to be affected. The ascorbic acid content of orange juice dried by sublimation is not detectably lowered. The lipoidal constituents of meat are not affected, and no rancidity develops in drying raw meat. This is equally important with many medical products. Blood plasma, in which the lipoids are unaffected during sublimation, is an example. With proper packaging, under either vacuum or inert gas such as nitrogen, many of these products may be kept satisfactorily for years without refrigeration.

It is for these reasons that this method, which only 15 years ago was brought from a laboratory curiosity into a workable procedure as discussed in Chapter 1, has become a commonly used process for drying in the biological and pharmaceutical industry.

Energy Relations

It has sometimes been erroneously considered that because drying by sublimation is carried out under high vacuum, less heat is required. Actually, the latent heat of sublimation of ice is greater than the latent heat of evaporation of water. Thermodynamically, the energy required to sublime a gram of ice at any given temperature to produce vapor, for example, at room temperature, is equivalent to the heat of fusion of ice and the heat of vaporization of water at room temperature plus the heat necessary to raise the temperature of ice to the freezing point and water to room temperature. This quantity of heat is naturally related, whether the process is carried out slowly at atmospheric pressure or rapidly under vacuum.

Table 1 gives at five temperatures the latent heat of sublimation of ice to produce vapor at the same temperature. These temperatures are those commonly used for a variety of products. As will be discussed in a later section, the actual requirements for the temperature of a product during drying by sublimation vary with different products. Naturally, the higher the temperature which can be used the more readily drying can be carried out and the

TABLE 1

VARIATION IN LATENT HEAT OF SUBLIMATION
WITH TEMPERATURE *

Temp., °C	Joules/gram	BTU/lb
0°c	2833	1220
−10°	2807	1210
−20°	2786	1200
−30°	2771	1192
−40°	2758	1186

* Data compiled by Dr. T. B. Hetzel of Haverford College. Refers to ice and vapor at same temperature. Values accurate to ±1.4%, varying with type of ice involved.

lower the cost. As for the actual energy relationships concerned, it is necessary to consider the heat required to carry the vapor up to full room temperature, inasmuch as the vapor lines are usually exposed to room-temperature air. However, as a practical matter, the amount of heat required to raise the temperature of the vapor is not significant, most of it being obtained readily from the room as the vapor passes through the vapor lines. If these are not exposed, and if the vapor is condensed back to ice, this additional heat is not required. The refrigeration load required for condensation is reduced accordingly. Similarly, if the cold vapors are removed by combination with a desiccant, there is less heat to cause excessive rise in temperature of the desiccant.

Basically, the amount of latent heat required in drying by sublimation is not a significant factor in comparing the cost of drying from the frozen state with the cost of drying by other means. As will be discussed later, the significant factors in such a comparison are the higher cost of handling a solid as compared with a liquid and of carrying out the process in equipment which must be designed for high vacuum. Also, a major factor is that the vapor evolved in drying must be removed by condensation, or otherwise, at very low pressure. For example, in condensation of the water vapor the temperature of the condensing medium is below that of the frozen product being dried. This is more costly not because of the greater amount of heat to be extracted from the vapor, but because of the low refrigeration temperatures at which this heat must be extracted and at which compressors produce lower tonnage.

When the vapors are removed by combination with a desiccant, an exothermic reaction is involved. Usually a regenerable desiccant and the vapor pressure of the desiccant increase rapidly with increase in temperature. Since these desiccants themselves are invariably poor conductors of heat and since they are combining with water vapor under vacuum conditions, the heat produced is taken away slowly. The resultant rise in temperature of the desiccant results in lowered efficiency as the vapor pressure increases.

In types of equipment in which the vapors are pumped directly without being condensed at freezing temperature and without entering into combination with desiccant, they are compressed directly to the liquid state. In the case of direct pumping by a steam ejector, condensation occurs in the first interstage barometric condenser. In the case of direct pumping mechanically the heat of condensation is removed by the cooling water of the pump.

Initial Freezing of Products

In many cases rapid freezing is required. A few years ago it was believed that to accomplish rapid freezing it was necessary to use extremely low temperatures such as are produced by Dry Ice. This is erroneous, however, because the speed of freezing is controlled by the rapidity of heat transfer. Using temperatures as low as $-78°C$, *e.g.*, Dry Ice, is of course a factor in rapid transfer of heat, but it is possible to design equipment for accomplishing rapid freezing at more economical temperature levels. Description of the various available means for carrying out freezing will be discussed in Chapter 5.

Vacuum evaporation may be relied upon for freezing certain products where there is little frothing and bubbling. Bubbling may be controlled somewhat by slowly degassing the solution under partial vacuum, after which a higher vacuum is drawn to induce freezing.

Medical products dispensed in small containers frequently are frozen directly within vacuum chambers by lowering the temperature of the chambers. This is one accepted procedure for vitamins, in the preparation of which the chambers are arranged for chilling to −40°C, as well as for control at any temperature from that up to the final drying temperature of +60°C or higher. In small-scale operation, containers frequently are arranged on manifolds so that Dry Ice may be used for convenience in freezing. With medical products convenience is frequently a more important factor than cost, and Dry Ice is used for this reason as well as for rapid freezing.

In the case of medical products dried in larger quantities per single container (e.g., blood plasma), it is necessary to "shell freeze" by rotating the containers in a low-temperature bath. In this way, by freezing around the inner periphery of the bottle, the depth of the layer is reduced and the time for drying shortened.

In drying industrial products such as foods in bulk, self-freezing frequently may be used, especially with solid products like meat. Sometimes self-freezing under vacuum is more economical because of simplification of equipment. On the other hand, as will be discussed in connection with various individual products, it sometimes is necessary to pre-freeze even solids before evacuation in order to get proper quality.

Removal of Water Vapor under High Vacuum

Three general methods may be used to maintain low water vapor pressure in the vacuum system: (1) condensation at low temperature,[1,2] (2) combination with desiccating substances, and (3) direct pumping.[3] All three methods are used industrially, but the one best suited to a given application depends on a number of factors.

1. *Condensation at low temperature.* Such condensation is carried out with condensers chilled either with Dry Ice or mechanically with refrigerants like "Freon" and ammonia. Originally, Dry Ice was the most widely used refrigerant. However, because of cost it is now used only with products which have a high value, like medicinals. The low temperature of Dry Ice is not necessary. Fundamentally, to establish and maintain a given pressure of water

vapor, it is the temperature of the condensing surface which is determinant, and not the temperature of the refrigerant. The condensing metallic surface does not long remain clean, as a thin film of ice is soon formed. The proper temperature required for the condensing surface depends upon the coefficient of heat transfer at the cold surface, which is influenced by the non-condensable gases which contaminate the water vapor, and the nature of the condensing surface. For example, a metallic surface has a better factor than glass or ice. Further, the area of condensing surface should be large to keep at a minimum the amount of heat to be transferred per unit area. The lower the amount of heat to be transferred per unit area, the less the required over-all differential between temperature of refrigerant and temperature corresponding to the pressure of water vapor in the system. The required temperature for the refrigerant in part depends also upon the thickness of the layer of ice built up on the condenser. This must be taken into account because of the poor thermal conductivity of ice.

The non-condensable gases account for the differential ("split") between the temperature corresponding to the vapor pressure of ice, equal to the total pressure in the system, and the actual temperature of the surface of the ice on the condenser. This differential may also be expressed as the ratio of partial pressure of water vapor to the total pressure in the system, and has great influence on the efficiency of condensation. This effect on transfer of heat is controlled by using tight vacuum equipment and pumps of adequate capacity for non-condensables.

To accelerate the transfer of heat by controlling the nature of the condensing surface, metal surfaces of small area continuously de-iced (scraped by rotation of blades) have been used. This is an attempt to take advantage of better heat transfer at a clean metallic surface and at the same time to eliminate the usual slow-conducting layer of ice. In practice, a truly clean surface has not been achieved. A molecular film of ice provides a condensing surface of ice instead of metal, and is as bad as a block of ice insofar as transfer of heat to ice-condensing surface and from ice surface to adjacent metal surface is concerned. Consequently, to make such condensers of limited surface effective, lower temperatures of condensing surface must be maintained. This offsets any economy gained. If the layer of ice is reasonably thin, conductivity across it is faster than transference of heat from vapor to the ice surface, so it is the latter which controls the over-all rate of transfer. Ikan claims that vacuum-condensed ice conducts as well as metal.[4]

Accordingly, it becomes necessary to accept an ice surface with its poor heat transfer. However, by use of condensers of very large surface, whereby the heat to be transferred per unit area is kept small, a higher surface temperature is adequate. Also, the ice layer is kept as thin as possible, to minimize the poor conductivity, so that both effects of extending the condensing surface lead to higher permissible temperature of refrigerant.*

The net result of all these factors in combination may be expressed in terms of the effective partial pressure of water vapor which can be established within the vacuum system by the condenser during drying. Assuming that the equipment is designed to avoid restrictive orifices in vacuum lines and elsewhere, the differ-

---

* Friedman[5] misconstrued the previously published statements.[6] As the above discussion should make clear, it has not been postulated that "the heat transfer rate through solid ice is independent of the ice thickness." Heat transfer from the vapor to the condensing surface of the ice is independent of the thickness of the ice. Also, transfer of heat from the surface of ice adjacent to the metal of the condenser to the metallic condenser surface is independent of the thickness of the ice. This consideration is important in connection with the much better coefficient of a completely clean metal surface compared with an ice surface. Naturally, the thickness of the ice also is important in the over-all transfer from vapor to the metal, but in a critical analysis this factor must be separated from the factors of transfer from surface to surface.

Similarly, it has not been postulated that the condenser *surface* is limited to 55 per cent of the absolute vapor pressure of water at the temperature of the frozen material. This is fully discussed in the following pages.

Further, Friedman misinterpreted the article by Brown, Bierwirth and Hoyler,[7] which Friedman summarized as being an "article on *combined* dielectric and sublimation drying." In this article on use of dielectric heating for penicillin, method and equipment were described for low-temperature liquid evaporation, the temperature of the solution being of the order of +35°C. The principle is one of drying with sufficient rapidity so the time during which the product is exposed to this temperature is too short for deterioration to occur. In fact, the article points out that it is necessary to avoid too high a vacuum, about 20 mm. being the minimum pressure; otherwise arcing in the high-frequency field will occur. In freeze-drying operations, even for pure ice, the maximum permissible pressure is something over 4 mm. In practice, as has been pointed out, considerably lower pressures must be used because the products being dried must be maintained at much lower temperatures, in some cases −30°C and lower. This corresponds to a maximum pressure of 200 to 300 microns for such products. Naturally, with presently feasible frequencies, RF heating cannot be applied to drying by sublimation.

ential between this pressure and the vapor pressure of the evaporating product, such as plasma, determines the theoretical maximal rate of flow of vapor. The vapor pressure of the product at the temperature at which it should be dried, on this basis, determines the temperature at which the condenser should be maintained. Some products must be kept colder than others, as will be discussed later. In Fig. 2.1 is shown the pressure differential produced by various temperatures at the condensing surface in relation to four different temperatures at which products are kept during drying. This differential in pressure is the driving force. It will be observed that for each of the several temperatures of product, there is a minimal temperature of the condenser surface, below which very little further increment is gained by further reduction in condenser temperature.[1] This has been pointed out also by Greaves.[8] He states that with serum at −35°C and condenser at −45°C, there is a differential of 0.112 mm. Hg in pressure. With reduction of condenser temperature to that of liquid air, the same differential in pressure would lower the serum by only 4.5°, i.e., to −39.5°C.

Further, as drying proceeds, it is limited in rate by diffusion of vapor through the interstices of the porous dry outer layer of product, which act as orifices. By laws of adiabatic gaseous flow through orifices (Napier equation), a differential between the vapor pressure at the surface of the condenser and that at the ice surface within the product where the former is 55 per cent of the latter will result in the maximum rate of flow obtainable. This has been borne out experimentally using equipment in which the temperature of the condenser surface may be varied from −10 to −60°C. For example, with one batch of blood plasma being dried at −18°C, and the condenser at −25°C, drying was completed in 21 hours. In another run with the condenser at −40°C, the time was the same, but the jacket temperature of the drying chamber had to be raised after the first two hours from +65°C, used in the first run, to +90°C in order to keep the plasma at −18°C. In fact, if the jacket temperature is not raised in this way, drying is retarded to 27 hours with a −40°C condenser, the plasma drying at about −32°C. Pressure was 500 microns in both cases, but if the jacket had not been raised to +90°C with −40°C condenser, the

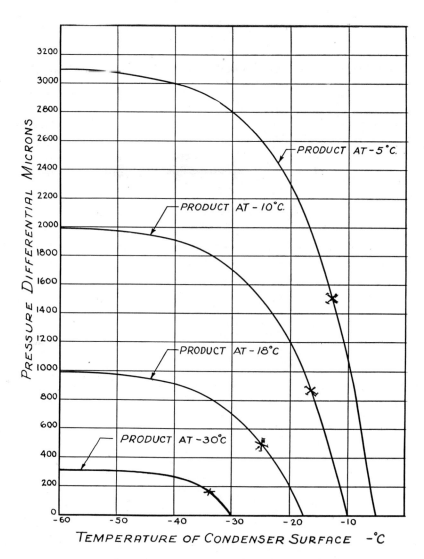

Fig. 2.1. Driving force in terms of differential in pressure produced by various condenser temperatures for products maintained at three different temperatures. "X" on each curve represents the temperature of the surface of condenser ice giving rise to the maximal differential of any value according to the Napier Equation, assuming no restrictive orifices in pipe lines, etc., other than in interstices of the porous dry outer layer of product itself. This applies to the first stage of drying when ice is being sublimed.

pressure would have had to be 225 microns. The efficiency of transfer of heat to the plasma is all-important in rapid drying, provided the ice-condensing surface is below the critical level discussed for obtaining the most rapid flow of vapor.

In drying by sublimation the pressures are well above one micron and the laws of flow of fluids apply to the movement of the water vapor. These laws as applied above are based upon the conditions of "screening" set up at an orifice when the downstream pressure is decreased below the limiting value. This screening accounts for the apparent discrepancy in not obtaining faster flow as a result of a greater differential in pressure. At pressures below a micron the mean free path of the molecules approaches the diameter of the pipe line and the laws of flow of fluids no longer govern. Movement of the vapor is then controlled by the natural diffusion of molecules, but this condition is not reached in drying by sublimation.

This comparison of differentials in pressures assumes no restrictions in vapor lines, necks of ampules, or elsewhere in the high-vacuum system. Otherwise, the temperature of the condensing surface would need to be reduced in order to produce a lower partial pressure of water vapor on the side toward the condenser of each restriction or orifice. Such reduction to less than 55 per cent of the pressure on the drying side of each orifice, by laws of adiabatic gaseous flow, can produce no further increment in rate of flow through the orifice. In other words, beyond a certain point, lowering of the temperature of the condenser cannot compensate for small vapor lines or restrictions.

By use of condensers of great surface having "constant efficiency," and by a proper balance of all *other factors* concerned, a very important practical conclusion is obvious as a result of applying this law of flow. Condensers may be operated at temperatures much above any originally believed possible and without sacrifice of effectiveness. With plasma at $-21°C$, a temperature of ice on the condenser of about $-27°C$ produces a vapor pressure equal to 55 per cent of that of the plasma and lower temperature at the ice surface is of no advantage.

2. *Desiccating substances.* Chemical desiccants such as phosphorus pentoxide and sulfuric acid have been suggested. These are impractical, however, on any scale of operation because of high cost, difficulty in using them, and other reasons. Regenerable desiccants having a low enough vapor pressure have much in their favor under certain circumstances.[9] The previous discussion of vapor pressure and condenser temperature applies also to the use of desiccants. Inasmuch as these desiccants are regenerated by heat, and since heat also is produced as a result of reaction of the desiccant with water vapor, a problem is introduced in properly maintaining low vapor pressure of the desiccant as drying proceeds; that is, the desiccants have a high thermal coefficient of vapor pressure. The heat of reaction is not readily conducted away in vacuum, as the desiccants themselves are poor conductors. The problem can be controlled, however, either by regulation of the quantity dried in relation to the amount of desiccant used (based on heat capacity of the entire bulk of desiccant), or by special means of cooling the desiccant. The desiccant can be either of the type which forms a fixed chemical hydrate, such as calcium sulfate, or of the physical type which combines with water by adsorption, such as silica gel or alumina. In the latter case the problem of warming the desiccant during drying is magnified because the vapor pressure, even at fixed temperature, rises with each small increment of water vapor adsorbed.

One rather complicated apparatus has been used which utilizes silica gel cooled by mechanical refrigeration. Cooling to low temperature in this fashion accomplishes two purposes: removal of heat adsorption of water and minimization of the effect of the gradual increase in vapor pressure as saturation of the desiccant is approached. Then, by changing to a fresh batch of refrigerated desiccant for completing desiccation, the final residual content of the dried product may be reduced to a satisfactory level. However, specially prepared calcium sulfate ("Drierite") in controlled amount without cooling has proved particularly satisfactory and is widely used, since it maintains a constant vapor pressure at any given temperature until saturated.

3. *Direct pumping* of the water vapor provides one of the simplest commercial procedures.[3] Again the same pressures must be produced as are obtained with condensers and desiccants. In this case, the same means is used to pump out non-condensables as

Fig. 2.2. Four-stage steam ejector with one inter-stage condenser between second and third stages. The condenser is of the barometric type ("leg" 34 ft. long not shown). This ejector is used in conjunction with the drying chambers (see Figs. 24 and 25, Chap. 5) and takes the place of a condenser.

establishes the low partial pressure of water vapor. Either an ejector pump or an oil-sealed rotary pump may be used. In the latter case, the pump must be equipped with means for continuously removing water from the oil of the vacuum pump, such as by a centrifugal clarifier. In this way, even though the oil-sealed pump is carrying water vapor through it, freshly clarified oil from which all condensed water has been removed by centrifugation is returned to the high vacuum side of the pump and its efficiency is not impaired. A multistage steam ejector with interstage condensers is suitable and is widely used in large-scale operation (Fig. 2.2). Combinations of these or of other accessory means, such as oil-diffusion or oil-ejector pumps, may be used. In any event, the volume occupied by the water vapor under expanded conditions of such a high vacuum is tremendous. The pumps used must have an exceedingly high volumetric capacity under these conditions.

On casual consideration it might appear that an ordinary oil-sealed mechanical rotary pump would have insufficient capacity because of the low efficiency under conditions of high vacuum. However, inasmuch as the water vapor is condensed on the high-pressure side of the rotary pump, at a pressure equal to the vapor pressure of water at the temperature at which the pump is operating, the pump is able to operate against a back pressure which is much below atmospheric. This is generally of the order of 125 mm of Hg. In effect, this approximates a second stage for the pump, so that under actual operating conditions of pumping water vapor the efficiency of a single-stage oil-sealed rotary pump will be maintained close to 100 per cent at 100 or 200 microns.

Even so, the capacity of any mechanical pump within practical limits is such that in larger-scale operation a jet-type ejector is preferred. Whether the ejector, in the case of steam, is of four or five stages and whether more than one interstage condenser is to be used, are engineering considerations of detail. The availability and relative costs of steam and cooling water must be considered; large quantities in any event are required. By-product facilities for these may be available in certain locations and the cost of operation is then low.

Stages of Drying

There are two stages in drying by sublimation: in the first, ice is evaporated from a frozen mass; in the second, moisture is removed from the final dry solid to lower the residual content to a minimal level. During the first stage, depending upon the product, some 98 to 99 per cent of all water is removed. In the second, the residual moisture content is reduced to 0.5 per cent or less of the final solids, which represents removal of over 99.95 per cent of the original content of water (assuming 10 per cent solids originally). In the first stage, temperatures are well below 0°C; actual temperature varies with the product, as will be discussed later. Suffice it to say at this point that few products can be dried at a temperature higher than −5°C during the first stage. Some food and medical products may be dried in the range of −5 to −10°C. A temperature of −10°C is critical with many. Some medical products must be at −20°C and others as low as −30°C. An impure penicillin may have to be kept as low as −40°C; streptomycin below −30°C.

During the final stage of drying, the dry product is taken to as high a temperature as it will stand in order to reach minimum moisture content in the shortest time. Some products, even in the final dry condition, are less stable than others, so that the final temperature varies widely. For example, certain dry biological products, like viruses and many living bacteria, cannot be taken much above normal room temperature. On the other hand, blood plasma may be taken as high as 80°C. The various temperatures for specific products are discussed in the next chapter.

DEGREE OF VACUUM AND TEMPERATURE OF PRODUCT DURING FIRST STAGE OF DRYING

During the first stage of drying, at which time the product is well below 0°C, if efficient vacuum pumps are used and there is little leakage of air into the vacuum system, the total pressure will be largely that of water vapor and will correspond closely to the temperature of the product being desiccated. With products such as plasma this is in the range of 500 to 800 microns; some may be higher, in some cases as high as 2000 to 3000 microns. In the case of penicillin the pressure must be as low as 200 to 300 microns. Most biological products, such as serum and plasma, have an initial freezing point a fraction of a degree below 0°C. However, as desiccation proceeds, a eutectic separation occurs (or gradual separation of a small proportional part of concentrated solution resulting from frozen-out solute and more dilute solution), and an apparent partial softening or melting (puffing) of the product may occur at temperatures even well below −1°C. The condition is more apparent than real, since close examination of the product reveals it to be grossly hard and brittle. Nevertheless, such a condition if of serious proportions should be avoided; hence a lower maximal temperature is required. In the case of serum, a product temperature of −9 to −12°C is sufficiently low, but with plasma the temperature must be −20 to −25°C. An examination of the vapor pressure of ice in these two temperature ranges will show that over three times as high a pressure can be used in drying serum as with plasma. Because of the marked decrease in vapor pressure with temperature, for greatest efficiency the temperature of the product being dried must be no lower than necessary.

Greaves[8] suggests the following as a means for determining the temperature at which a solution should be held during freeze-drying for sublimation to occur from the solid state. The first procedure is to measure the eutectic of the solution. This is found by placing some of the solution in a conductivity cell adapted for temperature measurement, and plotting conductivity and temperature on cooling and warming. The eutectic is shown by a plateau in the cooling curve coinciding with a sudden increase of resistance to an infinite level. This method works well with simple salt solutions, but with complex salt and protein solutions eutectics do not appear to be situated at temperatures which one might expect from consideration of the salt content alone. For example, with serum, whose main salt is sodium chloride, with a eutectic point at −21.4°C, no plateau is found on a cooling curve below −1.5°C, though the resistance does not become infinite until very low temperatures are reached. A more practical approach is to dry at different temperatures and observe what happens. A preliminary idea may be obtained by freezing, inverting the bottle, holding it at different temperatures, and noting whether any liquid separates from the ice at these temperatures.

When estimating eutectics by drying, the points to observe are: (a) any tendency for bubbles to form on the surface, (b) contraction in volume of the dried material when compared with the original liquid volume, and (c) "scaliness" of the dried material. Basing his conclusions on these points, Greaves states from practical experience that it may be said that sera will dry well if held below −10°C during the first stage of drying, plasma at from −10 to −25°C, depending upon the citrate to protein ratio, and sodium penicillin at below −25°C if impure (the purer solutions will dry satisfactorily at higher temperatures). Samples of broth may dry well at −30°C, though in some cases it may be necessary to go as low as −60°C to obtain perfect desiccation; this is important, since it is frequently convenient to dry virus and bacterial suspensions in broth.

TABLE 2

DRYING TEMPERATURES AND PRESSURES

Product	Drying-temperature Range (°C)	Vapor Pressure Range (Ice) (mm Hg)	Average Vapor Pressure (mm Hg)
Serum	−9 to −12	1.8 to 2.3	2.05
Plasma	−20 to −25	0.5 to 0.8	0.65
Penicillin	−28 to −32	0.2 to 0.3	0.25

In Table 2 is shown this relation between the pressures required for drying serum and plasma, based on the vapor pressures of ice in the ranges of temperature which are satisfactory. Accordingly, in any direct pumping system (with either steam ejectors or rotary pumps) about three times as great a volumetric capacity is required to dry plasma at the same rate as serum because of the higher vacuum needed. Otherwise a product which has partially thawed or softened during drying will be obtained. The capacity of the vacuum pump is a volumetric factor which is constant regardless of the degree of vacuum (except for lowered efficiency near the limit of the ultimate vacuum producible by the pump). Therefore, at higher vacuum a proportionately smaller weight of water vapor is withdrawn in pumping the constant volume.

DEGREE OF VACUUM AND TEMPERATURE OF PRODUCT DURING SECOND STAGE OF DRYING

The final temperature to which the product may be taken in the second stage of drying and the hygroscopicity or vapor pressure of the product at that temperature also have a bearing on the required temperature for the condenser or pressures needed in direct pumping. This relates to the final residual content of moisture obtainable. Whatever the vapor pressure of the dry product, the condenser or chemical or pump must establish a pressure which is lower. With a desiccant, vapor pressures of 10 microns and lower are readily obtainable, and with condensers or pumps a pressure of 100 microns presents no engineering problem. A condenser temperature of $-40°C$ is adequate to assure this. Few products encountered have a vapor pressure of less than 200 microns at 50°C when containing 0.5 per cent moisture. Plasma may be raised at the end of drying to 60° to 80°C and a large differential readily obtained. This is, however, a higher temperature than that to which orange juice can be taken.

In cases of hygroscopic products not stable at higher temperatures a regenerable desiccant may be used advantageously to yield low partial pressure of water vapor during the final stage—either calcium sulfate or a perchlorate.[9] Since such a small actual weight of water is removed in this stage, regeneration of the desiccant is infrequent. This is a less expensive means than refrigeration to produce lower final condenser temperature or a steam ejector for lower total pressure.

It appears that the "puffing" which occurs during the first drying stage of certain products is due to a plastic condition of the frozen material. Such products as are extreme in their tendency to puff, e.g., orange juice, penicillin and amino acids, have freezing points between 0 and $-5°C$ at reasonable or normal concentrations. Tests with a penetrometer indicate that these products possess a degree of hardness similar to that of pure water-ice. At temperatures around $-30°C$, they are almost the same as ice. Even at temperatures of -10 and $-6°C$, the degree of hardness is not much different from that of ice. At the actual melting points of the several products, the degree of hardness is the same as that of ice at its melting point, although, of course, pure ice is then a few degrees higher in temperature.

In spite of the foregoing considerations, at temperatures as low as $-10°C$ and even in some cases as low as -25 to $-30°C$, there is some apparent "bubbling" or "puffing" of the product. This condition does not set in as it would in the case of an actual liquid; in some instances as long as an hour or two may be required for the formation of a single bubble. Naturally, with any given preparation, the lower the temperature the longer the time required for puffing and the less extensive it is. Only at temperatures below about −40°C do such products become brittle so that they can be cracked and broken up in a granulator.

This situation during drying does no harm provided that the expansion of the product is not sufficient to carry it out of the container in which drying is taking place. In fact, within certain limits, the rate of drying can be accelerated as the result of the greater amount of surface exposed for evaporation. In any event, the degree of puffing varies with temperature, and in the case of all preparations of penicillin dried at a puffing temperature, the puffing has been shown by Cavelti[10] to be the result of bubbling *in vacuo* of microscopic droplets of eutectically and highly concentrated viscous penicillin solution dispersed throughout the solidly frozen hard mass of solvent being sublimed. The condition may be aggravated by a component of low surface tension. With certain penicillin preparations, this component is apparently an impurity present in particularly small amount. The tendency to puff in such instances decreases as the purity increases, and the concentration of total solids drops. The actual units of potency per milligram of solids is not an index of tendency to puff, since all impurities of normal occurrence do not have this same characteristic.

Heating Frozen Products without Thawing

Recognition of critical relationships governing the supply of the latent heat of sublimation to the evaporating frozen product was first recognized in 1935 and described in connection with drying in containers attached to a manifold.[1,2,3] This marked the departure from previous desiccator methods in which the products were either vacuum-insulated from the room or any other source of heat, or were even chilled by refrigeration, being in direct contrast with positive and controlled heating of the product after proper freezing and other factors.[2,11,12] The uncertainty of results and the failure of the older method with delicate preparations, in contrast with present-day successful results, is discussed in connection with the preservation of bacterial cultures in Chapter 3. A proper balance of supply and loss of heat through evaporation in order to maintain a temperature below freezing is accomplished by controlling the ratio of the evaporating surface to the surface of the frozen product adjacent to the outside wall of the container. Heat is supplied at the latter surface and utilized at the former. The size and shape of the container, the quantity of product frozen in a given size container, together with its position, and the shape in which the product is frozen must be carefully controlled to satisfy the critical ratio of the surface mentioned. Medical products which are usually dried in the container to be used for their distribution require different methods of freezing. Blood plasma, of which a dose is a relatively large volume, is "shell-frozen" around the inner periphery of the bottle by rotating it in a liquid freezing bath or otherwise, as described earlier in this chapter. The type of equipment used for this purpose is discussed in Chapter 5. In this way a relatively large evaporating surface is obtained with minimum thickness of layer. The evaporating surface represents a hollow core through the center of the frozen product. As evaporation proceeds this surface expands with the receding ice layer. A notable increase of the rate of drying occurs, therefore, after the first few hours, when the first stage of drying is about 20 to 30 per cent completed. More heat may be applied to the product without raising its temperature when this point is reached.

When long cylindrical containers are used for smaller volumes, the products often are frozen in the form of a long "slab" on one side of the container. The containers are merely placed on their sides in a freezing bath of liquid or in a low-temperature refrigerator. In the case of products like penicillin, where a few cubic centimeters are to be dispensed in a bottle which may be of 20 or 30 cc capacity, the bottles remain in an upright position so that the product is frozen as a "plug" on the bottom of the container.

The faster heat can be supplied, the faster drying can be carried on, but the temperature of the product must not be allowed to rise above its liquefying point. Either manifolds, mentioned above, or vacuum chambers may be used. Vacuum shelf dryers are widely used for this purpose. These are designed either for direct electric heating or for circulation of the heating medium, such as warm water, through the jacket and hollow shelves to supply the latent heat of vaporization more rapidly under controlled conditions. Recently, improved efficiency in the means of vapor withdrawal has made it possible to use even steam (at pressures as high as 40 lbs per sq in) with some products like meat, without melting the frozen product. This greatly shortens the drying time. As drying nears completion and there is less evaporative cooling, the high temperature of the heating source must be lowered so that the final dry product is not taken above its safe limit.

The vacuum shelf dryer has proved very satisfactory and is now the most widely used single piece of equipment for plasma, serum and streptomycin in the United States and Canada. It is coming into use in England and elsewhere in combination with both direct-pumping steam ejectors and low-temperature condensers. Electrical sources of heat, such as resistance heaters, induction heating, high-frequency fields or dielectric heating, and infrared lamps, as well as other forms of energy may be utilized. Oil baths also may be employed. So far, simple hot water has been used most widely. It is important for fast drying that heat be supplied rapidly. In order that drying may proceed with proper uniformity, it is essential that the hot water system be properly designed for even distribution of heat to the product. When using manifolds, warm or hot air may be blown by fans at the bottles of drying material.

With baths, either within vacuum chambers or around manifolds, closer control is possible and heat units can be introduced more rapidly from lower temperature sources. This provides less danger of overheating dried portions of products in the container toward the end of drying. At the outset the temperature of the bath is held below freezing but, of course, it must be higher than the temperature of the product in order to supply the necessary latent heat of sublimation. As drying proceeds, the temperature of the bath is gradually raised. It should be pointed out that in the vacuum chamber, when the bath is held below room temperature, it is not necessary to chill the bath but rather to heat it, even though it is held at low temperature. Finally, the temperature of the bath is set for the maximum to which it is safe to take the final dried product. In this way drying can be accomplished as rapidly as with higher-temperature sources, such as steam in shelves, which must radiate the heat across the vacuum space. The baths accomplish this at the lower temperature because of better transfer of heat by direct contact from liquid to solid surface. Although the period of drying is reduced to a minimum, baths are more complicated in operation and do not necessarily reduce the cost of equipment or of operation. Special metallic holders may be used for increasing the rate of heat transfer, and give nearly the same results in simpler fashion.

Many varieties or combinations of chambers and manifolds can be used efficiently. These are described in greater detail in Chapter 5. The fundamental difference between them is the manner of supplying heat and in sealing the final containers. With manifolds, a greater number of leak-subject vacuum connections are required, but manifolds provide for convenient sealing of the final containers aseptically under the original vacuum.[2] Also, manifolds provide flexibility when the same machine is used for different types of products or varying quantities of material in the containers of a single batch.

Greaves[8] points out that control of the supply of the latent heat of sublimation is the most important single factor in freeze-drying. Greaves has given the following analysis of the variables involved:

The latent heat of evaporation of ice at different temperatures can be calculated from Clapeyron's equation:

$$\frac{dl}{dT} = \frac{\lambda\,(v_2 - v_1)}{T},$$

which gives a value of 672 cal/g between −25 and −30°C. Within the accuracy of this analysis it is fair to assume an average value of 670 cal/g of ice over the whole range. Upon verification of this figure in condensation freeze-drying apparatus, a figure of 901.5 cal/g was obtained. Greaves ascribes this higher figure to losses in the system, but he advises its adoption when calculating requirements for equipment.

Greaves states that from Clapeyron's equation it is clear that the speed of drying depends solely on the rate of application of heat. How quickly the heat can be applied will depend upon: (a) the duty of the refrigerator at the condenser temperature required; (b) the highest "safe" temperature at which the material may be dried: for a given heat input, this temperature will depend upon the degree of obstruction to the flow of vapor and upon the condenser temperature; (c) the highest temperature at which it is considered safe to operate the heaters; and (d) the rate of transfer of heat through the frozen material. If the heat input is too high there will be a tendency to thaw at the point of contact of the frozen material with the heater surface.

During the early stages of drying a steady and balanced heat input can be arranged, but as drying proceeds the rate of heat absorption by the drying material will drop. Greaves found the following over-all average figure useful for preliminary calculations: *1 watt heat input will dry 1 ml in 1 hour.* For example, if it were required to dry 2,000 ml in 10 hours, the heat input required would be 200 watts, and the refrigerator duty must handle this load at the required temperature.

The heat applied to the frozen material during drying produces a vapor pressure difference between the evaporating and the condensing surfaces, and this reflects a difference in temperature between the two surfaces. The system consists therefore of: (1) a pressure difference, (2) an obstruction, and (3) a rate of flow. The relationship between the three is similar to that in Ohm's Law:

$$\frac{\text{Vapor pressure difference}}{\text{Obstruction to flow}} = \text{Rate of flow}$$

Since the rate of flow depends upon the heat input in watts (Clapeyron's equation), the formula may be expressed as follows:

$$\frac{\text{Vapor pressure difference}}{\text{Obstruction to flow}} = K \times \text{watts}$$

Greaves defines the unit of obstructive resistance as that which, under a vapor pressure difference of 0.01 mm Hg, passes vapor at the rate at which it is liberated by a heat input of 1 watt.

Then $\dfrac{P}{R} = \dfrac{W}{100}$

where: P = vapor pressure across the resistance in mm Hg
R = the obstruction expressed in the units proposed
W = the heat input in watts

Greaves does not assume that this analysis takes into account all the physical factors concerned, but over the pressure and temperature ranges normally encountered in this technique, he assumes that calculations based on these assumptions will be reasonably accurate in practice.

By making R infinitely small, W can be infinitely great without producing any significant rise in P. Drying cannot be made instantaneous, however, because the infinitely great W would cause an extremely high heat density and high temperature. This would cause melting at the contact surface of the frozen material because of its relatively low thermal conductivity. Nevertheless, in applying this formula to the drying of serum in open dishes as contrasted with open bottles or filter-capped bottles, Greaves concludes that serum in open dishes should dry much more rapidly than in bottles, particularly when capped with filters. However, we have found that by use of bottles with openings of the proper size, as customary in the United States, there is not nearly as wide a difference in time required for drying as the calculations of Greaves would imply. In the next section we shall consider other factors involved in determining the ultimate rate of drying which are equally if not more important in determining the control of heat.

Greaves applied his formula to experimental data to ascertain the various R values of the different parts of the system as follows:

(1) *Serum in open dishes*
P = 0.02 mm Hg
W = 250 watts
therefore, $R = \dfrac{0.02 \times 100}{250} = 0.008$

This means that 0.008 unit of obstruction exist in the system, the result of the presence of non-condensable gases and of the path the water vapor has to take in order to reach the condenser.

(2) *Serum in open bottles*
   $P = 0.25$ mm Hg
   $W = 7.14$ watts per bottle, total 250 watts for 35 bottles

Here are 35 resistances (due to the necks of the bottles) in parallel, and one resistance (that of the system) in series with this group. Considering one bottle only, the equation becomes:

$$P = \frac{RW}{100} + \frac{rw}{100}$$

where: $R =$ resistance of the bottle neck
     $W =$ heat input to each bottle
     $r =$ resistance of the system (determined above)
     $w =$ total heat input to all the bottles

$$R = \frac{100 \ (P - \frac{rw}{100})}{W}$$
$$= \frac{100 \ (0.25 - 0.02)}{7.14} = 3.22$$

Therefore, 3.22 units of obstruction exist in the neck of the bottle, which has a diameter of $\frac{7}{8}$ in and a length of $1\frac{3}{4}$ in.

Drying Rates

It is not possible to set up drying curves which will apply equally to the wide variety of products which may be freeze-dried. Further, the rates vary with the shape in which the product is frozen. For example, when blood plasma is "shell-frozen" within a bottle, at the outset the only surface for evaporation is that exposed at the narrow inner core running longitudinally through the bottle. As drying proceeds, the ice layer gradually recedes from the initial surface along this core and expands in area. Consequently, drying takes place at a continuously accelerating rate until the ice layer is completely gone. As a result of this, it is possible to apply heat more rapidly as drying proceeds without raising the temperature of the product. In the case of sprayed particles in freeze-drying, this situation is reversed, so that a more rapid rate of drying takes place initially.

For uniform conditions we can consider the rate of drying

liquids which are "bulk" dried in flat pans or trays. Similar uniformity would apply to products "plug-frozen" in bottles but not to products "flat-frozen" on the sides of bottles where the amount of surface decreases as drying proceeds.

Generally speaking, under uniform conditions, products of average characteristics may be dried at the rate of about 1 mm of depth per hour. This assumes optimal differential in vapor pressures and efficient means of heating. Naturally, the rate varies with the maximum permissible temperature for any given product. The 1 mm per hour rate assumes drying at $-18°C$. Under these circumstances the rate of drying is constant and on a straightline basis during the entire first stage of drying, which is until all the ice is gone. This requires about 80 per cent of the total drying time. With most substances this accounts for approximately 95 per cent of the total weight of water to be removed. During the remaining 20 per cent of the drying time the final 5 per cent of initial weight of water is removed. The moisture content generally will be reduced to about 1 per cent at the end of 90 per cent of the time (which corresponds to 99.9 per cent removal of initial moisture) and the final 10 per cent of the drying time is used to bring the moisture content below 0.5 per cent (see Figure 2.3).

The above final content of moisture assumes a vapor pressure at the desiccant surface or refrigerated surface well below the final vapor pressure of the product at the ambient temperature of the dryer. The rate given assumes a porous final product like dried blood plasma and other protein solutions containing not over 10 per cent of solids initially. With higher concentrations the greater density of the product retards the removal of residual moisture. A similar situation exists with products such as orange juice, in which case the final material does not have a completely porous structure. With unconcentrated orange juice the time required to lower the moisture from 1 to 0.1 per cent is as much as 20 per cent of total drying time. This time is even increased in drying preconcentrated orange juice.

The rate of drying penicillin varies widely with purity of product. The average amorphous product today resembles concentrated orange juice rather than plasma in drying characteristics.

In the case of porous products having a vapor pressure over 50 microns at the final drying temperature, a condenser ice surface temperature of −45°C is sufficiently low to accomplish the above-mentioned rates in reaching 0.5 per cent final moisture content.

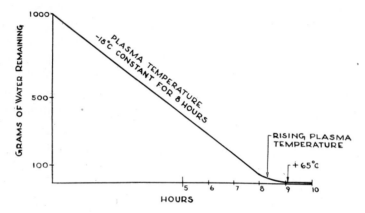

Fig. 2.3. Rate of drying 10% plasma protein solution frozen in uniform flat layer 10 mm. thick.

In other words, the length of drying cycle cannot be predetermined for any single product or class of product in the same way as is possible with more conventional methods of drying. Physical considerations are important in determining the temperature at which the product can be dried. Because of unlike phase conditions in different substances, the temperature below which it is necessary to dry if puffing is to be prevented varies widely from one product to another.

Further, quantities of products dispensed vary from a fraction of 1 ml to around a liter. In some cases, it is necessary that the size of the bottle be as small as possible in relation to the volume of product being dried. Blood plasma is a good example of this: 600 ml is dispensed in bottles as small as 750 ml. In the case of penicillin, as little as 1 ml is dispensed in a 20- or 25-ml container. Consequently, drying may be carried out much more rapidly in the latter case because of the reduced depth of layer per ml of material. The evaporating surface is much greater per ml.

When drying in bulk, with products like orange juice and amino acids, it is advantageous to allow the temperature to rise to a puffing point to increase the amount of evaporating surface. Although this affects the conductivity of heat through the material, generally more rapid drying can be obtained because of the greater surface exposed to evaporation.

As indicated, drying rates are determined by the variation in the conductivity of heat through different solid masses. This is in marked contrast with the conditions existing in boiling liquids, where there is essentially little or no thermal gradient from the heating source to the evaporating surface. Accordingly, with any given material, it is necessary to determine experimentally the rate at which drying can be carried out. Reference has been made to the reason for more rapid drying in thin films or fine particles. With thicker layers, as in a range of a few millimeters up to about 30 mm, products which do not "puff" in the range of -10 to $-20°C$ usually may be dried at the rate of about 1.0 mm depth per hour. In thin films, this rate may be doubled or quadrupled. On the other hand, when drying certain of the more difficult products, such as concentrated solutions of amino acids, this rate may be as little as 0.2 mm depth per hour.

Most Rapid Drying Cycles

Basically, during the first stage of drying a maximal rate of evaporation of the frozen product must be obtained. To achieve this, heat must be introduced into the frozen product as rapidly as possible without causing it to soften or melt. At the same time a maximal rate of flow away from the evaporating surface must be established. To accomplish this rapid flow adequate passageways must be provided for vapor, and this must then be condensed or evacuated efficiently.

Highly efficient condensers of adequate capacity for rapid removal of water vapor in the vacuum system may be used. Also, high-capacity steam ejectors for direct pumping or evacuation of vapor are available. Therefore, the controlling factor for rapid evaporation becomes the rate of supply of heat to the frozen product. In this there are certain basic limitations.

Heat must not be carried to the walls of the container which holds the product faster than the heat can be conducted through the frozen mass to a free surface where it is utilized to induce evaporation. Otherwise melting adjacent to the container wall will occur. Heat can be carried down directly to the evaporating surface itself in order to avoid conductance through ice, but even here there is a limitation. As soon as sublimation has proceeded to an appreciable extent the ice layer has receded from the level of the original surface, so that the evaporating surface has become confined within the interstices of the outer framework of porous dry solid. The heat must then be carried across this porous structure, but the temperature of this dry portion of the product must not be brought above the level at which it will be harmed.

All of this means that the ultimate speed of drying is determined and limited by the speed at which the heat of sublimation can be carried to the ice surface, and this limitation is one of conduction through poor conductors. When heat is applied rapidly to a product during sublimation, measurement of the temperature at different levels throughout the frozen layer reveals that there is a considerable thermal gradient from the outside surface up through the ice to the evaporating surface.

The only remaining unexploited means that can be foreseen at present for further acceleration of drying lies in development of a means for rapid generation of heat at the evaporating and receding ice surface only. Thin films assist materially in this direction. This can be realized only in bulk drying because, when drying medical products in market containers, it is desirable for other reasons to use as small a bottle as possible. When drying in bulk, thin films cannot be used in the batch type of equipment because very short cycles increase the number of loading and unloading operations per day. These require not only more labor, but also more time than would be saved as the result of the faster drying rate. For this reason, in batch drying of products in bulk, longer cycles are more conventional. In a continuous type of dryer advantage can be taken of the faster rate of drying in thin films or fine particles, but this introduces other problems in the way of equipment which will be discussed in Chapter 6.

In the final stage of drying the rate of supplying heat is not so critical because the actual weight of water being evaporated is small. The high porosity of the product allows the ready escape of vapors.

Bradish, Brain, and McFarlane[13] and Bradish[14] believe that the rate of drying is controlled more by limitations in the rate of transfer of water vapor from the frozen product to the ice surface of the condenser than by the preceding considerations of transfer of the latent heat of sublimation to the evaporating surface, as set forth by Greaves. Bradish states that the retardation effect of the porous dry mass above the receding ice surface of the material being dried is small. He believes that the transfer of vapor is limited by the rate of diffusion. He quotes Knudsen[15] that the maximum rate of vaporization from an ice surface at absolute temperature T is expressed by the equation

$$G_{max} = 0.244 \ ac\frac{P_T}{v^T} \text{ g per sq cm per sec}$$

where P_T mm Hg is the saturated vapor pressure in equilibrium with the ice surface and may be obtained from the physical tables. The numerical constant is a function of the molecular weight of the vaporizing material and a the condensation coefficient, which expresses the fraction of vapor molecules entering the mass of ice following collision with its surface. The fraction $I - a$ is reflected on collision and remains in the vapor phase. Bradish states that Knudsen has confirmed this equation and has shown that the condensation coefficient is unity for certain metals. It is pointed out that there is some doubt as to the value and temperature dependence of the condensation coefficient of water vapor. Bradish then quotes Tschudin[16] and Alty[17] as reporting conflicting values. However, Bradish feels that experimental and theoretical evidence favors the assumption of a unit condensation coefficient and he accepts this value. He says that the implication of a unit condensation coefficient is simply that every molecule colliding with an ice surface is immediately condensed, although it may be reevaporated later. Thus every molecule leaving the evaporating surfaces will suffer collisions in the partially dry material and interspace and will eventualy collide with, and condense on, the surface of the frozen material or of the condenser ice. The effective rate of sublimation is not equal to the rate of vaporization from the surface of the frozen material, but to the mass of water vapor actually transferred in unit time from frozen material to condenser ice.

Bradish says that if the interspace gap is so short that molecules are transferred almost without collision, then the sublimation rate is equal to the rate of vaporization at the surface of the frozen material minus the rate of vaporization at the surface of the condenser ice. If numerous collisions occur in the interspace this simple difference equation no longer applies, and must be modified to include terms expressing the proportion of molecules which traverse the interspace, as distinct from those which eventually condense on the surface from which they were evaporated. In drying systems in which the evaporating and condensing surfaces are widely separated, or in which the permanent gas partial pressure is high, the sublimation rate is low as a consequence of the numerous molecular collisions in the interspace.

Bradish further claims to have obtained rates of drying much faster than those reported by Greaves, which Bradish attributes to the placement of a cold condenser just above trays containing the materials being dried. If faster rates are actually realized there is no definite evidence to indicate that this may not have been purely as a result of better transfer of heat to the evaporating ice surface. As long as passageways to carry the vapor are adequate in diameter, no pressure drop can be detected between the condenser and the zones near the material being dried. This would seem to indicate that, as long as a properly efficient condenser and adequate passageways to carry the vapor are provided, faster drying depends not upon the actual rate of diffusion but upon the rate at which heat is carried to the evaporating surface. Here definite measurable gradients of substantial magnitude are readily demonstrated. This may be as much as 5 or 10°C in rapid drying from the bottom of a tray to the top evaporating surface where the heat is being carried to the tray from a hot shelf supporting it. This is far in excess of any differential in terms of microns from the area just above that of the evaporating surface to the region of the condenser, even when the condenser is as far as 10 or 15 ft. away, with large interconnecting vapor lines.

Final Moisture Content

The critical relationship between stability of the final product and extremely low moisture content was recognized in 1935 and for the first time set forth as a requirement.[2] A final moisture content of 0.5 per cent was first obtained at that time and recognized as a desirable level for maximal stability of most medical products. In no case should a moisture above 1 per cent be allowed if the product is to be stored for more than a few months, particularly when not under refrigeration. At 5 to 8 per cent moisture, the potency of even such a relatively stable product as diphtherial antitoxin falls off more rapidly than that of the original liquid product when kept at a corresponding temperature. There is also a rapid loss in rate and completeness of solubility with a moisture content in this higher range.[18] This is illustrated by data of Table 3.

Greaves[19] states that the current British practice is to eliminate all residual moisture from blood plasma and serum. To accomplish this, a three-day cycle of drying using −41 to −44°C condensers produces a residual moisture of 0.4 per cent. The residue is then removed by two successive secondary drying periods of two days

TABLE 3

LOSS IN POTENCY OF DIPHTHERIAL ANTITOXIN
Horse Serum
Effect of initial content of moisture; stored at 37°C—all-glass containers

	Initial Moisture (%)	Potency, units per ml				
		Initial	6 weeks	6 months	18 months	3 years
Liquid........	—	550	550	<45	0	—
Dry..........	0.5	550	550	550	550	450
Dry..........	5 to 8	550	<45	Insoluble	—	—

each over P_2O_5. This consumes a total drying time of seven days per batch. In the United States, procedure occupying a total drying time of 20 hours or less (as little as 8 hours) is able to produce 0.2 to 0.5 per cent H_2O. Whether the time consumed in the British practice of complete elimination of the final traces of moisture is justified in terms of degree of increased stability of blood plasma is still an open question and only time can answer it. Current regulations of the National Institute of Health in the United States specify a maximal moisture-content of 1 per cent for dried biological products. Determination of the residual content of moisture in these products may be made either, (1) by phosphorus pentoxide under vacuum[2,20] or, (2) in a vacuum oven (under 100 microns pressure) at 50° C for 24 to 48 hours under conditions as described,[20] only the first being approved by the N. I. H.

The following is the procedure followed for these two methods: For use with samples of approximately 1 gm. (the solids from 10 ml of serum), low form, flat-bottom weighing bottles (50 mm diameter) with well ground stoppers* are used. These are prepared by cleaning in chromic acid solution, followed by thorough rinsing with distilled water. The bottles with the lids tilted open are then placed in the oven† for 2 hours under a vacuum at 50°. The oven is connected directly to a Cenco Hyvac pump. The tubing should be short and all connections should be sufficiently tight to permit evacuation to 0.1 to 0.2 mm of Hg (McLeod gage). The bottles with the lids closed are then removed from the oven and placed directly in a desiccator to cool. The desiccator should contain a large freshly scraped surface of P_2O_5. In 1 hour, temperature equilibrium is attained and the bottles are removed from the desiccator one by one and weighed to 0.1 mg as quickly as possible.

The bottles are now filled quickly with amounts of samples believed to be about 1 gm each. The lids must be replaced on the bottles with as little delay as possible after transferring the sample.** The bottles are reweighed quickly in order to obtain the exact weight of the sample.

---

* Arthur H. Thomas Company, catalogue No. 9965 or equivalent.

† Weber vacuum oven. Arthur H. Thomas Company, No. 7886, No. 7888 or equivalent.

** It has been found that the moisture content will be increased by as much as 1 per cent of the weight of the solids in 1 minute of standing with the lid off (relative humidity of 68 per cent).

The bottles are then placed in the desiccator with specially scraped P_2O_5. The lids are tilted on the sides. The desiccator is evacuated to a pressure of 50 to 100 microns. After two days, it is opened and the bottles reweighed, carefully closing the lids before removal from the desiccator. They are then returned to the desiccator for another drying period of 24 hours and this is continued until constant weight is reached.

In using the vacuum oven, a similar procedure is followed. With the lids tilted, the bottles are placed in the vacuum oven regulated to $50° \pm 1°$. The lids should not be opened until after the bottles are placed in the oven; otherwise drafts may blow away small particles of the light and fluffy sample. The Cenco pump is turned on and allowed to run continuously for 22 hours with a pressure of 0.1 to 0.2 mm of Hg. A pressure of 0.2 mm of Hg should be reached within an hour or less.

In 22 hours the pump is shut off and air is slowly admitted to the oven. The precaution of admitting dry air into the hot oven has been found to be unnecessary. The lids are replaced instantly and the bottles removed to the desiccator for cooling. They are weighed after an hour to 0.1 mg as previously.

By this procedure, any detectable errors which might arise from atmospheric conditions are avoided, even on days when the relative humidity approaches 100 per cent. This method is fully satisfactory for carrying out a large number of routine determinations.

Penicillin may be an exception in the degree of low final moisture required, but the matter is still at issue since no complete and convincing data have been published. In the type of container currently being used for penicillin there is some opportunity for permeation of water vapor through the rubber stopper, as will be discussed in Chapter 5. As a result, over a long period of time, particularly when the containers are stored under adverse conditions of temperature and humidity, there may be some increase in the moisture content. This is another reason for drying as completely as possible because it provides a greater storage reserve for subsequent increase in moisture.

For the best keeping qualities in most foods it is imperative that moisture content be reduced to below 2 per cent, and preferably to 0.5 per cent, regardless of the method of drying; but in carrying it out from the frozen state, there is available a means of achieving such low moisture content without harming most foods. To achieve this low moisture by other means the product must be taken to excessive temperature. The general porosity and nature of the product obtained by sublimation make this stable condition readily attainable.

Determining the Completion of Drying
and Temperature of Product

An important practical consideration in any program for the control of drying is to know just when the proper degree of dryness has been attained. At the end of desiccation, as dryness is reached, the rate of evaporative cooling decreases markedly. The temperature of the product passes $0°C$, then approaches and finally reaches the jacket temperature of the chamber. (When using containers on a manifold, ice frost on the outside of the containers turns to liquid and then disappears as the product finally reaches the temperature of the atmosphere or bath around the containers.) A thermometer placed within a bottle and observed through a sight-glass in the drying chamber measures this. A thermocouple also may be used; although it is more accurate, the closer reading is not fully significant because of variations from one ampoule to another. A thermocouple has a greater advantage where the layer is too thin to permit satisfactory use of a thermometer bulb. With regard to variations from ampoule to ampoule, uneven heating, variation in thickness of the frozen layer and other factors are responsible for such non-uniformity. Allowance in drying time must be made for ampoules which are slower in drying than the index ampoule. The attainment of the final upper temperature, as measured by a thermometer, provides a practical index of completion of drying.

When measuring the temperature of plasma in standard transfusion bottles, a Weston type of metallic stem thermometer may be used with success. The entire stem is surrounded by the "shelled" material. Even toward the completion of the first stage of drying when the ice layer has receded to nearly the outer periphery of the bottle, there is a complete ice shield from the source of heat and the vapors passing through the layer of porous dried material are at a temperature corresponding to the evaporating surface. For this reason the thermometer gives an accurate index of the temperature of the ice until it is almost completely sublimed, after which the thermometer indicates the rise in temperature of the final dried product during the second drying stage.

Similarly, in bulk drying, to be discussed later, when the product is in open pans, the thermometer can be inserted through a hole in the side of the pan at any level. By placing thermometers at different levels, the temperature gradient may be measured. Then, when the ice layer is nearly gone (and even before), a thermometer in the upper layer of dried material does not reflect the temperature of the layer of ice at the bottom because of heat radiating downward from the shelf above. Short-stem Weston-type thermometers placed in small bottles like those used for penicillin reflect in large measure an average of heat radiating from the warm drying chamber and the temperature of ice in the bottles. Thermometers can be used in this way as an index even though they do not give accurate temperatures.

For accurate temperatures a small thermocouple frozen into the bottle is the only satisfactory means. In this case, the thermocouple should be placed at the lowest part of the layer of frozen material and adjacent to the container wall in order to be of greatest value in indicating completion of drying. Copper-constantan couples are quite satisfactory, ice-water being used for the constant-temperature junction. Greaves[8] suggests that the constant-temperature junction be held at the temperature corresponding to the highest to which the product is to be taken, in order to avoid giving attention to the maintenance of an ice bath.

Some additional time must be allowed for further drying to eliminate the final traces of moisture. This is accomplished by maintaining the product for a specified length of time at the above-mentioned final maximal temperature. With efficient apparatus, 15 per cent additional time is usually adequate, but the length of time actually required is also a function of each specific product. This relates to its hygroscopicity, the temperature to which the stability of the product will permit it to be taken (shorter times required at high temperatures), and the thickness of layer of product in the container.

As desiccation proceeds, the pressure in the apparatus will decrease, ultimately reaching that of the residual air in the drying chamber. It is controlled by the rate of leakage into the equipment and the efficiency of the vacuum pumps. The lower the pressure of air, the more sensitive is the index provided by total pressure, since the less air there is in the system the greater the portion of the total pressure due to the partial pressure of water vapor. Determination of the true total pressure of water vapor in a vacuum system is an important matter requiring separate consideration.

Measuring Water Vapor Pressure

In spite of the fact that the McLeod gage first appeared in 1874[21] it still remains the basic type of instrument used for measurement of high vacuum. Since that time, although various modifications and improvements have been proposed,[22,23,24] all utilize the basic principle described by McLeod. This method provides the only satisfactory known means for absolute measurement of the extremely fine pressures of high vacuum. Technically, the high vacuum range is usually regarded among engineers as applying to pressures below 5 or 10 mm Hg and runs on down to the zone of microns and fractions thereof. A micron is 0.001 mm Hg and provides a convenient term for expression of low pressures.

A closed-end manometer or a U-tube type of mercury manometer of sufficient length may be used for measurement of absolute pressure, but such a device is limited in sensitivity by the difference in the level of mercury which can be read. Lenses or other means of magnification of reading are not suitable since there is insufficient movement of the mercury with a slight difference in pressure. Inertia of movement under slight pressure differences, together with frictional resistance, nullifies use of lever and float arrangements for increasing sensitivity. For direct measurement in terms of absolute pressure of mercury, therefore, only the McLeod type of vacuum gage is suitable.

THERMAL ELECTRIC GAGES

All other gages for measurement of high vacuum are based on some other property in the vacuum system, and accordingly all other gages must be calibrated against the McLeod type. For example, one type of electrical gage is based on the thermal conductivity of the residual gases in the vacuum system. A source of heat, such as a hot wire element, is used and either a thermocouple or resistance thermometer wire is used to measure the amount of heat transmitted to it. Still another type of thermal gage operates on the temperature of the hot wire or filament itself, the temperature of this wire being fixed by the rate at which heat is carried away from it. The temperature of this wire is determined by change in resistance. The Pirani gage is of this type. Hydrogen and even water vapor conduct heat to a greater extent than air at the same pressure and consequently a gage calibrated for air would give inaccurate readings with other gases and vapors. With hydrogen, the error would be a high reading in terms of air calibration. Hence, in freeze-drying, a different calibration would be required at various times during the drying cycle as the proportion of water vapor to air changes. It might vary in drying even from one batch to another, as the leakage of air into the equipment is subject to daily fluctuation, depending upon how tightly valves and doors are closed, the condition of packing, and other factors.

Furthermore, with this type of gage, the surface characteristics of the heating wire become altered with age so that recalibration against the McLeod gage is necessary frequently, even with air measurement alone. This gage is sensitive only in the range of 1 to 100 microns. At higher vacuum, thermal conductance is too small to enable the method to be used and at higher pressures the change in conductance is too small to confer proper sensitivity.

IONIZATION GAGES

An ionization type of gage is also used, but does not operate at pressures above about 0.5 micron. In fact, if the ionization tube is not turned off at pressures above this, it will be damaged permanently, so that there is serious limitation in its use. (For a short period, pressures up to 200 microns will cause no damage.) Briefly, the principle of the ionization gage makes use of the fact that an electron emission current from the hot cathode of the three electrode vacuum tube will cause ionization of gas molecules in the tube by bombardment. These ions flow to a plate maintained at a sufficiently high negative potential with respect to the hot cathode. Then, by means of a meter in the plate circuit, the ion current is measured to indicate directly the vacuum in microns.

MISCELLANEOUS GAGES

Other types of gage have been designed, such as those depending upon a calibrated leak through a fine capillary; or a differential bellows by means of which a comparison is obtained against a known reference vacuum; or still another type in which a U-tube carrying a fluid of specific gravity much less than mercury is used. Above this fluid in one arm a known reference vacuum is maintained so that, by difference in level, the exact vacuum in the system may be determined. With all these gages, a McLeod gage must be used either to check the "reference vacuum" or to calibrate the scale.

MCLEOD GAGE

In spite of the limitations of the gages described, there frequently are special applications where gages of these kinds are well adapted. Unless some special reason exists, however, the McLeod type is always to be preferred since it is the ultimate reference standard. The McLeod gage does not require batteries or other electrical connections for operation and it is rugged; hence, it is used directly for all ordinary vacuum measurements in drying by sublimation. Also, the McLeod type may be used over a much wider range of vacuum, as from a fraction of a micron up to 5,000 microns. With other gages a series must be used for such a range, each covering a small portion of the total range of interest in freeze-drying. Further, in the swivel type of McLeod gage, one has available all of the above-mentioned advantages of the McLeod type, in combination with portability.

With the McLeod gage, non-condensable gases other than air, such as hydrogen, cause no error in reading but condensable vapors such as water or alcohols cause serious error unless the gage is properly designed and used. For this reason it is imperative to

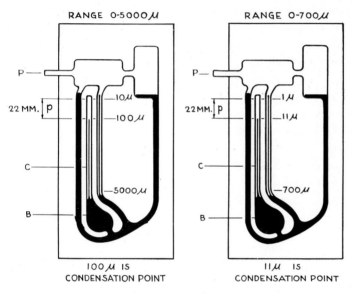

Fig. 2.4. Comparative condensation errors in gages of different scale range.

give careful consideration to a suitable McLeod type gage in freeze-drying during all portions of the cycle, including that portion when there is largely water vapor in the system and also at the end, when there is nearly pure air.

The portable, swivel type[23,24] (Fig. 2.4) gage is one of the most convenient and is widely used. Other forms of McLeod gage are bulky and cumbersome and also require large quantities of mercury. Many of them are fragile and may require an auxiliary vacuum for operation. For this reason, in the following discussion, the McLeod gage will be discussed in terms of the swivel type, although the basic principles apply equally well to all forms of McLeod gage.

Principle of operation. Turning the swivel gage from a horizontal position to the vertical position, as illustrated in Fig. 2.4, cuts off a definite volume V of the rarefied air at the unknown pressure P of the vacuum system, and compresses it to a smaller volume v at a higher pressure p. It will be observed that V is the combined volume of the measuring bulb B and the center tube C (closed end or measuring capillary). The value of p is equal to the difference in level of the mercury in the center tube C and the right outside tube compensating capillary. Boyle's law is used in calibration of the scale.

During compression, the pressure to volume relation of Boyle applies only to noncondensable gases. With condensable vapors like that of water, there is much greater contraction since they withstand only a small degree of compression before condensing. If the pressure p exerted on the vapor trapped in the center tube exceeds the condensation pressure (which varies with temperature), the vapor condenses. As a result of the greater contraction in volume in the center tube from this cause, the mercury will rise farther than otherwise to indicate a far better vacuum than actually exists. There is no simple correction or multiplication factor that can take account of this.

Water Vapor Effect. 1. Condensation; Higher Pressure Range—Compare two gages, as in Fig. 2.4, one having a range of 0 to 5,000 microns and the other 0 to 700 microns (the gages having about the same scale length), connected to the same vacuum system. With water present, different readings will be obtained, but neither will be correct. This is because it is the difference in level p of the mercury in the two capillaries which sets up the pressure resulting in condensation of the moisture. At a temperature of 24°C the vapor pressure of water is 22 mm. In other words, if the difference in level p of the mercury in the two capillaries is 22 mm or more, the vapor will be condensed. This point on the measuring capillary, corresponding to the difference in level which is equal to the vapor pressure, we may call the condensation point.

In the wide-range gage, reading from 0 to 5,000 microns, the condensation point corresponds on the scale to a pressure of about 100 microns; on the narrow-range gage, to 11 microns as indicated in the drawings. Consequently, if there is largely water vapor in the gage, at a pressure of 250 microns, and very little air, say 2 microns, the vapor will condense to liquid (invisibly small in amount) and the contraction in volume will cause the mercury to rise in the measuring capillary to within 22 mm of the top—which corresponds to the vapor pressure of the condensed water.

Comparison of the two gages will thus result in the wide-range instrument indicating 100 microns and the narrow-range one, 11 microns. In this example, where the total pressure of air and water vapor combined is 252 microns, it is seen that the total pressure is far above 11 microns and even above 100 microns. All the operator knows, however, is that the pressure of the air alone is not over 11 microns, because if it were more, it would prevent the mercury from rising so high.

When there is enough air in the system to yield readings above 100 microns, the two gages would come into closer, but still not exact, agreement. Both readings would still be in error. For example, take a case at 24°C, where there is 100 microns pressure of air and 1,500 microns pressure of water vapor, yielding a total pressure of 1,600 microns. With the wider-range scale, p would comprise 22 mm of length for the compressed air plus another 22 mm for the partial pressure of water vapor under compression which sets up saturated conditions. Thus 44 mm of scale length would indicate a pressure of 450 microns. Similarly, with the narrower-range scale (0 to 700 microns), p would comprise 51 mm for the air and 22 mm more for water vapor, a total length of 73 mm, indicating 200 microns. Both gages would give exactly these same fictitious readings in microns with actual pressures even as high as 5,000 microns, if only 100 microns of this total pressure were due to air and the remaining 4,900 to water vapor. Similarly, with 100 microns of air and 150 microns of vapor, a total of 250, the wide range gage would read about 175 microns and the narrow range instrument 200 microns. Drying the gages will correct these errors.

2. *Outgassing; Low Pressure Range*—At total pressures below the condensation point, condensation cannot occur and accurate readings are obtainable. Water vapor coming slowly from the glass or mercury in the gage, however, may not be pumped

away completely enough to establish equilibrium with the system, in which case a fictitiously high reading is obtained. Generally, this is at pressures below 10 microns and pressures as low as this are normally not encountered in freeze-drying. However, drying the gage will correct this error also. Outgassing of non-condensables from glass or rubber can be corrected only by pumping sufficiently long. Furthermore, at very high vacuum, rubber connections must be eliminated.

Condensation Correction. 1. Hot Gage Method—This is applicable where the range of operating pressures is such that, at some reasonably high temperature, the condensation point will exceed all pressures to be encountered. For example, at 38°C, the 5,000 micron range gage will give true total pressures up to 500 microns; and at 48°C, up to 2,000 microns (the 700 micron range gage being correct up to 250 microns). At 66°C either gage would give true total pressures up to the maximum of its range. This method will not always function at the highest vacuum, *e.g.*, where moisture from the mercury itself is not pumped away rapidly enough; indeed, then errors of fictitiously high readings due to outgassing are magnified.

2. Air Flush Method—This means is applicable where a high capacity vacuum pump is used. A tee tube is placed in the line to the gage. By means of a stop-cock or a pinch-cock, the gage is closed off from the vacuum system and air is admitted to the gage through the tee tube. The gage is then evacuated again to flush out most of the water vapor. In about two minutes a reading is taken and it will be found higher than the original, before flushing, in proportion to the amount of water vapor initially present. As further readings are taken, however, it will be noted that they gradually lower again as vapor diffuses back into the gage. Whenever a reading close to the true total pressure in the system is desired, the gage must be flushed. This is not applicable at higher vacuum.

3. Chemical Trap—This is the simplest method of all. A glass tube large enough in diameter to cause no undue restriction of flow is used. It is filled with a chemical selected on the basis of a vapor pressure well below the minimum pressure to be encountered in the high vacuum system. By suitable selection, chemicals for vapors other than that of water which cause similar errors, such as alcohol and oil, may be removed. An indicator chemical may be used so that time for replacement may be determined readily. At highest vacuum, say at pressures below 0.1 micron, it may be necessary to cool the chemical trap.

4. Freezing Trap—A low-temperature condenser kept cold by means of Dry Ice, liquid air, or liquid nitrogen may be used for freezing out the moisture at a properly low vapor pressure. The necessity for continual supply of the refrigerant and for frequent removal of condensate makes this method less convenient.

The chemical or freezing trap causes true *total* pressures to be indicated even though there is only dry air in the gage at all times. This air is present in quantity so that its pressure exactly balances the total pressure of water vapor and air in the system on the other side of the trap. Even traces of moisture will cause some degree of error and new gages (or old ones that have just been cleaned) may require several days under vacuum, protected by a moisture trap, for complete removal of moisture in order to insure accurate readings. Always keep the gage protected and admit only dry air to it.

Readings When McLeod Gage Is Wet. Since the wider the range of the gage the higher the condensation point, a moist gage of wide range can be used up to higher pressures than one of narrow range before errors of condensation arise. A condensable vapor trap is recommended to exclude permanently all vapors, the chemical type being the most practicable. Using two gages of different scale range and obtaining identical readings is the best means of knowing with certainty that accurate readings are being secured.

With a McLeod gage of the recording type for producing a continuous record of vacuum, a proper trap for moisture is indispensable.

After a given freeze-drying system has been properly designed and put into operation and capacities have been established on a daily routine, a McLeod gage without a condensable vapor trap can be used as an index of the proper operation of vacuum pumps and also to show that there is not excessive leakage into the vacuum system. In other words, when the same kind of product is being dried daily and there is the same water load at the condenser (or other device for removal of water vapor) there is not necessarily need for knowing the true total pressure. Presumably, drying cycles have been worked out and there may not be any necessity for knowing the true total pressure to determine when drying is finished. In such a case, it is entirely suitable to use a McLeod gage without a condensable vapor trap. If a major leak develops, the gage will register a major change, even if not accurately.

With the wider range gage mentioned above (having a condensation point at 100 microns on the scale at 24°C), and with moisture in the system, any reading of more than 100 microns should be interpreted as indicating an air pressure about equal to the actual reading, or a little less, plus an unknown amount of water vapor (since the water vapor would be condensed in the capillary to just a fraction of its ordinary volume).

Readings near 100 microns (in the range ±25 microns or less) should be interpreted as indicating an air pressure of not more than the reading, plus an unknown amount of water vapor. In this case, the actual air pressure might be only a few microns and the rest of the pressure would then be caused by water vapor. However, the actual amount of water vapor might be very much more than the reading on the gage, since most of the vapor might have condensed to a smaller volume.

Readings below the 100 micron point but above 10 microns can be interpreted as indicating close to the true total (air and water vapor) pressure in the system.

The same interpretation applies to narrower-range gages (such as one reading from zero to 700 microns), but in this case also the interpretation would be based on whether the reading is above or below the condensation point (11 microns instead of 100 microns). The wider the range of the gage (as one of zero to 5,000 microns as compared to one of zero to 100 microns) the greater the proportion of water vapor which is permissible before error by condensation results.

In other words, in the above-mentioned example, any major leaks in the vacuum system or any fault in the vacuum pump, which would result in an excessive pressure of air in the system, would immediately be reflected in a reading well above 100 microns. The operator would know that if the gage reads 100 microns this is not necessarily the true pressure, particularly during the first stage of drying by sublimation. However, he would further know that everything is in proper operating condition in his plant, and with the gage registering 100 microns, the particular batch is off to a good start in drying without excessive leakage. If he obtains a reading of only 500 microns or 1000 microns on the gage, he knows that it must be due to air.

Bradish[14] has summarized the freeze-drying work of Greaves in England. An exception must be taken to one statement of Bradish, "The permanent gas (air) partial pressure is observed by means of a McLeod gauge and liquid air trap." As discussed, this method of using the McLeod Gage does give a true reading of the *total* pressure as proved experimentally.

Sherwood,[25] in experimental work with freeze-drying penicillin, has used an "icy-ball" as a means for determining the vapor pressure of water in his experimental "dryer." A thermocouple was embedded in the center of a 9 cu cm block of frozen distilled water and the temperature so indicated was used on the basis of the vapor pressure of ice at that temperature to establish the pressure of vapor within the chamber. Although Sherwood did not attempt to use this method to determine the ratio of water vapor pressure to that of non-condensable gases, this could readily be done by use of a McLeod Gage, properly protected with a trap which would give total pressure as described above. Sherwood noted that the suspended icy ball vaporized at a very much lower rate than did the ice in bottles. This would apparently be due to the fact that the only heat which would reach the ball would be by radiation across the vacuum space.

Drying in Market Containers

MEDICAL PRODUCTS

It was as a direct result of the development in 1935[2] of a practical method for drying in the final container that freeze-drying, or lyophilization as it was most commonly called at that time, came to be of use in the medical field. Not only was it necessary to take the old laboratory art of drying in an ice-box and develop it into a physically workable drying procedure, but it was essential to carry out the process with sterility. Most medical products to which it was of interest and advantage to apply freeze-drying are used parenterally. Hence the necessity of maintaining rigid sterility. The distribution of any bulk-processed material always has presented a difficult problem (and still does) where a hygroscopic and sterile product must be handled. This is the more important since most products after drying are in the form of a cake and must be broken up, then possibly ground and subdivided. In the case of grinding protein substances there are the dangers of denaturation, absorption of moisture, and bacterial contamination. Often, these products are highly potent and need to be weighed or measured accurately. Although penicillin bulk-processing with final transfer to market containers was carried out on a limited scale, it was soon abandoned by most firms in favor of the method originally developed in 1935 for processing in the final container. Streptomycin, because of other considerations, is largely bulk-dried and subdivided.

It was stated in 1935[2] that "This procedure has already proved satisfactory for operation on the scale required in the research laboratory, on a scale suitable for large hospital and board of health uses, and on a semi-industrial scale. There is little doubt that it can readily be adapted to full industrial scale operation.

"The essential problems that had to be solved in developing the several models of apparatus to be described were (a) the securing of automatic regulation of temperature during the processing of the product in the individual containers in which it is to be stored and distributed, (b) the completion of the dehydration within reasonable time, (c) the provision of practicable means of sealing and severing the containers individually without loss of the original vacuum, and (d) the preservation of asepsis throughout the process."

Temperature control was made automatic by regulating the rate of sublimation of water vapor from the product undergoing desiccation. Quoting further from the same source, "Regulation of the rate of sublimation is accomplished by apparatus which satisfies certain critical relationships between the rate of heat intake from the atmosphere at the exterior glass surface of the containers, the rate of heat loss at the evaporating surfaces of the product, and the rate of escape of water vapor from the product to the condensers. Adequate condensing surface must also be provided. The essential features which have established this automatic regulation of temperature on a satisfactory basis are as follows:

"*a.* The product is frozen in containers of proper size and shape, in such a way as to give the correct relationship of the evaporating surface of the frozen product to the surface adjacent to the glass, through which atmospheric heat is transferred to the frozen solid.

"*b.* The product in its containers is brought to a very low temperature before attachment to the desiccating apparatus.

"*c.* Very rapid attachment of the containers to the manifold of the apparatus is provided for.

"*d.* All connections between the containers and the condensers are made with bore large enough to offer a sufficiently free passage for the escaping water vapor.

"*e.* The rapid establishment and maintenance of a high vacuum throughout the apparatus is provided for.

"Completion of the process within a reasonable time has been effected by regulation of the relationship between the above-mentioned surfaces of the frozen product and its volume and depth."

Freezing of the product was carried out with cotton plugs in the mouths of the containers. Therefore, with contraction of the air in the containers during freezing, air drawn in from the room was filtered free of bacteria. The plugs had to be removed for drying, but during this step all flow of vapors was outward. At the conclusion of the process of drying the containers were sealed under the original processing vacuum. Accordingly, there was never opportunity for bacterial contamination or absorption of water.

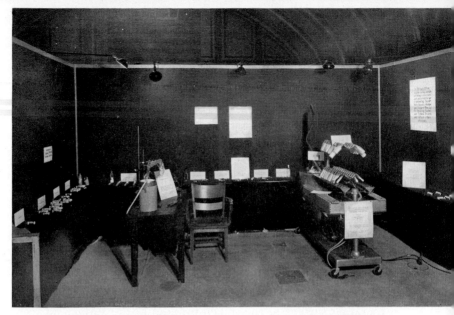

Fig. 2.5. Author's exhibit of dry-ice type of lyophile apparatus which received the award of Honorable Mention at the scientific exhibit of the American and Canadian Medical Associations in 1935 at Atlantic City. The apparatus on the left is a small glass miniature laboratory type and the one on the right is the hospital size for human sera. Also shown are samples of freeze-dried convalescent serum used at the Children's Hospital as discussed in Chapters 1 and 3.

Furthermore, during drying itself, the containers were placed on a manifold in such a fashion as to permit no solid matter to fall into them by gravity. In most types of equipment used today many of these principles are still utilized.*

With respect to medical products, there is generally an aversion to the appearance of any product which has "puffed" during drying. This situation undoubtedly has arisen from the fact that in many products such an appearance is a sign that deterioration may have occurred, particularly if they are proteins. Mortality of

---

* Practical lyophile Dry Ice apparatus of this type was demonstrated by the author at the meeting of the Society of American Bacteriologists in December 1934,[2] at the Atlantic City meeting of the American and Canadian Medical Associations in 1935 where the scientific exhibit illustrated in Figure 2.5 received the award of Honorable Mention,[26] at the meeting of the American Public Health Association in 1935, and of the Second International Microbiological Congress in London in 1936.[27] The cryochem machine illustrated in Figure 2.6 subsequently was shipped to Africa for work with Rinderpest as discussed in Chapter 3 in 1938.

viruses and bacteria is particularly high if such a condition exists. Accordingly, a high standard of appearance is recognized as a physical index of proper drying. In the case of certain products such a situation would be of no consequence, but even so, the same high standard is maintained for all products. Further, the amount

Fig. 2.6. First manifold type of Cryochem machine using a regenerable chemical desiccant and with built-in electrically heated regenerator. The apparatus is of the manifold type and has been operating for ten years successfully in Africa in connection with Rinderpest as discussed in Chapter 3.

of "puffing" which can occur in an ampoule is highly critical, since if it exceeds a certain degree, the product will expand out of the container and proper drying cannot be controlled. Therefore, it is preferable to prevent all puffing when drying in final containers.

Bulk Drying

For many purposes, even for medical products, it is desirable not to dry in final ampoules. This applies when carrying out desiccation as a step in general processing in which the product is not stored or distributed in dried form. Examples of this are fractionated products of blood plasma such as serum albumin. During the war serum albumin was dried from the frozen state because it was the most practical means of assuring elimination of all final traces of alcohol used in its preparation without harm to the protein. On the other hand, it was not necessary to obtain extremely low content of residual moisture since the product was stable in solution and hence better adapted for distribution in solution. After drying it was dissolved and bacteriologically filtered so that it was readily sterilized. There are other medical products for which similar reasons exist for drying in bulk.

Similarly, but for other reasons, many labile medical products may be concentrated in this fashion. In these cases special stainless steel sterility pans, with lids designed to keep out microorganisms during drying, or large glass bottles may be used. If bottles are used, they may be placed either on a manifold or within heated vacuum chambers. Penicillin is dried by some manufacturers in bulk with aseptic distribution by weighing the dry powder into final ampoules. Here it is necessary to carry out weighing and filling into ampoules in special cubicles or hoods which are fed with air of relative humidity preferably maintained as low as 1 per cent and arranged for maintaining complete sterility. This is done by using filtered air, installing ultraviolet lights, and by covering the front of the hood with aprons having sealed-in sleeves for the operator's hands. In this way, the operator is out of all direct contact with the interior of the cubicle. This procedure has met with disfavor in some quarters because of greater technical difficulty of being assured of sterile manipulation. If there is contamination when products are distributed into final containers as a liquid, there is greater likelihood that a sample bottle, or bottles picked at random, will be representative because of greater uniformity of mixing than is the case when products are distributed in solid form. Apparently either method can be used; bulk drying is more difficult but lower in cost if properly set up on a large scale.

For many industrial products, bulk drying is the only manner in which they may conceivably be handled economically. Aside from the matter of easier handling, other advantages accrue from drying in bulk. Heating of the product is more readily controlled, particularly at a rapid rate. In drying continuously in thin films lowest cost is realizable. A further advantage is that when drying in bulk it is possible to permit a greater degree of "puffing" of plastic solid material and still maintain proper control without having the product get out of hand. In a word, bulk drying should always be used where the nature of the product will permit it; indeed it is a "must" with low-cost products such as foods.

When drying in bulk the products may be in direct contact with heated surfaces on the other side of which heat-exchange fluid is circulated. This direct contact permits greatest efficiency in the transfer of heat because of the minimum number of surfaces involved through which the heat must pass and also because of greater uniformity. Alternatively, but less efficiently, radiant heat may be carried directly down to evaporating surfaces. If separate pans are used, uneven transfer of heat may occur, this being greatest at points of best contact of the pan with the shelf. The result is either overheating or retardation of drying rate.

BIBLIOGRAPHY

1. Flosdorf, E. W., Hull, L. W., and Mudd, S., "Drying by sublimation," *J. Immunol.*, **50**, 21 (1945).
2. Flosdorf, E. W., and Mudd, S. "Procedure and apparatus for preservation in 'Lyophile' form of serum and other biological substances," *J. Immunol.*, **29**, 389 (1935).
3. Flosdorf, E. W., Stokes, F. J., and Mudd, S. "The Desivac process for drying from the frozen state," *J. Am. Med. Assoc.*, **115**, 1095 (1940). U. S. Patent No. 2,345,548.
4. Ikan, E. *Chem. Eng. Progress*, **43**, 348 (1947).
5. Friedman, S. J. "Drying," *Ind. Eng. Chem.*, **39**, 20 (1947).
6. Flosdorf, E. W., "Advances in drying by sublimation. Blood plasma, penicillin, foods," *J. Chem. Ed.*, **22**, 470 (1945).
7. Brown, G. H., Bierwirth, R. A. and Hoyler, C. N. "Radio-frequency dehydration of penicillin solution," *Proc. Inst. Radio Engineers*, p. 58W (Feb., 1946).
8. Greaves, R. I. N. "The preservation of proteins by drying with special reference to the production of dried human serum and plasma for transfusion," *Med. Res. Council*, Special Report Series No. 258 (1946).

9. Flosdorf, E. W. and Mudd, S. "An improved procedure and apparatus for preservation of sera, micro-organisms and other substances—the cryochem-process," *J. Immunol.*, **34**, 469 (1938).

10. Cavelti, J. E., *Private communication.*

11. Reichel, J., Masucci, P., McAlpine, K. L., and Boyer, J., *Unpublished work* (See Ref. 12).

12. Reichel, J., U. S. Pat. Re. 20,969 (1939).

13. Bradish, C. J., Brain, C. M., McFarlane, A. S., "Vacuum sublimation of ice in bulk," *Nature*, **159**, 28 (1947).

14. Bradish, C. J., "Freeze-Drying," *Chemical Products* (July–August, 1947).

15. Knudsen, M., *Ann. Phys.*, **47**, 697 (1915).

16. Tschudin, K., *Helv. Phys. Acta.*, **19**, 91 (1946).

17. Alty, T., *Phil. Mag.*, **15**, 82 (1933).

18. Flosdorf, E. W., Data obtained in collaboration with Mr. G. Willard Webster of Sharp & Dohme, Inc.

19. Greaves, R. I. N. "Production of blood derivatives to meet war requirements in Great Britain—with a note on the large scale preparation of a dried product," *J. Am. Med. Assoc.*, **124**, 76–79 (1944).

20. Flosdorf, E. W., and Webster, G. W. "The determination of residual moisture in dry biological substances," *J. Biol. Chem.*, **121**, 353–359 (1937).

21. McLeod, *Phil. Mag.*, **47**, 110 (1874).

22. Kaye, G. W. C. "High Vacua," p. 127, Longmans, Green & Co., New York, 1927.

23. Flosdorf, E. W., "A simplified and portable McLeod Gage," *Ind. and Eng. Chem.* (*Anal. Ed.*), **10**, 534 (1938).

24. Flosdorf, E. W., U. S. Patent No. 2,278,195.

25. Sherwood, T. K. *Personal communication.*

26. Scientific Exhibit at Meeting of American Medical Association, *J. Am. Med. Assoc.*, **105**, 51 (1935).

27. Flosdorf, E. W. and Mudd, S., "Rapid drying of serum and microorganisms from the frozen state for preservation," p. 45; and McGuinness, A. C., Stokes, J., Jr., Flosdorf, E. W., and Mudd, S., "The clinical use of lyophile human serum," p. 352 of Second International Congress for Microbiology, Report of Proceedings, ed. by R. St. John-Brooks, London, 1936.

CHAPTER 3: APPLICATIONS

Medical Products

CONVALESCENT HUMAN SERUM

The first application of freeze-drying on a production scale was the preservation of convalescent human sera.[1] Back in 1933 it was recognized that serum prepared at the close of one epidemic, particularly in the case of children's diseases, might have much to offer in the prevention and control of further epidemics in subsequent years. The problem of the deterioration of the sera had always been a major deterrent to intensive investigation of their use. The possible value freeze-drying might have with these sera was the motivating stimulus which resulted in the development of a workable freeze-drying procedure which could be applied to human products, with necessary sterility being maintained during drying for parenteral use.[1]

By 1935, when the method appeared in scientific publication, sufficient favorable experience had been accumulated with the dried products, prepared during the development, to thoroughly justify the efforts spent. Those sera were collected in, and distributed from, the Philadelphia Serum Exchange.[2,3] Processing and drying of all the first sera was carried out by the author in the Bacteriological Department of the School of Medicine, University of Pennsylvania. The dried sera were used both for prevention and for treatment in clinical trials. All the sera distributed by the Philadelphia Serum Exchange since 1933 have been in lyophile form. The Philadelphia Serum Exchange, indeed, owes its origin and continuance to the successful development of freeze-drying

69

as applied to such human products. Convalescent measles, scarlet fever, chicken pox and mumps sera and pooled normal adult sera had been administered by early 1935 in "lyophile" form to a total of more than 600 persons. It was felt at that time that the distinctive advantage of lyophile sera was demonstrated for such work because it could be harvested at the optimum time and used when and where needed. It was pointed out[1] that if the sera in question are especially perishable, as in the case of pooled normal adult sera, or are only occasionally needed, the method of preservation could make all the difference between practicability and impracticability in the use of serum. It was also felt that the method of preservation could be a powerful aid in the utilization and further investigation of the values of sera and other products from human sources for many purposes.

Also, convalescent sera were preserved from epidemics whose etiology and nosology were still under investigation. Convalescent sera from epidemics of influenza in Philadelphia and in Alaska[1] were collected and preserved for distribution to various parallel investigators for cross-protection tests.

More recently, McGuinness, Stokes and Armstrong have reported on the results of an eight-year study of human sera used, after freeze-drying, in the prevention and treatment of certain common communicable diseases.[4] These vacuum-dried sera, it was found, could be given successfully either by intravenous or by intramuscular injection. It was noted that the former is just as innocuous as intravenous injection of the same serum prepared in the liquid state. Originally, febrile and shock-type reactions had been observed occasionally following intravenous injection. This may well have been due to the lack of proper precaution in the preparation of glassware and in failure to carry out other steps to avoid pyrogenic contamination. Although pyrogens were recognized before 1935, the extent to which they could be responsible for such reactions was not as generally and fully appreciated as it is today. None of the early products were tested in rabbits for pyrogen.

McGuinness, Stokes and Armstrong customarily dissolved the powdered residue from each 10 cc of serum in 4 cc of sterile and pyrogen-free distilled water. This represented a large decrease in the bulk of material to be injected. Of course the serum may be restored to its original volume for intravenous injection if desired.

Preservatives are unnecessary in the dry serum, but it has become customary to add some such agent as merthiolate as a precaution for when the product is not dry. This minimizes the danger of contamination by the physician after restoration of the dry product to the liquid state, this being the step least subject to careful routine control and check. Accidental transfer of syphilis is not possible. In addition to the fact that all blood programs for either serum or plasma require testing according to the technique of Wasserman, Kahn, or the like, and only negative blood is used, *Spirochaeta pallida* do not survive freeze-drying. This is discussed more fully later in this chapter in connection with the preservation of cultures of bacteria, viruses, etc.

Dry normal adult serum in pools containing the blood of a minimum of 50 individuals has been found to be particularly interesting because convalescent serum is more difficult to obtain in sufficiently large quantity to be of general practical value. The use of large pools of normal serum provides a product which is uniform from pool to pool. Although larger doses are required when pooled adult serum is employed, this disadvantage is largely offset when using dried products which can be concentrated to less than one-half the original volume when restored for use. Human sera dried by sublimation gave satisfactory results, as were reported from the eight-year study just mentioned, in passive immunization against measles, scarlet fever and whooping-cough; in the case of the latter two, in treatment as well. Measles is caused by a virus. After a virus has become established within body cells and the disease is in progress, serum treatment fails, since it does not reach the proper site to combat the infectious agent. Neither liquid nor dry serum has been found effective either in passive immunization or treatment of chicken-pox. With mumps the data are insufficient to be conclusive, but they suggest that serum may be of value in prophylaxis. The major conclusion is that vacuum-dried sera may be stored over long periods of time, and administrated in concentrated form, and that the clinical results are comparable with those obtained with fresh liquid sera.

Another interesting application is the drying of human hyperimmune serum. This has been most widely employed for whooping-cough. Such serum may be prepared and titrated according to the method described by Flosdorf, McGuinness, Kimball and Armstrong.[5] The serum is obtained from the blood of individuals who are known to have had pertussis in childhood and who, in addition, have received repeated injections of pertussis vaccine. This produces a high agglutination titer. McGuinness, Armstrong and Felton employed such hyperimmune serum in the immunization of 308 infants and children subsequent to their exposure to whooping-cough and in the treatment of 442 patients with whooping-cough following the onset of paroxysms.[6] They report that the serum was of considerable value both in prevention and in treatment of the disease.

HUMAN BLOOD PLASMA AND NORMAL SERUM

Plasma is the liquid part of the blood and differs from serum mostly in the method of preparation. In both cases, the red cells, as well as the white, are removed. In preparing serum, this is accomplished by allowing the blood to clot. In order to obtain the best yield of serum, the clotted blood is usually centrifuged and the liquid part free of cells is siphoned off. To prepare plasma, "citrate solution" or another suitable reagent is used when collecting the blood to prevent clotting. Centrifuging is then used for sedimentation of the cells and the supernatant liquid is removed.

Accordingly, since clotting has been prevented in plasma it contains fibrinogen and thrombin. Also, the complement fraction will be preserved for a somewhat longer time in stored liquid plasma than in liquid serum since citrate has some preservative effect on complement.

The relative merits of plasma versus serum have been widely debated. Serum has the advantage of greater ease in the collection of the blood initially and in preparation of the final product. Less expensive equipment is required, particularly since centrifugation does not need to be at as high a speed or as long. On the other hand, the proponents of plasma point out that there are additional components present in plasma. There is some question whether these are of value for a large majority of the purposes for which blood or serum transfusions may be given. The fact is that both human blood serum and human blood plasma were used with success during the past war. In the United States, plasma was used exclusively. In Canada, serum was used exclusively and in Great Britain both were used, with reported equal results. An excellent review by Greaves[7] describes the production, for transfusion, of human serum and plasma in England during the war.

Either blood serum or blood plasma may be dried successfully from the frozen state. Around 1935, at the time that work was being carried on with convalescent human serum, human blood plasma was dried by the author successfully for the first time.[1] As a result of this development in drying from the final containers, drying by sublimation rapidly was applied as a major research tool in many laboratories on various medical research projects. Among these was the use of normal human serum and plasma for treatment of hemorrhage, secondary shock, and burns.[8] To this extent, development of drying by sublimation represents one of the three major streams[9] of investigation that gave rise to the blood plasma program of the American Red Cross. One of the other streams of investigation was that involving the laboratory study of the mechanism of secondary shock resulting from hemorrhage, trauma, toxemia, and burns. This investigation indicated that the major factor is one of a reduction of the volume of blood below the minimal capacity of the vascular system. The third stream of investigation was one of accumulation of clinical experience with the administration of liquid human plasma and serum as a substitute for whole blood in treatment of secondary shock and allied conditions. It was even found that in certain cases, for example, where there is shock without hemorrhage, blood plasma is superior to whole blood since it is only the liquid part of blood and not red cells which is lost from circulation. The confluence of these three streams of investigation resulted in an extensive program for taking dry and stable blood plasma to the battlefield and resulted in an enormous reduction in fatalities among our war casualties. Dried plasma is stable for years without refrigeration and is instantly available (within 5 minutes) for transfusion. Typing is not required.

It may be stated definitely that the extended program of blood plasma and serum in the United States and other countries had its origin in and came about as a direct outgrowth of the early work and development of dried human convalescent serum for use with children's diseases.[1] The sequence of steps in expanding the medical application of dried human blood serum and plasma from this point on has been well set forth by Freeman and Wallace,[10] by Mahoney,[11] and by Taylor.[12] Before 1941, of course, it was well recognized that blood plasma or serum in a stable form had many advantages for emergency use.[13] The subsequent development in use of dry blood plasma for transfusion as an outgrowth of the work with other freeze-dried human blood products[1] was as follows: In 1936, Hughes, Mudd and Strecker[14,15] were the first to report the use of concentrated solutions of human blood serum in the treatment of cases of increased intracranial pressure and shock. These authors pointed out that the great therapeutic value of dried human blood serum for reducing intracranial pressure and for shock was that it could be given in concentrated form for its dehydrating effect, and that even where concentration is not needed it could be more immediately available than either liquid serum or whole blood, and also that it could be given without regard to blood type.

Bond and Wright,[16] following this clinical report, began investigating the effectiveness of concentrated serum in the treatment of experimental shock in animals. Their experimental findings established that serum, concentrated four times, was very effective in restoring blood pressure to normal in animals which had been previously in a state of experimental shock. Consideration of the important subsequent experimental and clinical literature is beyond the scope of this book. This use of serum, regenerated from the dry state, helped also to bring to the attention of clinicians the fact that fresh undried serum and plasma had a wide usefulness, a fact that had been previously pointed out in scientific literature but had been largely neglected in clinical medicine.

It is now well known that normal human plasma may be stored as a liquid for a period of many months. The optimal temperature of such storage is about that of the room and not lower. At lower temperatures, precipitation occurs. The danger of such method of storage by way of gross bacterial contamination constitutes a serious hazard. Also, labile components in the plasma are lost. Lozner, Lemish, Campbell and Newhouser have pointed out that accidental contaminants during preparation may multiply to dangerous proportions during preservation as a liquid for even short periods. They further emphasized that after a few months, liquid plasma is adequate as a human colloid only. The liquid plasma becomes devoid of blood coagulation factors, complementary activity, and probably many antibodies. It should not be administered to patients with either hemorrhagic diatheses or infections, who require these components specifically. The use of the product should be subject to the same precautions regarding excessive dosage as is human serum albumin.[17]

Plasma may also be stored in frozen form, this requiring less expensive equipment than for freeze-drying. The product is well preserved. Disadvantage lies in the fact that freezing chambers are necessary for storage and distribution. Also, melting of the product requires 5 to 10 times as long as restoration of the dry product with water. On the other hand, because of the lower cost in institutions where large quantities are used, frozen blood plasma finds extended usefulness. Based on predicted daily consumption, plasma is thawed every morning as a matter of routine. For reserve and for special emergencies, dry plasma frequently is used to supplement frozen plasma.

R. deRohan Barondes[18] reported that while assigned to a prisoner of war camp he administered freeze-dried blood plasma orally and observed that it exerted beneficial effects on such gastrointestinal disorders as hyperchlorhydria, gastritis, enteritis, ulcerous and malignant processes and diarrheas. The plasma acts as a buffer for gastric acidity, exerts a soothing influence on inflamed and diseased tissues, is a fibrinogenic agent through its plasma globulin content, aids tissue regeneration and possesses antitoxic and antibiotic properties. In addition, it aids in the capacity to fabricate antibodies and increases resistance to infection. The dried plasma is well tolerated when mixed with palatable cool mixtures. Hot fluids are not used as excipients because coagulation of the plasma occurs, with loss in its therapeutic properties. An excellent agent for incorporation with the dried plasma is apple powder, which is likewise a valuable agent in treatment of gastrointestinal disorders. Plasma is superior to amino acids and protein hydrolyzates in quickly combating hypoproteinemia, maintaining nitrogen balance and restoring the electrolyte equilibrium. This would be especially so in the presence of a severely damaged liver. Both fresh egg-white and freeze-dried eggwhite are effective also, ameliorating the symptoms of gastrointestinal disorders. These desiccated products can be prescribed in enteric-coated capsules or mixed with cool fluids.

FRACTIONS PREPARED FROM PLASMA

Various fractions of human serum prepared by Dr. Harry Eagle were dried successfully a good many years ago by the author.[1] Serum albumin, serum pseudoglobulin and euglobulin, as well as such labile substances as fibrinogen and prothrombin were found to retain their solubility and biological activity for a year or longer.

In preparing fibrinogen and prothrombin it was noted that the dried material, on resolution, was often distinctly more alkaline than the original preparation, presumably because of loss of carbon dioxide during dehydration. In some cases this alkalescence was sufficient to inactivate the product unless due precaution was taken either to buffer the original solution strongly, or to acidify it slightly just before processing. Dr. Eagle also observed this condition in guinea-pig complement and antisera from various sources which had been dried; however, the alkaline shift was apparently insufficient to affect biological activity. Lens protein, serum albumin and highly purified egg albumin also were dried and were found to maintain all their native characteristics for a period of years.

More recently, freeze-drying has been applied extensively to fractions prepared from plasma collected by the American Red

Cross during the past war. Cohn[19, 20] and his co-workers succeeded in preparing various components of blood in a high degree of purity so that they might be used for many specialized purposes. For example, serum albumin in high concentration could be used instead of whole blood plasma for osmotic effects, etc. The main advantage in the use of serum albumin during the war was for the benefit of landing parties where small bulk was important. The product is stable in solution, which fact contributed to ease in administration. However, as this method of preparation involves the use of alcohol, it was found that the most practical means of removing alcohol completely and with certainty was to dry the product from the frozen state. In this case, extremely low final moisture was of course unnecessary because the product was then redissolved for distribution. With respect to certain other fractions, such as thrombin and fibrin foam, the final product is dried from the frozen state for distribution. Globulin is not distributed in freeze-dried form.

Cohn states[21] that he has prepared fractions which are water-soluble containing over 50 per cent lipid. The lability is far greater than that of albumin or gamma globulins, of fibrinogen, or of thrombin. Cohn found that when freeze-dried, some but not all were denatured. The cloudiness of the resuspended dry plasma he believes may be attributable to these substances. These products require further study, since knowledge of the chemistry and the functions of the lipid proteins has just begun to be acquired.

As indicated above, Cohn made extensive use of freeze-drying in the development of his system of fractionation. He avoided salting out, which is the classical procedure for separation of proteins, and in this way eliminated dialysis. Depending upon the relative solubility of various blood derivatives under conditions of varying salt content, pH and temperature, especially using relatively low temperature (0 to $-10°C$) as well as other means, the proteins are precipitated. By varying these conditions in proper sequence, separation into different fractions is accomplished.[20] Many of these fractions are then dried from the frozen state to yield stable purified products which can be redissolved at any concentration in the appropriate diluent.

OTHER SUBSTITUTES FOR PLASMA

Koop[22] reports that, of the plasma substitutes studied extensively during the recent war years, only human serum albumin and gelatin solutions seem to be both safe and effective on the basis of reports available at this time. Human serum albumin derived from plasma itself, is not, strictly speaking, a substitute. Gelatin, in addition to being safe and effective, is also cheap, and when fortified with amino acids or protein hydrolyzates it is a readily available source of parenteral protein. As was pointed out in Chapter 2, freeze-dried gelatin has excellent solubility at around room temperature, which means that this lends itself to use under aseptic conditions just as well as blood plasma. Also, amino acids or protein hydrolyzates may be freeze-dried and are available commercially.

The polysaccharide, gum acacia, was used in World War I. It was found later, however, that its antigenicity and toxicity rendered it unsuitable. It has a particular tendency to produce liver disfunction and hypoproteinemia.[22]

Bovine albumin has been prepared by fractionation using Cohn's method, just as with the human substance; freeze-drying has also been used in similar fashion. However, it is necessary to separate the globulin fraction completely; otherwise, alarming reactions are produced upon intravenous injection into other species.[22] When it is properly prepared, a low reaction rate is obtained, but even so a non-bacterial chill-producing substance has apparently not been separated from the albumin. Reactions with the purified albumin include urticaria, diarrhea, fever, nausea, vomiting and chill. Further, since bovine albumin is a potent antigen, there is a possibility of subsequent cross-reaction upon eating beef products.

Koop[22] reports that pectin as a substitute for plasma is inferior to serum, less safe than gelatin, and no better than saline in post-hemorrhagic prolonged hypotension. Methyl cellulose and polyvinal alcohol have been used, but not widely. Although they are effective in shock in animals and are not antigenic, they show excessive storage in the viscera. Koop also reports that hemoglobin, when given intravenously to animals, elicits untoward reactions, such as the blockage of renal tubular lumina by hemoglobinous pigments. This can be eliminated by improved methods of preparation. Globin prepared from erythrocytes has been used; in Koop's review it is stated that in certain conditions satisfactory results are obtained. However, work with dog globin indicated that the substance is less effective than saline.

When using gelatin there is a choice in the raw material to be used. The viscosity, gel strength, modulus of rigidity and temperature of solidification are directly proportional to the size of the molecular chain, whereas the fluidity and melting point are inversely proportional to molecular chain size.[22] All the molecules give rise to a higher osmotic pressure, but are retained for a shorter period in the circulation. Gelatin is the only plasma substitute originating elsewhere than in blood, which is protein. However, it is an incomplete protein and is non-antigenic.

ANTITOXINS AND OTHER ANTISERA

The same advantages that accrue to human sera may be gained by drying animal sera. In many instances, the liquid animal products are relatively more stable than the liquid human products discussed. However, with storage under unfavorable conditions, say at 30 to 40°C, the liquid sera may lose potency rapidly. For example, liquid diphtherial antitoxin, equine, will lose all detectable potency upon storage for six months at 37°C. In the dry product no detectable loss begins to appear for three years.

It is usual practice in the biological field for stocks of horse sera and other similar products to be kept on hand in bulk quantities to be available rapidly in time of disaster and other emergencies. The major amounts of such supplies are stored in bulk for various reasons. One important reason is that this practice permits final assay of such products to be made as dispensed immediately prior to time of shipment. Furthermore, the demands in respect to size and type of package are not always known in advance.

Lyophilization in bulk affords a convenient means of carrying large stocks with minimum losses. At the time of final dispensing, the products are restored and, in the case of serum, filtration is carried out. The liquid is then packaged in the usual fashion and either distributed as a liquid or again lyophilized. There is one possible disadvantage which off-hand is not so obvious. Some products, such as certain antitoxins, undergo initially a loss of potency and then reach what might be considered a standard or "steady" state. At this level, potency is fairly stable for a period of time. There is some advantage in allowing this initial loss down to the steady state to take place during bulk storage of liquid. Then, when the product is finally dispensed, the assayed potency as appears on the label will be maintained for a longer time. Accordingly, the advisability of freeze-drying reserve quantities of material in bulk is a matter requiring consideration of all the various factors and conditions for a given product.

As will be discussed in Chapter 4, certain sera develop turbidity upon reconstitution. This condition comes about as a result of lipoidal substances that are present. With human serum and plasma this is particularly pronounced, especially if blood is obtained from a non-fasting donor. Lyophobic sols do not reconstitute well, even in the presence of protein. This condition also occurs to a lesser degree with rabbit serum. It is not noticeable in horse serum.

The turbidity which occurs in human and rabbit sera causes difficulty in carrying out precipitative reactions, as with rabbit-precipitin. It has been a drawback to the use of dry standardized syphilitic human serums for calibration and standardization of diagnostic test procedures. Such standard sera could facilitate comparison of test results from different laboratories. The difficulty with lipoids may be overcome by drying twice with intermediate Seitz-filtration.[23,24] At the time of filtration of the reconstituted serum following the primary drying, the titer of the serum may be adjusted by dilution to a desired point. It is then dried for the second time. Accordingly, the final dry product has a predetermined definite titer and is stable.

CONCENTRATED GLOBULINS AND OTHER PROTEINS

As indicated, egg albumin, lens protein and many other products which ordinarily are considered difficult to handle without alteration may be successfully dried from the frozen state. The variety and types of proteins studied are quite extensive, and there is no need to consider them all. Suffice it to say that proteins are particularly well adapted to freeze-drying. The porosity and friability of the dehydrated material make it responsive to rapid and thorough extraction with ether, petroleum ether, alcohol and similar lipoid solids. Denaturation of the proteins on such extraction is greatly reduced as compared with extraction in solution.

It has been the established practice in the biological industry to separate the globulin fraction of immune horse sera. The antibodies are largely contained in this fraction and by separation it is possible to effect a high degree of concentration. This is desirable to reduce the volume to be injected and also to reduce the amount of unnecessary foreign protein to as great an extent as possible. This is most important with animal sera, to avoid allergic reaction to protein of foreign species, with possible fatal anaphylactic shock.

Such globulin fractions can be dried successfully from the frozen state. There is no loss in activity during drying and potency is well maintained in storage even at elevated temperatures. Concentrated globulin preparations, however, restore very slowly at time of reconstitution for injection. Instead of being a matter of a few minutes, in some cases the time may be extended to as much as one-half hour. However, there are products such as snake antivenom in which the globulin cannot be properly preserved in the liquid state. This is particularly true in hot deserts and in the tropics. Carrying liquid products for days, often with exposure to hot sun, results in early spoilage. For this reason, even though some additional time is required for reconstitution, the use of freeze-drying is justified in that the product may be had where needed and where it would be unavailable otherwise. Lahiri,[24a] who has worked with Major General Sir Sahib Singh Sokhey of Bombay, India, and with Doctor K. Ganapathy and Mr. M. K. Habbu, reports that the low solubility of the salted out immune globulins seems to be due to the lipid containing proteins, which are separated in the same fraction. As Cohn *et al.* have pointed out (*loc. cit.*) these lipoproteins are altered during freeze-drying this fraction. The immune globulins are also precipitated out as part of fractions II and III of the Cohn et al. procedure (*loc. cit.*) by ethyl alcohol at controlled pH, ionic strength, temperature and protein concentration as discussed elsewhere in this chapter. Lahiri states that for this reason the alcohol precipitated immune globulin fraction if not further purified by sub-fractionation would possess the same difficulty of freeze-drying as the salted out immune globulin fraction. Lahiri points out that immune globulins must be separated as a major fraction to facilitate economical large-scale processing. To overcome the problem, Lahiri found thât the bile salts, sodium taurocholate and sodium glycocholate do not precipitate the proteins and they do improve the solubility of the freeze-dried product. The two salts are equally effective. The salt must be added and intimately mixed with the serum before drying, adding it to the dried serum not being the slightest bit effective. It is preferable to add the bile salt two to three days before drying.

Lahiri used anti-snake-venom serum which was fractionated in small lots and cooled afterward. The pH was adjusted to 7.2 and it was made isotonic. After clarification, the serum in 6-liter amounts in 9-liter bottles was cooled at 0° and 6 grams of sodium taurocholate was added to each bottle. After gentle agitation and mixing, the serum was stored at 0°C for two days and then was extracted by 2 liters of ether at 0°C for each bottle. For extraction, the bottles were shaken vigorously. Ether was then separated by decantation and centrifugation for 15 minutes at 2,000 RPM at about 30°C. Three layers are obtained, the top consisting of excess ether, the intermediate of extracted and condensed lipids of white color and the bottom layer of clear sera. Then they separated the sera by siphoning, and this was pooled in 9-liter bottles and the dissolved ether removed by means of an air jet blown over the surface of the serum at room temperature. After removal of the ether, one gram of sodium taurocholate was added per liter of serum and intimately mixed. Two days later, a few samples were distributed in 10 ml. containers and freeze-dried as usual. After freeze-drying, the product was tested again for solubility. It was found that sometimes further extractions were required, but never more than a total of four. Serum which required fewer than four extractions generally required 0.1 per cent bile salt to show satisfactory solubility but if the serum was extracted four times, no additional bile salt was added.

Lahiri states that in spite of all of this treatment, the product did not show any loss in potency and its safety for use in man was not impaired in spite of the bile salt which was added. The final product was better than the original in that it was less viscous and presented a crystal-clear appearance.

In summary, extraction of lipids with ether in the presence of bile salt improved solubility without any loss of the immune bodies and without making the product unsafe for use in man. Neither the extraction of lipids alone, nor the addition of the bile salt alone, was enough to improve the solubility of dried product to the desired extent.

Major General S. S. Sokhey has done much to extend and apply freeze-drying effectively to anti-venoms for snakes of India. In the United States such preparations are available commercially for snakes of the western hemisphere.

GUINEA-PIG COMPLEMENT

The complementary activity of guinea-pig serum affords a sensitive index to the effectiveness of drying. The duration of its potency is extended from a matter of a day or less in the liquid state to five years or more in the dry state, storage being at about +5°C in both cases. In Fig. 3.1 is given a summary of data obtained from tests carried out over a period of five years.

In the preparation of guinea-pig complement, it is important to use the best of practice in handling the serum before drying. Only healthy and large male adult guinea pigs should be used. Pools from large numbers of animals should be prepared, preferably never less than ten animals. In large-scale production the pools must be kept below the size at which excessively long storage without freezing would be necessary to complete them. If the serum must be stored overnight or even for a few hours before drying, it should be kept frozen. Unless cold rooms are available for centrifuging and other manipulations with the liquid serum, it is inadvisable to work with large quantities of complement during summer months. There should be a minimum of handling and preferably the product, if stored at all before drying, should be frozen in the final containers properly dispensed for drying.

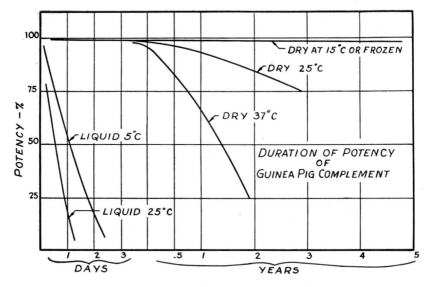

Fig. 3.1. Summary of data obtained over a five-year period of storage. The curves representing results obtained at 25° and 37°C. are schematic and are an average representation of data obtained in tests from a number of laboratories. Certain modifications of tests for syphilis utilizing complement-fixation are more rigid or sensitive in their requirement of complementary activity, therefore, the curves are drawn assuming that about 90% of full original potency is required in those tests which are more exacting in their requirements. Some tests can be carried out satisfactorily simply by an adjustment in dilution even if the potency is reduced by as much as 50%.

Residual moisture content should be reduced to less than 0.5 per cent. Close attention to the type of containers and vacuum seal must be given. This subject will be discussed in Chapter 5, but it should be pointed out here that in the case of guinea-pig complement it is imperative to use a type of seal which will completely exclude water vapor. It is not only because of the small volume in which the products are dispensed, but also because of the extreme sensitivity of guinea-pig complement to excessive moisture.

In Tables 1, 2 and 3 are given typical experimental results of the testing of guinea-pig complement.[25] The data presented in these tables were obtained in testing according to the method of Boerner and Lukens.[26] Similar results are found when carrying out titration according to the technique of Kolmer as used in his

TABLE 1

HEMOLYTIC TITRATION WITH 0.75% SUSPENSION OF ERYTHROCYTES COMPLEMENT LOT 472–C–1, DE-GASSED AND SELF-FROZEN, 2 YEARS OLD

Complement Dilution	Amboceptor Dilution					
	1:5000	1:7500	1:10,000	1:15,000	1:20,000	1:30,000
1/30	C	C	C	C	C	±
1/40	C	C	C	C	C	C
1/60	C	C	C	C	C	C
1/80	C	C	C	C	C	±
1/120	C	C	C	C	±	1
1/160	C	C	±	±	1	1

C = complete hemolysis. All readings are on a basis of "4" as indicating no hemolysis. ± = hemolysis approximately 90 per cent complete. 1 = hemolysis 75 per cent complete.

TABLE 2

HEMOLYTIC TITRATION WITH 0.75% SUSPENSION OF ERYTHROCYTES COMPLEMENT LOT 472–L, DRY-ICE FROZEN, 2 YEARS OLD

Complement Dilution	Amboceptor Dilution					
	1:5000	1:7500	1:10,000	1:15,000	1:20,000	1:30,000
1/30	C	C	C	C	C	±
1/40	C	C	C	C	C	±
1/60	C	C	C	C	C	±
1/80	C	C	C	C	±	±
1/120	C	C	C	±	±	1
1/160	±	C	±	±	1	1

C = complete hemolysis. All readings are on a basis of "4" as indicating no hemolysis. ± = hemolysis approximately 90 per cent complete. 1 = hemolysis 75 per cent complete.

TABLE 3

HEMOLYTIC TITRATION WITH 0.75% SUSPENSION OF ERYTHROCYTES FRESH COMPLEMENT

Complement Dilution	Amboceptor Dilution					
	1:5000	1:7500	1:10,000	1:15,000	1:20,000	1:30,000
1/30	C	C	C	C	C	C
1/40	C	C	C	C	C	C
1/60	C	C	C	C	C	C
1/80	C	C	C	C	C	±
1/120	C	C	C	C	±	±
1/160	C	C	C	±	1	1

C = complete hemolysis. All readings are on a basis of "4" as indicating no hemolysis. ± = hemolysis approximately 90 per cent complete. 1 = hemolysis 75 per cent complete.

complement fixation tests. It is observed that there is no essential difference, whether self-freezing or Dry-Ice freezing is used.

Under conditions where rapid handling of serum at low temperature is not possible, a stabilizing solution consisting of sodium acetate and boric acid may be added before drying. In this way a product is prepared which keeps well and which also maintains stability without detectable loss of potency for a period of several days following restoration. This is of particular convenience for the use of the desiccated product in small hospitals and laboratories.

Further, Giordano has recommended testing the serum from individual guinea pigs and then using the serum from satisfactory ones only.[27] When drying complement this would necessitate freezing of many small amounts and then thawing, probably for practical purposes not thawing until the next day, in order to pool the proper sera. This would be inconvenient; however, not to freeze would mean that the final product would not be equivalent to that prepared from fresh serum with respect to ultimate duration of potency in the dry state. Therefore, in order to follow Giordano's recommendation, it is necessary to add the stabilizing solution immediately after separating the liquid serum from the clot, to avoid use of intermediate freezing.

The use of sodium acetate, according to Rhamy, for preservation of complementary activity has long been known.[28] Rhamy has given an extended historical sketch of this subject.[29] For some purposes the degree of preservation afforded by such chemical preservation is adequate. Eagle states that the exact duration of unaltered activity is uncertain and may vary from batch to batch.[30] Therefore the advantage of the greater certainty and extended duration of uniformity of the complementary activity of serum in dry form seems to warrant the use of vacuum desiccation from the frozen state.[30] In this latter connection it is necessary to consider the size of the investment being made in animals for a large pool; the method of preservation must be completely reliable. Also better results are obtainable with a dry reagent because it can be used reliably for a standard over a long period.[30] Some economy may be effected by taking advantage of an annual low seasonal price of animals in order to prepare in advance a supply for a year or more.

By combining the two methods of preservation, advantages may be realized that are possessed by neither one alone. To summarize, in the first place, only a dry product has reliable stability. Second, the serious losses in activity, which may result from delaying the desiccation too long after bleeding the animals, are eliminated by use of the stabilizing agent. Large uniform pools may be obtained which contain satisfactory serum on Giordano's basis which also have the full initial high potency of freshly bled animals. Also, daily liquid residues from restored containers of the dry serum need not be wasted, and this permits drying even two or three days' supply in a single container to lower the cost.

It is desirable to use a minimum concentration of sodium acetate so as not to lower the freezing point excessively. A concentration lower than the 20 per cent recommended by Rhamy is preferred.[29] The lower concentration, as originally recommended by Rhamy,[28] is quite adequate, particularly when the serum is to be kept in dry form for the major portion of the storage period. Toluene as a bacteriostatic agent is undesirable in a vacuum system of desiccation; hence, 4 per cent boric acid as recommended by Ruffner,[31] by Sonnenschein,[32] by Green,[33] and by Boerner and Lukens,[26] as well as Rhamy's original lower concentration of sodium acetate, provides the preferred solution for freeze-dried preparations.

The following is the exact procedure: Bleed the. animals and centrifuge the blood immediately after the clot has formed. To the individual portions of serum, immediately add an equal volume of the stabilizing solution containing 12 grams of anhydrous sodium acetate, or 20 grams of the crystalline salt, and 4 grams of boric acid per 100 ml of sterile distilled water. In bleeding very large numbers of animals it is advisable to separate the serum and to add this stabilizing solution without waiting to complete the bleeding of all the animals. Finally, before dispensing the serum into vials for desiccation, make a pool of the proper individual portions in a single large container. Finally, dispense the serum into individual final containers and dry it from the frozen state, preferably using equipment of the chamber type. Drying on external manifolds with the stabilizing solution present is somewhat more difficult because of a tendency to fuse and bubble out of the containers. Temperature conditions are more readily controlled in the vacuum chambers.

In physical form the final dry product is quite different, the higher salt content causing a "fused" appearance and a loss of the porous, net-like and friable structure which the desiccated products normally have. The solubility characteristics, however, are unimpaired and are excellent.

For use, the serum is restored in customary fashion by the addition of distilled water, using a volume equal to the *actual serum* placed in the individual container, *not including that of the stabilizing solution*. This yields a 12 per cent final concentration of sodium acetate, which is double that existing prior to desiccation. In the Wassermann reaction this original volume is then diluted further with 0.85 per cent salt solution as usual, but not until just before the complement is to be used in the test. Excess concentration of sodium acetate in no way interferes with the use of the complement in the Wassermann reaction; actually, the amount present becomes highly diluted as employed normally in the test. Even a saturated solution of sodium acetate, like sodium chloride, is not hemolytic or anticomplementary.[29] In the present case the stabilizing solution becomes diluted to about 0.12 per cent in the actual Wassermann test, which is only negligibly hypertonic, namely 10 per cent. This is too low to cause any inhibitory action on biological hemolysis.

Sera undergo a loss of carbon dioxide during desiccation, with a consequent elevated pH of the restored product.[1] Addition of the stabilizing solution lowers the initial pH of the serum prior to desiccation, so that the final value of the dry serum upon restoration is less elevated. None of the effects observed as the result of use of the stabilizing solution, however, are attributable to the pH. This may be demonstrated by duplicating the changes in pH using dilute hydrochloric acid to the amount of 1.2 ml of $N/1$ HCl per 100 ml of serum. The activity characteristics of a portion of serum so adjusted in pH will be found to be equivalent in all respects to the unadjusted pH portion of the same pool when duration tests are carried out. On the other hand, the characteristics of a third portion to which stabilizing solution has been added and in which a similar change in pH occurs will have the improved conditions of stability just described. The effect on pH in three such portions of a same pool is illustrated in Table 4.

TABLE 4

pH OF SEPARATE PORTIONS OF A SINGLE POOL OF GUINEA-PIG SERUM

	Before desiccation	After restoration of the dry product
Unadjusted	7.90	8.94
With stabilizing solution	6.80	8.05
Adjusted with HCl	6.75	8.05

In the event that in a given laboratory the undelayed desiccation after bleeding of the animals presents no problem, it is preferable not to add the stabilizing solution before drying because of the added difficulty in drying. Then the stabilizing solution may be substituted for distilled water used in the restoration of the dry product. In this way the advantages of a stabilized reconstituted product may be realized, a solution having full potency for several days.

BACTERIAL AND VIRAL CULTURES

Swift,[34] Elser, Thomas and Steffen,[23] and others have reported successful preservation of even some of the most delicate organisms for long periods of time. *N. Meningitidis* (meningococcus), *N. Gonorrhoeae* (gonococcus), *H. influenzae*, *H. pertussis*, *E. typhosa* and other similar organisms have been kept viable for a period of many years; upon reconstitution their growth may be started again to produce subcultures of unaltered characteristics.

It has been found that a protective protein greatly prolongs the keeping qualities of the organisms, and greatly increases the percentage viability. Serum or plasma may be used, but it must first be inactivated to remove bactericidal activity. Sterile skim milk (autoclaved) provides a most satisfactory medium.[35]

Cultures grown in liquid medium may be concentrated by centrifugation and then resuspended in milk. Organisms grown on a solid medium may be harvested by scraping into saline or milk. If saline is used, the suspension is added to an equal volume of sterile skim milk. This mixture is then distributed into small containers. Usually large numbers of containers of culture are dried at a single time. Small quantities per container are ordinarily adequate, as little as 0.05 ml being satisfactory. It is highly important, however, to use all-glass containers rather than containers which carry a rubber stopper exposed to the atmosphere. Otherwise, as will be discussed in Chapter 5, diffusion of water vapor through the stopper in a short time raises the moisture content of the culture to a point where the viability of many species is not maintained for long. As micro-organisms preserved in such small amounts are especially sensitive to this condition, it is necessary to use containers which may be sealed by fusion of glass.

When bacteria are dried in small volumes it is advisable to freeze the suspension of bacteria in milk by placing a freezing mixture around the containers before applying the vacuum. If larger quantities are dried per single container, degassing and self-freezing may be used,[36] as discussed in Chapter 2. In such cases it is not necessary to place a greater number of organisms in the

containers, but only to use more milk for a greater degree of dilution which provides more liquid for evaporation during self-
freezing.

Either vacuum chambers, manifold-type of equipment, or other
types discussed in Chapter 5 may be used for culture drying. Large
glass vacuum desiccators are suitable for the purpose, provided a
proper low-temperature condenser or a chemical desiccant in
adequate amount is used. Such equipment does have limited
capacity and is subject to technical inconvenience. Quite frequently such apparatus, by technical error, is inadequate in its
capacity for sufficient desiccant to complete the drying of the
volumes of liquid processed. Means for raising the temperature
finally to 25 to 35°C for proper low residual moisture are more
difficult to effect and control.

When drying cultures in small volume, a matter of a few hours
is usually adequate. Unless it is for commercial production it usually is simpler and safer to allow desiccation to continue overnight; the next day the containers may be hermetically sealed by
fusion of the glass with a flame. Evacuation of the containers before sealing is not always essential. Naylor and Smith[37] reported
that dried cultures of *Serratia marcescens* must be stored under
high vacuum to achieve a high survival rate; viability is rapidly
lost when sealed under air or tank nitrogen. They did not attempt
purification of nitrogen by passage over hot copper, or use of
special high-purity nitrogen (99.99 per cent). Frequently it is simpler to seal under original vacuum to avoid contamination.

The widest use of cultures dried from the frozen state is in
maintaining stocks of cultures. This not only eliminates continual
laboratory transferring and sub-culturing, but it insures preservation of the original characteristics of the organisms, these frequently undergoing variation and change when subjected to
weekly sub-culturing. Drying has been invaluable in maintaining
specially developed strains of *Penicillium notatum* for high yields
of penicillin. Otherwise, the strains would revert and be lost. Large
numbers of containers of every organism are dried at one time. A
new container is opened whenever a given organism is to be cul-

tured. It may be necessary to carry a culture through two or three culture generations after restoration to rejuvenate all the original characteristics.

Hammer applied desiccation from the frozen state to various viable bacteria.[38] Rogers employed the method successfully for lactic acid-forming bacilli.[39] Swift has used this system of desiccation extensively in his work with streptococci and pneumococci.[34] Siler and his associates at the Army Medical School have maintained their cultures of the now well-known S-58 virulent *Eberthella typhosa* without dissociation over a period of many years.[40] From Dr. H. Parker Hitchens I have learned personally that viability and type have been maintained for over ten years at room temperature. Preservation of this strain in this manner made it possible for Siler and his group to embark on a program of research lasting over a period of years. There would have been little justification for starting the program without having assurance that at the end they would be dealing with an organism of the same characteristics they started with, as could be established by freeze-drying. As a result of this program carried on by Siler and his associates, a much improved vaccine for preventing typhoid fever was produced and was available for World War II. This is another major, although indirect, contribution of freeze-drying to the great success of American military medicine during the war. Welch, Borman and Mickle reported successful preparation of *Klebsiella pneumoniae* in unaltered form.[41]

Flosdorf and Kimball reported on extensive use of freeze-drying for *H. pertussis*.[35] With pertussis, agglutinin absorption was the index to demonstrate that no dissociation occurs as a result of drying over a 12-year period. The fundamental importance in antibacterial immunity of the combination of agglutinins with surface antigens of bacteria is well established. With non-flagellated organisms such surface reactions as agglutination or phagocytosis therefore provide distinguishing methods of assay for effective surface reactants in either serum or antigen. Complement fixation, and precipitin testing with soluble antigens, are of diagnostic value but do not distinguish surface antigen-antibody combination from phenomena involving other antigens.

Appleman and Sears[42] reported that legume nodule bacteria (*Rhizobium leguminosarum*) retain both viability and their capacity to nodulate plant hosts and to fix nitrogen after four years of storage without loss. Bacteria tested were isolated originally from alfalfa, lespedeza, cowpea, pea, soybean, vetch, crown vetch and clover host plants. The cultures were grown on asparagus-Mannitol medium and then emulsified in sterile water for drying.

Freeze-dried viable cultures of molds and bacteria are now available commercially in the dairy industry as "starters" for first propagation in production of cottage cheese, buttermilk, butter acidophilus, bulgarian and yoghurt.

During storage of dried cultures ordinary refrigeration at about 5 to 8°C is used. This is not essential in all cases, but it is virtually prohibitive to carry out systematic studies of the effect of temperature on storage of the many hundreds of strains and numerous species of organisms of interest. Accordingly, it is safest to rely on refrigeration, particularly as the size of the containers is so small. The procedure to be followed in preservation of cultures depends somewhat upon the specific type of equipment used. For this reason, typical procedure is discussed at the end of Chapter 5.

In order to use the dry organisms the stem of the all-glass container is scratched with a file in usual fashion. After scratching the glass with a file, the container, for breaking, is wrapped under a cloth impregnated with antiseptic to prevent the spreading of dry organisms as air rushes in. Excess antiseptic should first be squeezed out of the cloth, however, to avoid sucking the liquid into the container when the vacuum is broken. Sterile water is then added. With a standard small loop, the proper culture medium, either liquid or solid depending upon circumstances, is inoculated. A somewhat longer incubation period may be required to obtain satisfactory growth of the first culture generation.

With regard to the percentage of viable cells remaining in cultures of bacteria after desiccation there is wide variation, depending upon the species and also the particular strain; this frequently may be as little as 5 per cent, but since the surviving cells keep well, there is adequate survival for the purpose of maintaining stock cultures. However, in the case of live bacterial vaccines, which will be discussed in the next section, the situation is entirely different and steps should be taken to improve it for economic as well as other reasons. This is also true for "starter" cultures in the dairy industry and yeast for baking. The essential steps are different in every individual case, but often it is possible to control conditions whereby 80 to 90 per cent survival may be achieved. Speck and Meyers[43] report that spray-dried cultures of *Lactobacillus bulgaricus,* when reconstituted with fluid at 37 to 50°C, give a higher percentage of viability than at 21 to 25°C. Reconstituting at the lower temperature with subsequent warming does not produce the same result. They found that freeze-dried cultures gave the opposite temperature effect.

Lord Stamp[44] has compared what he terms "slow drying of bacterial cultures in a desiccator over dehydrating agents *in vacuo* with 'more rapid freeze-drying'. " He states that it is simple drying in the unfrozen state, although the degree of vacuum is 100 to 300 microns of mercury and phosphorus pentoxide is the desiccant. In view of the latter condition, Lord Stamp could well be drying from the frozen state. It would depend entirely upon whether or not the small quantity (1 mm) in Petri dishes would be completely dried during evacuation before there would be time to freeze. If not, there would be nothing to prevent freezing; but, of course, because of the absence of the controlled means of heating, the rate of subsequent drying would be indeterminate and slow. In drying in a desiccator in this fashion it is quite possible that in some cases there would be partial freezing, in others complete freezing, and in still others no freezing at all. In other words, because of the absence of control and of any means of knowing how well or poorly the product is frozen, the matter is indefinite; and this may account for the variable results Lord Stamp reported, *i.e.,* with *Chromobacterium prodigiosum* in one experiment there was an 86.1 to 90.2 per cent survival and in another case, 60.7 per cent. Also, Lord Stamp has pointed out that his slow method proved unsatisfactory for preservation of more delicate organisms, such as *Neisseria meningitidis, Vibrio cholerae* and *Fusiformis fusiformis,* whereas these along with *N. gonorrhoeae* were successfully preserved by rapid freeze-drying.

Lord Stamp states that better results were obtained with these methods when gelatin was used as a medium. He also incorporated beef extract and peptone. Except where acidity is harmful, as with *Haemophilus pertussis,* he found that ascorbic acid further improved the results, which he interpreted as a result of the antioxidant effect.

The difference in results obtained by Lord Stamp by the so-called slow method in a desiccator as compared with rapid freeze-drying is of interest in demonstrating the great improvement in results obtained by this method as it has been carried out so extensively during the past decade by use of proper conditions of freezing, positive and controlled means of heating, and other factors.[1,45,46] Lord Stamp states that a lower final content of moisture was obtained by use of the rapid method of freeze-drying, where the containers were exposed to the atmosphere while attached to a manifold connected with a Dry Ice condenser.[1] This same uncertainty of results and undependability when applied to delicate organisms, as well as the lack of reduction to as low a final moisture content is characteristic of all similar desiccator methods reported by Swift,[34] Elser,[23] Hammer,[38] Rogers,[39] Shackell,[47] and others. The desiccator carried no means for actively and positively supplying heat under controlled conditions where the containers were actually placed in the refrigerator. Indeed, in some of the earlier work just cited, below-freezing refrigeration coils were placed in the drying chamber, which would actually inhibit or retard drying. This is in contrast with modern procedure, which employs the principle of carrying out drying as rapidly as possible but without melting or thawing and by positive heating, either in a vacuum chamber or with atmospheric air.

Weiser and Hennum[48] reported more rapid death rate in cultures of *Escherichia coli* which had been freeze-dried than in those which had been dried from the liquid state at 22°C. However, no determinations of residual moisture content were made, and in view of this fact it seems doubtful whether safe conclusions can be drawn. Furthermore, this organism is scarcely representative of the more delicate ones which have been successfully preserved over a period of many years, as discussed in the preceding pages. Also, it has been suggested that perhaps there may be a residual level which is being reached in the number of more resistant organisms, and that the rate would naturally be more rapid in the case of the cultures having had the lowest death rate because of the drying operation *per se.* On the other hand, even were this the case with this one particular organism, no conclusions could be drawn with regard to more delicate organisms, where there is no survival when the cultures are dried from the liquid state.

In 1936, Eagle[24] showed that *Spirochaeta pallida* does not survive the freeze-drying period. Rabbit chancres were emulsified, shown to be infectious for rabbits, and lyophile-processed by the author; the residue was re-emulsified and injected intratesticularly into six new rabbits. These rabbits showed no signs of syphilis, and after a year four survivors were found to be susceptible to the same strain of *Spirochaeta pallida.* More recently, Probey has reported similar findings.[49]

With viruses, there is usually less activity after processing, but the final desiccated product is well stabilized and little further loss occurs during storage.[50] Viruses are, in general, more difficult to dry than other substances. The temperature must be maintained lower than is frequently necessary with many other products, preferably well below $-20°C$.[36]

Harris and Shackell presumably used freeze-drying in the preservation of rabic brains.[51] Rivers and Ward have relied widely on freeze-drying in their work with an intradermal vaccine for Jennerian prophylaxis.[52] Siedentopf and Green have reported great success in the preservation of modified canine distemper virus (ferret passage).[53] It is known that some substances, after drying from the frozen state, may not maintain activity in the presence of atmospheric oxygen, even though completely dry and hermetically sealed. Typical of such products are those high in lipoidal content. In such a case, sealing is necessary either under original vacuum or under an inert gas such as nitrogen or argon. Siedentopf and Green report that this is so with their distemper virus. It should be pointed out that the release of the original vacuum with dry air and subsequent evacuation or replacement of air with inert gas does not operate satisfactorily in all cases, since oxygen may be absorbed by the highly porous solid matter and cannot be readily swept out. Also, for distemper virus the nitrogen must be purified by passage over hot copper.[54]

Influenza virus may be successfully preserved[50] and freeze-drying is used widely for carrying various strains of the virus in many research laboratories. Hoffstadt and Tripi[55] report successful three-year preservation of Levaditi and Cutter strains of vaccinia, herpes simplex, laryngotracheitis of fowls and Rous sarcoma viruses. On the other hand, they found inconstant maintenance of viability of the virus of infectious myxomatosis of rabbits over the three-year periods; whether this was because of non-uniform residual content of moisture or other reasons was not determined. Their culture of O A strain of Shope's fibroma did not survive the period. Other viruses which have been successfully kept are those causing hog cholera,[56] rinderpest, ovine ecthyma (sheep scabs), yellow fever and various fowl diseases, such as laryngotracheitis and fowl pox prepared from chick embryos. Wooley[57] has reported that lymphocytic choriomeningitis and St. Louis encephalitis after freeze-drying had been preserved for 378 and 833 days, respectively. Tests for longer periods were not made.

Libby[58] has used freeze-drying in immunochemical studies with tagged antigens involving radio-tracers, with tobacco mosaic virus tagged with radioactive phosphorus (P^{32}). Mice were injected with the tagged virus; 24 hours later the mice were killed in a Dry Ice-acetone bath, and 3 to 4 mm sagittal sections were prepared with a band saw. These sections, after freeze-drying, were impregnated with paraffin and 1-mm sections were prepared with a microtome and placed in intimate contact with x-ray film for exposure for varying periods to obtain autoradiographs. In this way it is possible to locate regions and organs of greatest concentrations of radioactivity.

The same methods as applied to the types of micro-organisms already enumerated are likewise applied to molds and other organisms. The method has been used quite widely during the development of the penicillin program and has proved invaluable in transporting to great distances the many stocks of molds which have been collected, as well as specially developed strains previously discussed. In the case of molds, spores rather than the vegetative forms may be dried.

BIOLOGICAL WARFARE

One of the unfortunate possible applications of freeze-drying is in the preservation of the various micro-organisms such as bacteria and viruses which are pathogenic for man and other animals, plant life and also products produced by micro-organisms. It has been said that bacterial warfare was invented in 1649 by the Venetians who sent a physician with a flask of buboes to spread bubonic plague among the Turkish army in Crete. Some of the recently developed possibilities have been set forth by Rosebury and Kabat.[59] Any of these agents such as pathogenic *Neisseria* may be preserved by freeze-drying for production of a carrier rate high enough so that cases would appear; for virus of mumps and measles, which are highly epidemic particularly among children and among adults from rural areas; and for yellow fever virus. The latter can apparently be transmitted without the aid of insect vectors under artificial conditions not met normally in nature, since the dry powder apparently can penetrate unbroken skin. Naturally, there may be many other applications developed in recent years which, for reason of security, are not being published. A fine dust of such a virus in freeze-dried form, as well as other materials, might even scatter sufficiently if merely dropped in a glass vessel, although of course much more efficient means could readily be developed. These authors point out what is now generally accepted, that bacterial warfare is feasible, although actual demonstration of its practicability is lacking, since the destruction or immobilization of men or of essential productive and military equipment and materials without excessive risk to the user has not been proved. For no other reason than possible retaliation there is risk to the user. In fact, biological warfare is similar to or in the same category as chemical warfare, in which a major reason for fully exploring the possibilities is to be fully prepared as a means for defense. Defensive measures mean not only measures of defense *per se*, but must include full exploration of the possibilities in offensive tactics as well. Freeze-drying plays a part, not only as a possible method for direct dissemination of infectious agents and for distribution of immunizing agents, but as an invaluable aid as a research tool in delimiting the possibilities.

The work of Rosebury and Kabat[59] as published and as referred to above contains only data that were publicly available before 1942; it was treated as confidential during the war emergency, and has only recently been published by virtue of the removal of war-time restrictions. It is to be hoped that biological warfare will never become a reality. If it does not, the tremendous effort will have been repaid by virtue of the major contribution to medicine in increased knowledge of the control of disease prophylactically, therapeutically, epidemiologically and otherwise.

BACTERIAL AND VIRAL VACCINES

It would seem self-evident that a method suitable for preservation of bacterial and viral cultures in viable form would also be suitable for preservations of vaccines made from them. However, there are several other considerations. First, with both bacteria and viruses, there is the matter of percentage viability remaining after drying, as has been discussed. Second, with bacterial cells, there is the question of the extent to which full original degree of dispersion is obtainable upon reconstitution, regardless of whether viability is maintained (many bacterial vaccines are prepared from killed organisms).

This "agglutinability" of cellular organisms has been suggested as a drawback in the use of freeze-drying for preservation. In addition, there is the point that if the organisms have been killed, the means of killing is quite likely to have caused so much change in the cells that little more would be likely to occur percentage-wise in the liquid suspension over any reasonable period of normal storage. With vaccines composed of living organisms, such as *Brucella abortus,* we have an entirely different situation in normal storage, since mortality of living cells is high in undried form.

A case where freeze-drying has been of value in the preservation of live bacterial vaccines is *Brucella abortus,* just mentioned, for control of Bang's disease in cattle. The organisms are suspended in a protein medium, such as serum or milk, preferably the latter. The pH is adjusted between 6.6 and 6.8, preferably with a phosphate buffer. Survival rates of about 50 per cent after drying are considered good, although by making other modifications in the suspending medium, survival rates as high as 90 per cent have been obtained. There is a minimum freezing and maximum final temperature for optimum survival, depending on strain variation, generally above Dry-Ice temperature for the former and above room temperature for the latter. The rate of temperature increase and time for drying are also critical.

The viral vaccine for prevention of canine distemper has been produced commercially in a small way. Various fowl viruses are produced by desiccation. Vaccine for the prevention of yellow fever in man has been successfully prepared on a rather large scale. In experimental work the virus of influenza has been freeze-dried. Vaccine for intradermal injection for immunizing against smallpox by Jennerian prophylaxis[52] has all been distributed after freeze-drying. There is question about the efficacy of this method of immunization but this has no bearing on freeze-drying *per se* (it relates to the nature of the material itself and the method of carrying out immunization).

One of the earliest applications of freeze-drying has been in the control of rinderpest (cattle plague) in Africa. The mortality for this disease is high, sometimes reaching 50 to 75 per cent. In preparation of the virus the blood of infected animals is laked and centrifuged. This separates the leucocytes with which the live virus is associated. Without drying, the virus remains viable and effective as an immunizing agent for a matter of a few weeks only. The virus survives freeze-drying well and its life is thus extended to months and years. Cattle are immunized by the simultaneous inoculation of living virus and immune serum, this being similar to the practice in immunizing swine against hog cholera discussed below.

Munce and Reichel[56] have shown that hog cholera virus of blood origin, when desiccated under high vacuum and stored *in vacuo* in flame-sealed ampoules, remained infective after exposure to a temperature of 60°C for 96 hours. At 37°C, the infectivity was maintained for 328 days. Phenolized liquid virus from the same mixture was non-infective after exposure to the higher temperature for only five hours. At 37°C the period of infectivity of the dried preparation was approximately 23 times as long as for the phenolized liquid virus. After storage at 20°C, the dried virus was still infective in these authors' last test, which was conducted after a storage period of 1125 days—12 times as long as for the corresponding phenolized liquid virus.

It may be pointed out that hog cholera virus, as commercially available, consists of the phenolized, defibrinated blood of artificially infected swine which are undergoing an attack of acute hog cholera at the time their virus-laden blood is collected. This virus preparation is frequently referred to as "simultaneous hog cholera virus" because it is used simultaneously with anti-hog cholera serum in the immunization of swine against hog cholera. The animals would not survive the injection of the live virus were they not protected simultaneously with the serum. When used in conjunction with anti-hog cholera serum, the virus possessing high virulence and the proper antigenic properties stimulates a strong, active immunity of lasting duration. The product, when dispensed as a liquid, must be preserved with phenol in the amount of 0.5 per cent. This agent exerts a viricidal action which gradually reduces the viability until it is no longer infective. For this reason, the United States Bureau of Animal Industry has assigned an expiration dating of only 90 days for the phenolized liquid from the date of the *production* (not sale) of the product. Accordingly, the results with the freeze-dried product are of particular importance, not only in extending the actual dating itself, but in assurance that the product will have not undergone partial deterioration when used.

Munce and Reichel have also reported that the freeze-dried samples maintained their infectivity for a longer period after freeze-drying when stored in flame-sealed ampoules than in rubber stoppered bottles, in both cases the containers being evacuated.

Although unpreserved liquid virus maintains its infectivity for a longer period than phenolized liquid virus from the same mixture and stored at the same temperature, Government regulations require the use of a suitable preservative for obvious reasons. Accordingly, the results of significance are those in comparing the longevity of the freeze-dried product with the phenolized liquid virus.

Smadel, Randall and Warren[60] have reported on the successful freeze-drying of Japanese encephalitis vaccine. This was supplied by the Army Medical Department, Research and Graduate School, for the Pacific Theatre. They used the "Nakayama" strain and produced a 20 per cent suspension of infected chick embryo tissue in buffered physiologic saline containing sufficient formaldehyde to inactivate the virus. The formaldehyde is finally neutralized with sodium bisulfite, penicillin is added to the final pools to make a final concentration of five units per cc, and the merthiolate is added at 1:10,000.

The vaccine is finally freeze-dried in apparatus of a type similar to Bauer and Pickels, and is described in Chapter 5. By means of external refrigeration, the vials supported on a vertical manifold, the air is kept around $-20°C$ for several hours. The temperature is then allowed to rise slowly and reaches $0°C$ about 20 hours after starting. The temperature is then raised quickly to $30°C$ and is maintained there during the 20 to 24 hour period. A pressure of 30 to 50 microns is held initially and at the end of the cycle, the pressure goes as low as two or three microns. Presumably, this low pressure is unnecessary, but is obtainable because of the inherent nature of the equipment which utilizes a Dry Ice condenser.

When drying is completed, vacuum is released by means of "super-dry, oil pump nitrogen which has a moisture content of less than 0.002%." This is further passed over a chemical desiccant. The nitrogen-charged ampoules are sealed by fusion of the glass stem. Storage of the vaccine is at $5°C$. Rehydrated vaccine must be discarded after about eight hours.

HUMAN MILK

It is well known that many mothers have large excesses of milk and others an insufficient supply. By means of human milk banks it is possible to maintain a fairly satisfactory balance of supply and demand. Occasionally an excess supply may carry the situation temporarily out of balance. Drying the excess by sublimation directly in nursing bottles was carried out as early as 1935.[1] Although application has not been widespread the possibilities are considerable, particularly in making the product available in smaller communities where the population does not permit the maintenance of a milk bank.

PENICILLIN, STREPTOMYCIN AND OTHER ANTIBIOTICS

An antibiotic is an agent produced by living microorganisms which exerts antagonistic effects upon other living organisms. Penicillin is produced by *Penicillium notatum* and although it was discovered originally in 1929, not until World War II were its great clinical potentialities fully realized. Extensive clinical testing was carried out, and the product finally put into mass production. A somewhat extended discussion of freeze-drying amorphous penicillin follows because it represents a difficult material, hygroscopic, labile and requiring lower than usual temperature. Since about 1948 most commercial penicillin has been crystalline, not requiring freeze-drying.

Early work was not directed toward evaluating the possible clinical usefulness of penicillin presumably because its lability seemed to make it unsuited as a therapeutic agent.[61] However, when later research had resulted in demonstrating the effectiveness of penicillin,[62,63] it was natural that desiccation from the frozen state should be called upon to stabilize it, as freeze-drying had in the meantime become highly developed for commercial use.

In many respects, the problems with freeze-drying plasma and penicillin were similar and, indeed, even many parts of the equipment used were identical. On the other hand certain peculiarities in the nature of penicillin introduced problems quite different from any encountered earlier. Although penicillin is essentially labile, more so than many other biologicals, it is not in the same class as guinea-pig complement. It is desirable to dry penicillin at temperatures even lower than that required for many other biological products including blood plasma. Penicillin does not remain in a completely satisfactory physical condition unless the temperature is below about $-20°C$, and in some cases preferably below $-25°C$. The exact temperature varies with the degree of purification and with the concentration of the product; nevertheless, even the least exacting of preparations should be processed at a lower temperature than plasma. Some commercial preparations require $-40°C$. Frozen penicillin may be considered as a partially thermoplastic material, the degree of thermoplasticity being greater at the higher range of sub-freezing temperatures. Furthermore, penicillin solutions have a low surface tension. If penicillin is not kept at the low temperatures indicated above during drying, this thermoplasticity in view of the low surface tension allows a certain degree of apparent bubbling; if allowed to proceed too far, this would be sufficient to introduce serious problems of practical control. Therefore it is desirable to maintain a temperature low enough to avoid this condition. This is discussed more fully in Chapter 2.

Carr and Riddick[64] determined the hygroscopicity of various penicillins. Their published curves show a critical point in humidity above which there is rapid absorption of water by the dry material.

Drying of a biological product intended for parenteral use may be carried out either in bulk or in the final container in which the product is to be stored and distributed. At first virtually all parenteral penicillin was dried in the final container, as proposed in 1935.[1] Some parenteral penicillin is now dried in bulk. However, drying in bulk has not met with favor in all quarters because of the obvious problems of maintaining sterility while sub-dividing dry powder into ampoules for distribution. The problem is made more difficult because of the hygroscopic nature of dry penicillin and the fact that the size of doses requires accurate weighing of small amounts. Drying penicillin in bulk for transfer of dried powder to final ampoules is the first time that this method has ever been tried in the routine commercial production of a biological product.

Originally, preconcentration of penicillin was carried out in bulk by partial freeze-drying, with transfer of concentrated liquid to ampoules for final drying. This reduced the size of the final ampoules required, particularly where the original penicillin was very dilute. However, highly concentrated solutions of penicillin are now obtained directly by improved methods of chemical extraction, so that this preliminary step of concentrating by evaporation is no longer necessary. It should be pointed out, however, that when concentrating in bulk, as just described, the same problems of sterility are not encountered as when drying completely in bulk. This is because a representative sample of the concentrated liquid is readily obtained for bacteriological culturing; if it is found sterile there is reasonable assurance that the entire batch is sterile. This is in contrast with the ineffectiveness of proper bacteriological sampling of dry powders.

There are no particular limitations with regard to the temperature of freezing other than it be sufficiently low to prevent excessive separation of ice crystals from concentrated penicillin. As indicated above, a temperature of $-20°C$ represents about the maximum to be used if the product is to be dried without excessive apparent bubbling of the thermoplastic solid. The Food and Drug Administration has used Cryochem freeze-drying in test work and standardization with penicillin after shell-freezing, presumably with a Dry Ice bath.[65]

There is a further complication in the large-scale production of penicillin in contrast with plasma. Because of the larger bulk of material in a single plasma bottle and the lower surface to volume ratio, its contents will not thaw quite so quickly when removed from the freezing-bath. With penicillin the amounts are so small that unless special precautions are taken there is considerable hazard of partial thawing after removal from the freezing-bath or from the frozen storage vaults. This happens during loading of the drying chambers and evacuation to pressures that enable the frozen state to be maintained by evaporative cooling. For that reason, drying chambers of the type used widely for blood plasma[9] have been modified to the extent that they can be chilled to subfreezing temperatures. The product, after being loaded into the chambers, is held in a frozen condition in this way until the proper degree of vacuum is obtained. Then the chilling medium is removed from the jackets of the chambers and the heating medium is circulated at the proper temperature.

A still simpler procedure has now been introduced which greatly reduces the labor of handling the bottles. Those containing the liquid penicillin are introduced into the chilled drying chambers. As soon as the penicillin has been frozen, which may be within as little as half an hour, the chamber is evacuated and then heated in the usual fashion.

Because of the high hygroscopicity of penicillin, low final moisture content is somewhat more difficult to obtain. One procedure which has met with favor is to use steam ejectors or refrigerated condensers in the first stage of drying for the removal of the bulk of the water vapor from the frozen penicillin solution. This affords the most economical way of carrying out the process, since a vacuum of no better than about 250 microns is required. To complete the drying a chemical desiccant may be used. By choice of the proper desiccant partial pressures of water vapor as little as a fraction of a micron are readily obtainable, making it possible to reduce the final moisture content in penicillin to as low a level as necessary.[9] Inasmuch as the amount of actual water to be taken up by the desiccant in this second stage is small, weights of desiccant which are reasonable will last for a long time before replacement or regeneration is necessary. The Food and Drug Administration has used Cryochem freeze-drying in test work and standardization of penicillin to sufficiently low moisture.[65]

As an aid in reduction to proper final moisture content, the temperature of the penicillin may be raised toward the end of drying to increase the vapor pressure. This in turn raises the pressure which it is possible to use for obtaining final dryness. Although originally it had not been considered safe to take the dry penicillin to above 40°C, there seems now to be evidence that the final product may be raised to considerably higher temperatures, even as high as 110°C. This, of course, simplifies the problem of obtaining a low moisture point at the end of the process.

Although exhaustive data are not yet available which relate the stability of penicillin at various temperatures to the actual content of moisture in the dry product (among other things, it varies with the degree of purification) it is generally agreed that the lower the content of moisture the greater the stability. There is considerable difference of opinion as to just what is the critical level. In some States it was early required by regulation that the product be reduced to below 2.5 per cent, and there is evidence that a final moisture content of 0.5 per cent is necessary for *maximal* stability.

The foregoing discussion applies to amorphous penicillin. Crystalline penicillin can be reduced to dryness by means other than freeze-drying, but in some processes final reduction of the product to low moisture parallels the second stage of freeze-drying.

Streptomycin is likewise being freeze-dried. As with other products, longer datings may thus be permitted. Furthermore, sterilization of the pure product just before filling the final containers is difficult. The uncertainty of sterile handling of liquid products, which are not readily sterilized by the normal procedure of filtration or heat or by addition of bactericidal preservatives, has been discussed in Chapter 2. If a batch of liquid product is free enough from contamination that organisms cannot be found in standard test procedures, the product is freeze-dried and there is definite assurance that it will be safe for use upon restoration. This is in contrast with the situation where the product would be dispensed in a large number of bottles as a liquid and a few might be slightly contaminated. During storage these few bottles would become heavily contaminated as a result of multiplication of the few isolated organisms which missed initial detection. Streptomycin is more like plasma in its physical drying characteristics than penicillin except a temptrature less than $-30°C$ is necessary.

Naturally, freeze-drying is applied to other antibiotics, both to control lability and to make control of sterile distribution easier, such as bacitracin.

During the war, Sherwood[66] and his collaborators at M.I.T. carried out extensive studies on drying penicillin and arrived at certain theoretical considerations. These were in connection with drying from bottles, centering entirely around the type of bottle established by the W.P.B. for distribution of the antibiotic. In the Appendix will be found a portion of the reports made of this work.

HORMONES, AMINO ACIDS, BILE AND OTHER BIOLOGICALS

A wide variety of biological products has been dried successfully from the frozen state; there is no change in general in biological or other properties, and the dry products have excellent characteristics of solubility. A brief reference will be made to some of these. Bacteriophage from many organisms including that of dysentery has been dried.[67] Highly purified tuberculin protein satisfactory for skin testing in control of tuberculosis has been dried successfully by lyophilization. Seibert, who has contributed more than anyone else to the chemistry of tuberculin, has studied the effects of freeze-drying and various procedures of applying it. She has found no change in this protein material detectable by some of the most sensitive means available today.[68] Langner and his associates have applied freeze-drying to organisms to be chemically extracted and to the extracts obtained from them. This was in connection with studies in allergy.[69,70,71] Casals has applied freezing and drying to various antigens of a non-virulent nature to be used in complement-fixation tests with central nervous system virus infections. These have been frozen and dried and distributed to various laboratories for use in hospital diagnostic work.[72] Small-pox and BCG vaccines are dried in U.S.S.R. with excellent results for shipment to remote places.[73] Hetherington has used lyophile serum, embryo juice and plasma media for tissue culture.[74] An adequate supply of material can be kept on hand for continued use to avoid considerable routine labor and at the same time provide a constant medium for use in a long series of comparative experiments. The product has been found excellent in connection with the growth of cardiac explants for white mice. Souter and Kark have produced a stable thromboplastin suitable for use in the Quick prothrombin test.[75] Material ready for immediate use with the addition of distilled water permits the performance of the test by the physician in his own office and makes it possible to carry out the test with greater ease anywhere.

Teague, Galbraith, Hummel, Williams and Macy report that the removal of water from feces, urine and milk by dehydration *in vacuo* from the frozen state permits preservation of the dry material indefinitely in an undenatured form if stored under proper conditions.[76] This method of dehydration has many advantages over oven-drying. Oven-drying at 70°C and under hydrolyzes the soaps in feces, causing exaggerated values for the free fatty acids and a reduction in the soaps, although the total free fatty acid plus soap values is the same for both methods of drying. The nitrogen contents of the Cryochem samples of feces, urine, and milk approximate those of fresh specimens. In obtaining energy data by the bomb calorimeter, the Cryochem-dried material permits greater accuracy in analyses and economy of time and materials, and eliminates one nitrogen determination and the correction for nitrogen loss in drying.

Dried human blood cells are available commercially for topical treatment of slowly healing wounds, burns, and ulcers. The product apparently has the property of stimulating the growth of healthy granulation tissue when sprinkled in liberal quantity over the affected area. It also serves as a medium for the growth and extension of epithelial cells over the granulating surface. The cells represent the residual cell mass after plasma is withdrawn from fresh human citrated blood. The preparation also contains a small amount of residual plasma, the stroma and the contents of the cellular and acellular elements of the blood. The freeze-drying operation is carried out readily to produce a highly satisfactory product. The dried product is unabsorbed by the dressing and clings to the wound site. It is highly stable for an extended period of time.

Bile has been prepared in dry form so that a stable product may be stored ready for dissolving to use in obstructive jaundice. It is believed that the abnormal bleeding which occurs is due to the failure in the absorption of vitamin K in the absence of bile in the intestines.[77]

Farr and Hiller have reported on the successful drying of hemoglobin.[78] They found that applying the method of freeze-drying to oxygenated hemoglobin solution resulted in preparations in which the hemoglobin had lost 25 to 30 per cent of its oxygen-binding capacity, by change to methemoglobin. However, when hemoglobin solutions were first deoxygenated by repeated evacuation of all gases, so that over 99 per cent of the oxyhemoglobin was changed to reduced hemoglobin, the reduced solutions could then be frozen and dried in ampoules and the dried hemoglobin kept *in vacuo* for months without methemoglobin formation. In redissolving the reduced hemoglobin it was necessary to prevent even momentary access of atmospheric oxygen to the dried material before it was dissolved; otherwise, methemoglobin was formed. After the reduced hemoglobin was in solution, oxygenation did not inactivate it and the solution was stable in air. At 4°C the solution could be kept several weeks without significant change.

Drabkin reported[79] that excellent results were obtained with hemoglobin which the author prepared in 1937[80] by freeze-drying. These original samples were dried on a manifold type of Dry Ice condenser apparatus and were sealed in individual containers.[1] Drabkin stated that samples of dog cyanmethemoglobin kept in storage for nine years in a refrigerator remained unaltered. Preparations of hemoglobin tested over a five-year period were partially oxidized to methemoglobin but were undenatured in the sense that total pigment still remained completely convertible to hemoglobin by means of $Na_2S_2O_4$. This change toward ferrihemoglobin is not unusual; it occurs slowly and progressively in dilute solutions of oxyhemoglobin exposed to the air and also in the case of solid precipitate obtained in dialysis against saturated ammonium sulfate when not stored under vacuum. Of all the preparations, Drabkin found that cyanmethemoglobin proved to be the most stable, and in all his studies he has used freeze-dried preparations as his hemoglobin standard.

Amino acids are now available commercially after having been freeze-dried. In production, casein prepared by acid digestion is hydrolyzed to give a mixture of amorphous amino acids. In some cases certain of the amino acids are reduced in their natural amount, such as glutamic and aspartic acids, and others such as tryptophane are supplemented. The product may be used parenterally as a 10 per cent solution in the same way that blood plasma is administered, say at rate of 50 to 60 drops per minute. Clinical experience at the present time is not broad, but as the result of nutritional therapy expected benefits are a contribution to antibody formation, hemoglobin formation, maintenance of liver function, regeneration of tissue required for the healing of wounds, maintenance of water balance (by effecting a reduction in and the disappearance of edema), prevention of edema, and other advantages. Reported indications for parenteral administration are whenever food cannot be eaten or digested, when it is not permitted as a pre- or post-operative precaution, and for restoration of nitrogen balance when sufficient protein is not available.

These mixtures of amino acids present somewhat greater difficulties in drying than certain other substances because of the lower temperature required. It has been reported that some of these troubles may be overcome in part by concentrating the solution *in vacuo* and adding dextrin to the concentrated solution.[81] For this purpose it is claimed that of the carbohydrates, only dextrin or starch is suitable; sucrose or cerelose is reported not to aid in subsequent lyophilization.

With proper type of equipment, vacuum concentration of the protein hydrolyzate may be carried out at temperatures below say about 50°C without an antifoaming agent. This concentrated hydrolyzate may then be shell-frozen and lyophilization carried out as usual. The above authors state that not over 10 per cent of the total volume of the bottle should be filled with the product, but the author has found it possible to fill the bottles up to about 50 per cent of their capacity, as is the case with blood plasma.

Many enzymes have been dried without loss in their activity.[1] To cite but one unusual case, crystalline beef liver catalase has been dried; the properties of the dried product compared favorably with those of undried crystalline beef liver catalase. Dounce and Howland[82] report that the dried material is not crystallizable.

On a small scale, freeze-drying has been applied to the histologic fixation of tissues. In this case drying is slow and heat is not used. Altmann was perhaps the first worker in the field to report on such an application.[83] Gersh has extended the use of this technique for fixation[84] and Hoerr advanced the technique by more rapid freezing and by using a lower temperature of dehydration.[85] This topic is the subject of a later section.

One rather interesting application of freeze-drying has been in the dehydration of orchid seeds by Svihla and Ostermann.[86] It was found that seeds which were dried from a suspension of blood serum would not germinate upon reconstitution, but those dried from a suspension in coconut liquid germinated well and grew satisfactorily. Seeds of tuberous begonia and snapdragon failed to survive desiccation and did not grow.

Hormones are dried quite widely on a commercial scale and their commercial distribution as a result has been greatly assisted. Chorionic Gonadrotropin from the urine of pregnant women, and also of bovine origin, is perhaps one of the best examples; also anterior pituitary extracts of bovine origin. A wide variety of minced glandular materials is dried.

VITAMINS, PHARMACEUTICALS, CHEMICALS

Up to the present time the major application of various products in this class has been for parenteral use. The method has several advantages (1) the lability of the product; (2) the greater ease in controlling the sterility, as has been discussed in connection with antibiotics; and (3) the increased rate of solubility. The last is particularly important where an ampoule of product must be opened by a physician and dissolved at a temperature not lower than that of the room and not above that of the body and made ready for immediate injection. Rapid solubility frequently makes the difference between whether or not a product is suitable for such clinical use. Considerable quantities of vitamin B preparations are now dispensed commercially after freeze-drying for parenteral use. Aqueous solutions in high concentration have instable solubility characteristics, which is another reason for freeze-drying.

ELECTRON MICROSCOPY

Wyckoff has reported on the use of quick-freezing and desiccation from the frozen state to prepare specimens properly for use in electron microscope studies.[87,88] Fig. 3.2 shows a micrograph of a frozen-dried tobacco mosaic preparation. This contains a net-

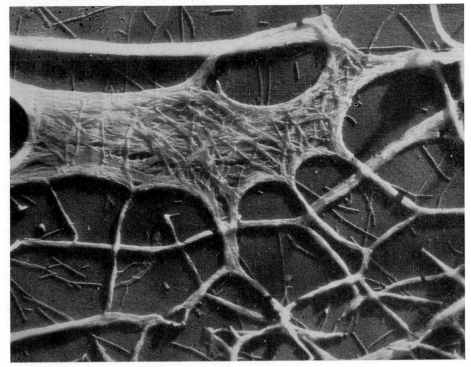

Fig. 3.2. Micrograph of a freeze-dried tobacco mosaic preparation. Magnification 24,000x. Courtesy of Dr. Ralph W. G. Wyckoff.

work of thick bundles of particles, and the formation of these bundles by the curling up of fragments of a sheet can be watched under the microscope. The fact that some bundles overlie others is evidence that the sheets from which they were derived were at different levels. The magnification is 24,000 times. As Wyckoff points out, most native proteins are strongly hydrated, whether they are in molecular suspension or whether they form part of an organized biological tissue. When water is lost during air-drying, for electron microscopy, it is probable that the elementary particles of many proteins will shrink and distort. Dehydration cannot now be avoided; therefore techniques are needed which will desiccate with a minimum of alteration. Freeze-drying accomplishes this.

The solution to be studied is prepared by taking a microdrop and applying it to the usual collodion- or Formvar-covered screens which have been chilled with Dry Ice or liquid-air temperature. The cold block is then quickly transferred to a vacuum chamber and high vacuum drawn before the product melts. If the preparations are to be shadow-cast before microscopic examination, vacuum desiccation and shadowing can be carried on in the same apparatus without breaking vacuum.

Wyckoff has made electron micrographs out of frozen-dried bacteria, of plant and animal viruses, and of tissues. In the case of certain of the materials the pictures are indistinguishable from those of ordinary air-dried preparations, and there would seem to be no reason for freeze-drying. With others, however, very interesting and striking pictures have been obtained. Mysels[89] has reported excellent photographs of amorphous aluminum laurate prepared by freezing direct on the naked wire gauze of the object holder and then subliming the cyclohexane solvent. When evaporating the same dilute sol at room temperature, no structures were observable in the soap film.

Pease[90] points out that ionic constituents are free to move during drying even when frozen unless quickly frozen to a "glass" ice and dried below $-55°C$. He froze a myosin sol in $0.5M$ KCl at liquid air temperature and then dried it in a Dry Ice cryostat at $-72°C$. Then after fragmentation, examination with the electron microscope revealed the total absence of salt crystals. Only with thick specimens bound by membranes, e.g., muscle fibers, was unquestioned salt found to be retained in situ.

Two possible explanations offered by Pease assume that the fixed ions in the solid are not associated in a crystal lattice and that either the slightest jar disperses them as free ions (or molecules) or else there is literal evaporation of the ions or molecules. He states that if the first were true, one might expect at least occasional masses trapped in interstices, but none were observed. As to the second explanation, nothing is known about vapor pressure relations in systems of isolated ions on an evaporating solid surface where attractive forces might be different from those on a crystal face or fluid surface. Pease suggests experimentation with radioactive tracer techniques to determine if evaporated salt can be located somewhere in the condensing or pumping system.

In any event Pease has demonstrated that aqueous systems containing high concentrations of salt can be prepared by this method for effective use with the electron microscope.

HISTOLOGY AND CYTOLOGY[*]

Freeze-drying has been employed extensively for many years by histologists and cytologists. The technique as practiced is quite different from the use of freeze-drying today for biologicals, pharmaceuticals, micro-organisms, and other products discussed. The procedure is much slower and the products are maintained at lower temperatures without heating. It is for these reasons, as well as the fact that tissues are generally more difficult to dry than liquids, that the process is more time-consuming and requires more elaborate equipment.

It was nearly 60 years ago that Altmann[83] stated that biological materials could be dried without shrinkage at a temperature of −20°C. This was published in connection with his cytological work on bioblasts. Forty years later Gersh[84] described equipment for fixation involving the use of liquid ammonia to provide low temperature and a diffusion pump and phosphorus pentoxide for removal of the moisture. With this equipment Gersh was able to confirm the value of the procedure for fixation of some organs and tissues (skin, cartilage, smooth muscle, liver, pancreas). Gersh applied the technique successfully to the investigation of the excretion of uric acid and ferricyanide, the chemical nature of intracellular constituents, and the intracellular distribution of glycogen. Gersh also used the method for the preservation of vitally, or supravitally, stained preparations which fade in fixation or are incapable of satisfactory preservation by other means. He found that fixation of organs other than those just mentioned was less satisfactory, and that central nervous system material is exceedingly poorly fixed. A series of very interesting investigations on

[*] While this book was in press, a simple and relatively inexpensive freeze-drying apparatus for microscopic sections was described by Wang and Grossman in *J. Lab. Clin. and Med.*, 34, 292 (1949). Dry Ice and dimethoxytetraglycol are used for maintaining the temperature of the tissue at −31°C during drying. Use of this mixture without an excess of Dry Ice maintains this constant temperature for several days (Wikoff, Cohen and Grossman, *Ind. Eng. Chem., Anal. Ed.*, 12, 92 (1940)). A conventional Dry-Ice condenser is used for the removal of water vapor.

these subjects was then published by Bensley, Gersh, Stieglitz, Hoerr and others during the next three years.[91-97]

Goodspeed, Uber and Avery reported on interesting applications in plant cytology. They studied particularly the character of fixation and reported on chromosome structure in *lilium longi-florum*.[98]

In 1936, Hoerr introduced certain changes in Gersh's technique for Altmann fixation.[85] These changes involved more rapid freezing of the tissue by means of pentane chilled to $-131°C$, or isopentane chilled to $-195°C$. Dehydration was carried out quite slowly with the product at temperatures below $-30°C$, the tissue being permitted to warm very slowly from the freezing to the dehydration temperature. Paraffin was not used for embedding in microchemical studies. The lower temperature eliminated the greatest objection to the technique thus far for cytologic studies, by reducing the size of the ice crystals in freezing, thus bringing the artefacts below the visibility of the microscope.

Also in 1936, Scott and Williams[99] reported on "A Simplified Cryostat for the Dehydration of Frozen Tissues." This was constructed mostly of metal which permitted a dehydration temperature range for the product of 0 to $-70°C$. Scott and Williams claim low cost of operation. The apparatus is automatic in control of the temperature of the product and employs butyl alcohol and Dry Ice for the refrigerant. Thus we see that the entire trend is one of lower and lower temperature for the product. Scott has stated further[100] that $-20°C$ does not give particularly good results when one is interested in the electrolytes found in tissues. The reason is that the eutectic point of many of the salts normally found in tissue is considerably lower than $-20°C$. Consequently, it is impossible to keep them in a salt-ice equilibrium at $-20°C$.

The theoretical temperatures of dehydration run as low as $-54.9°C$, and even lower temperatures would not be out of place. But for practical reasons it is very difficult to dehydrate tissues in these extremely low temperature ranges. The vapor pressure of ice becomes very low, and adequate differential is difficult to obtain; consequently dehydration is retarded tremendously. It would take about six weeks to dehydrate 20 grams of ordinary tissue at $-65°C$, for example. Scott[100] sets a drying temperature of $-32.5°C$ and states that this is not theoretically correct but that it is practical and feasible; in general, Scott found that it gave very excellent results.

Richins[101] has reported on the preservation of vasomotor pictures in histological preparations by freeze-drying, using direct microscopic observation of the smallest arteries and arterioles responding to stimulation by intravenous administration of autonomic drugs. The abdomen of a white rat is opened sufficiently to allow extraction of a loop of duodenum. After drug administration, the duodenum loop is frozen quickly with Dry Ice to preserve the vasomotor picture. The frozen duodenum is cut and freeze-dried for fixing. Sections are then cut in paraffin at 10 micron thickness and stained with toluidine blue and eosin; Richins reports that the physiological pictures are well preserved. When atropine sulfate was injected into the femoral vein, the arteries in the subserosa and the arterioles in the submucosa of the gut were constricted. The capillary beds in the villi contained a small amount of blood. After administration of ergotoxine phosphate, the arteries and arterioles were dilated and the capillary beds in the villi were engorged with blood.

Food Products

FRUIT JUICES

Orange juice offers great promise for drying by sublimation. Not only are problems of juicing and of garbage disposal eliminated in institutional use, in dining cars and the like, but dehydrated orange juice also offers a greatly expanding market around the world where distribution of fresh fruit is impracticable. This applies also to the juices of many tropical fruits, such as those of guava, naranjilla and papaya. Even dehydrated pineapple juice may be brought to the American market with a flavor which only those who have been fortunate enough to travel to places like Hawaii have tasted.

From juices of vegetables such as carrots, celery and peas an excellent product is obtained which reconstitutes in a few minutes, with flavor comparable with those of frozen foods. With such products as these, however, the cost of the operation probably prohibits displacement of fresh vegetables, but for special purposes and specialty products there is wide opportunity.

Pretreatment may be used, in the case of tomatoes, for example, to produce a puree, or in the case of orange juice to make a concentrate, which may be dried. It must be borne in mind, however, that the quality of the final product is no better than that of the material as prepared for drying, so that no method of pretreatment or preconcentration can be used which will harm the quality. On the other hand, concentration may yield a product which, though satisfactory at the outset, lacks stability. Drying by sublimation can then stabilize the product at a much reduced cost over drying unconcentrated material, with increased output from the more expensive sublimation equipment. A semi-works freeze-drying plant is now in operation in Florida.

Many citrus concentrates, even when freshly prepared, are of such poor quality that there is little reason to dry them. However, by a new method of concentrating through slow freezing out of ice crystals and centrifuging, a satisfactory concentrate of 3:1 and 4:1 has been obtained. This has high quality when dried, although not the full equivalent of the dried product obtained from straight-run fresh juice. Another procedure which has been found satisfactory is to use a low-temperature vacuum concentrate to which a proportion of straight-run fresh juice has been added. This returns some proportion of volatile, aromatic constituents, improves the quality of the concentrate and when freeze-dried has good flavor. Another procedure is to improve spray-dried powder by addition of freeze-dried crystals.

By use of some such method of obtaining concentrate, sufficient product for a full year's operation of the drying plant can be accumulated during the citrus-growing season. This excess product is held in the frozen state and is drawn upon as needed. As a result, the output of the freeze-drying plant is increased in two ways. The daily output is increased by drying a product of higher total solids content, and the plant can be operated for twelve months per year instead of the five during the crop harvest.

A still further improvement in quality can result at relatively low cost. Sufficient concentrating capacities may be installed to accumulate a year's supply during a period of the best two months of the growing season. It is known that early- and late-season fruit from Florida, California, and other citrus-growing areas are not of optimum quality.

With orange juice, it is often helpful to include a small percentage of a gelatin stabilizer or other similar substance. Such a stabilizing solution may be used, with sugar if desired, with products other than orange juice. In the case of lemon and lime juices, however, another problem is encountered. The ratio of acid to sugar is high, and the citric acid is reduced to such a low moisture content that its hygroscopic effect slowly carbonizes the sugar to a slight degree over a period of time. The product after reconstitution has an excellent flavor, but is unattractive in appearance, but this may be overcome by addition of sugar to improve the acid ratio (U. S. Patent 2,471,678).

In carrying out the process, the product to be dried must first be frozen. This may be done either by freezing before placing it in the vacuum chamber, by self-freezing under vacuum, or by a combination of these procedures. The essential requirement usually is that freezing be rapid. Similarly, the product may be sprayed into a high-vacuum chamber, the moisture of the small droplets being rapidly sublimed after freezing. Varying proportions of the juice in this procedure are dried from the liquid state in freezing, depending upon the rate of input of heat at the same time that cooling is taking place to induce freezing. These particles may be allowed to dry while falling through a column, or they may be carried on a belt or similar device. In such fashion, either a semi-continuous or fully-continuous type of operation may be effected.

Burton has described[102] a process which utilizes the spraying of a concentrate onto the warm water-jacketed walls of a vertical, cylindrical tank. A layer thickness is built up so that after freezing, a drying time of about six hours is required to complete the drying of the batch. Because a vacuum-concentrated product is used in this particular process, the final product is apparently not the equivalent of fresh juice, since Burton states that the reconstituted powder compares in flavor to restaurant-type orange juice, which has been stored in a refrigerator for some time. The pressure of 500 to 700 microns which is used corresponds to a temperature of $-20°$ to $-25°C$ for the plastic juice. Final blank-off pressures as low as 20 microns may be used for reducing the final moisture content in the dried powder to less than 1.5 per cent.

Instead of spraying, the liquid may be carried onto a belt or other arrangement by other means as at Massachusetts Institute of Technology, namely, by spreading with the aid of scrapers or doctor blades. By the use of continuous injection with such methods and automatic unloading for removing the product into large vacuum reservoirs, semi-continuous operation may be effected. For fully continuous operation, high-vacuum locks may be used for removing the product from the drying chamber.[103] (In the M.I.T. apparatus, the product is below freezing even though there is apparent bubbling, as with penicillin.)

The product in continuous operation may be carried, if desired, through a cooler zone to aid freezing, after which it is passed through a hot zone. The material finally may either be cooled before unloading or unloaded while hot.

Orange juice at temperatures of about freezing (just slightly below $0°C$) does not become fully hard and brittle. As the temperature of the frozen product gets lower, however, the degree of brittleness increases. In dealing with concentrate, the higher the content of total solids, the lower the temperature before a fully brittle product is obtained. In freeze-drying particularly concentrated materials, it is unnecessary to dry at temperatures as low as those at which a fully brittle product exists. In fact, the drying may be carried out at temperatures as high as those where the solid is still quite pliable and plastic. Under these conditions the product may even gradually "puff" as the frozen material dries. Puffing frequently is not complete until as much as 80 per cent of the moisture is removed, the end point of puffing varying widely with both the type of juice and the degree of preliminary concentration.

A question often asked is, "Why does this condition not occur during freeze-drying of straight-run or unconcentrated juice to the same extent that it does when drying 'concentrate'? All stages of total solid content are apparently passed through when drying the straight-run juice." The answer is that the drying of a frozen product is not comparable to the vacuum-drying of liquids, since the ice layer in the frozen product recedes gradually. When drying is half completed there is an upper or outer layer of dry product; an under or lower layer remains, with an ice content the same as that of the original material. That is, the ice layer gradually sublimes and recedes, leaving an outer coating or framework of porous, solid material to cover the remaining ice-containing layer.

With respect to freezing the rate is not entirely a function of the temperature of the freezing medium, but rather a function of the rate at which heat is extracted from the product. By combining the external cooling of the container with evaporative cooling through application of vacuum, a temperature for rapid pre-freezing may be used which is relatively high—even above that at which desiccation subsequently is carried out. Self-freezing may be accomplished by means of the vacuum alone; but in this case, when the product is a liquid, it is necessary to combine the vacuum with a preliminary degassing step. This requires a gradual and controlled rate of evacuation.[9,104]

Juice is conveniently handled by piping directly into the freezing shelves of the dryer. The finished dry crystals can be removed by tilting the dryer trays or by other automatic means. When completely dry, the product flows readily so that there is no difficulty with sticking. Therefore, even in batch processing there is little handling.

When juices are dried as concentrate a product is obtained which may be soft and pliable, or plastic, at higher temperatures, such as 50 or 60°C, even when they are completely dried to a moisture content of less than 0.5 per cent to as low as 0.1 per cent. Therefore, when unloading such a product, it is advisable to lower the temperature somewhat so that a brittle material is obtained for handling. On the other hand, it is well to unload the product at as high a temperature as possible, to minimize the tendency to absorb moisture from any atmosphere through which the dry product passes during packaging operations.

A typical flow-sheet for vacuum sublimation of orange juice is given in Fig. 3.3.

During drying, vitamin C is retained without loss. Therefore, through freeze-drying not only is a dried product obtained which has flavor characteristics fully comparable with those of fresh juice,

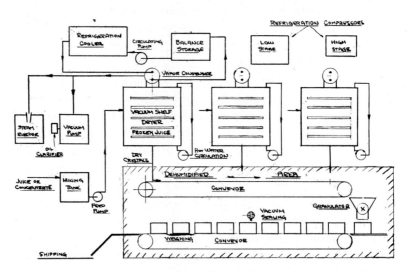

Fig. 3.3. Flow sheet for vacuum sublimation of orange juice. Three dryers, operated as batch units on a time cycle, permit practically continuous operation. The juice is de-aerated and frozen by the application of vacuum, then maintained below the freezing point, still under high vacuum, while heat energy is supplied by hot water circulated through the jacket and hollow shelves. Water sublimed from the frozen juice is condensed, the temperature of the condensing surface being maintained by the refrigerating cooler. The vacuum pump or steam ejector, or both, remove noncondsensible gases and air.

but a highly nutritious product is available as well. The ascorbic acid content is well maintained during storage also. From about 5°C up to 40°C, with a moisture content of under 1 per cent, no loss in vitamin C is detectable over a period of a year. At higher contents of moisture (about 4 per cent) there is still little loss during storage in a refrigerator. At 4 per cent moisture at room temperature there is as much as 50 per cent loss in vitamin C in six months, and at 40°C it is over 80 per cent. However, since the product becomes "caked" and loses its characteristics of solubility and high quality of flavor at the higher moisture content, the loss of ascorbic acid is of no consequence. In other words, if the residual moisture of content is below the point at which solubility and flavor are retained, then vitamin C is likewise well preserved. Comparable results have been found in other high vitamin C products, such as dried tomato juice and pulp.

MEATS

The fact that freeze-drying has proved itself so thoroughly useful for biological protein products would lead one to believe that excellent results might be obtained with meat. This is the case. However, successful results with meats are not quite as reasonable to expect as would appear on the surface of the matter. Since meat is a solid, or semi-solid, it is much more dense than the frozen solutions of proteins like blood plasma and serum. Connective tissue and other fibers further alter the situation. In spite of these facts, however, surprisingly satisfactory results are obtainable, particularly with ground meat products. Another difference is in the fat content of meat products. Of course, trimmable fat may be removed to a large degree, but dry meat products which do not have a high enough content of fat do not reconstitute to yield a savory and juicy product. The total content of fat should be in the range of 30 to 40 per cent dry weight.

Cost considerations of meats dried by sublimation are relatively attractive. The content of moisture to be removed is low with respect to the price of the product. As a specialty item freeze-dried meats can command a premium price. Since storage under refrigeration is unnecessary, it is a valued specialty in pantry storage for infant feeding, and for the unexpected guest; it is also practical for use on yachts, for campers and fishermen, and for many other purposes where fresh meats are ordinarily unavailable because of lack of even the ordinary degree of refrigeration.

As with other products in drying by sublimation, the raw meat first is frozen. The ice is sublimed under high vacuum, leaving the solids of the original fresh product more or less intact in shape and size. The dried product appears much like the original meat even in color.

Because of the sub-freezing temperature at which dehydration is carried out, not only are there no changes in the molecular structure, but bacteriological and enzymatic actions cannot occur. The loss of volatile components is almost nil.

As will be discussed in Chapter 4, proteins have been studied after drying from the frozen state more than any other chemical species. Chemically, antigenically, immunologically and electrophoretically, proteins have been shown to undergo no change whatsoever either in drying or in subsequent storage.

Fats, likewise, do not change chemically during drying from the frozen state, but they do undergo change with regard to their colloidal state of dispersion. Fats are lyophobic colloidally, whereas proteins are lyophilic. Because of this, proteins after drying in this way are taken back into solution rapidly and completely into their original form, whereas fats are not. For example, in blood plasma fat-like components, resulting from the diet of the donor, do not reconstitute, so that even though the protein of plasma restores to a perfectly clear solution, the fatty constituents cause a turbidity. Similarly, in meats, the fats do not restore to the original condition.

Furthermore, fats will undergo oxidation even in the dry state. This affords no particular problem, however, since the products may be stored either under nitrogen or other inert gas, or *in vacuo*. Hydrolysis of fats does not occur, however, since the final moisture of content is reduced to a very low level.

It is important that bacterial growth cannot occur during sublimation because of the low temperature. Accidental contamination can always occur during any processing which is not bacteriostatic or bactericidal in action. However, the frozen state is bacteriostatic, and even if there were accidental contamination, there would be no multiplication of organisms. Only the grossest degree of contamination would be serious. After the product has been dried, the moisture of content is so low that bacterial growth cannot take place.

The content of vitamins is well preserved without any loss in activity. Indeed, this very method of desiccation from the frozen state is used by pharmaceutical manufacturers for preservation of vitamins of the B Complex in purified form. Such pharmaceutical preparations are used for parenteral injection, and this signifies the extent to which reliance may be placed upon this superior method of drying and of preservation.

Experts and food technologists in the field of meat products agree that meats dried by this method after reconstitution are indistinguishable in flavor from fresh meat. This is true of ground beef, pork, and lamb. The fact that fats are lyophobic does not adversely affect the quality of the final cooked product in any way. In fact, the coalesence of the fat particles, particularly in the case of pork, accounts for the fact that upon cooking there is actually improvement in flavor. Whole cuts of meat, such as thin steaks, may be dried. It appears, however, that the first application in industry will be to ground raw beef and pork sausage products.

At room temperature in the range of 80° to 100°F for 18 months, raw beef, raw pork, and raw lamb have not shown any deterioration in palatability or in ease of reconstitution. Under ordinary refrigeration at 40° to 45°F, the products will probably keep indefinitely. At a temperature of 120°F, after about three weeks a gradual change sets in, but the meat is still edible after three months. After three months of continued storage at 120°F, the product develops what might be termed as a "brown" flavor, but if the meat is well cooked, this is not noticed. In fact, some persons have even felt that the flavor has been improved.

In all cases, the above testing has been done with meat to which nothing has been added as filler which could in any way affect the flavor of the meat itself.

It has not been necessary to add anything which would act as a binding agent in reconstituting the meat. On the other hand, if desired, many of the usual recipes may be followed in cooking which call for the addition of egg and other ingredients to make special dishes.

In summary, meats dried by sublimation are sufficiently stable so that under ordinary conditions of distribution, no special attention need be given to maintaining temperature below that normally encountered in temperate climates. It would be well, however, to place some warning notice on packages, as is often done with other products, "*Store in a cool place.*"

It has been well established that for pure protein it is essential for the final moisture content to be reduced to below 1.0 per cent and preferably to 0.5 per cent for maximum stability. However, in the case of meat, a minor degree of denaturation of protein is of no importance, since the proteins are subjected to heat in cooking; hence this low minimum content is not nearly so essential. On the other hand, a low moisture of content does assist materially in extending the time over which a high degree of palatability is maintained at higher temperatures of storage. In any event, it is preferable to have a moisture content no higher than 2.0 per cent.

As a result of drying by sublimation, there is now available what a few years ago would have been considered an almost spectacular meat product. Raw meat may be stored without refrigeration for a period of months and years without danger of spoiling or of bacterial contamination. Within a matter of minutes the product can be reconstituted to produce a fresh raw meat containing all its original juiciness and flavor and ready for cooking in the usual fashion.

Goresline [105] has pointed out that dried and dehydrated foods have a remarkably clean bill of health from the standpoint of poisoning and other infections. Dried foods are among the safest; however, proper sanitary precautions must be taken because some types of pathogenic bacteria are so well preserved in dried form. Of main interest is the fact that minor contamination will not result in gross multiplication during storage.

OYSTERS, CLAMS, FISH FILLETS, ETC.

Oysters and clams may be dried, either whole or ground. In the case of oysters, the final product is naturally more satisfactory if dried whole. Since no problems are involved, this is the method to be recommended. It is important, as might be expected, that the oysters and clams be frozen immediately after opening. Deterioration of such products is so rapid, even when stored at about 5°C, that there is no alternative to freezing. As a result of drying, there is some shrinkage and shrivelling of the whole oyster and clam.

Upon reconstitution, these products return to their original shape in a surprising manner. For reconstitution, it is advisable to add iced water to the oyster and clam packages (preferably tin can) immediately upon opening. The can should be kept cold for 15 to 30 minutes to allow complete penetration of the restoration water if the product is to be eaten raw; if it is to be cooked, such long standing is unnecessary.

Fresh clams for chowder or stew are always cut up or ground. For this reason it is better to freeze-dry the clams in the cut-up form, since the final product then requires one less operation in preparation for cooking. With both oysters and clams the juice may be dried at the same time, so that upon reconstitution of the final product this also is obtainable in the original condition. Fig. 3.4 illustrates a batch of oysters being dried in a laboratory pilot plant.

Cod fillets and other fish fillets have been dried successfully. In the case of such products, care must be taken in packaging to avoid breakage in shipment, since the dried product is highly friable.

MILK

The qualities of rapid reconstitution and flavor are such that dehydrated cow's milk may some day find a wide market. But for goat's milk there is an outstanding opportunity. It is a higher-cost milk product. A strong odor may develop in liquid goat's milk during distribution. By drying from the frozen state, this odor is avoided and drug-store counters eventually may carry a product which people will find indistinguishable in taste from the cow's milk to which they may be allergic. Goat's milk dried or concentrated by other methods has an unnatural flavor.

New methods of vacuum-concentrating milk at low temperature above the freezing point have now been developed to yield a product which has a quite satisfactory flavor. Unfortunately, however, before distribution this product must be sterilized; pasteurization is insufficient. Although pasteurization destroys pathogenic organisms, many others are not destroyed, which will cause deterioration during storage of the evaporated milk. Sterilization is necessary even though this produces the characteristic unnatural flavor of ordinary evaporated milk products and therefore little advantage

Fig. 3.4. Pilot drying of oysters.

is gained from the new method of low-temperature concentration just referred to. However, such concentrates may be dried from the frozen state, thereby avoiding the necessity of sterilization.

COFFEE AND TEA EXTRACTS

Highly satisfactory soluble dry coffee extracts may be prepared by freeze-drying. According to technologists in the field the product is superior to that obtainable by any other commercial method available. To bring the cost within range, it is necessary to produce extracts containing 40 to 50 per cent solids. Such concentrated extracts are obtainable commercially today; indeed, concentrations as high as 70 per cent have been reported. The dried product has excellent solubility characteristics; and because of the low temperature used in drying, most of the aromatic constituents are retained. Drying of the extract is similar in method to drying concentrated citrus juices. Cream or milk may be added to the liquid extract before drying, although for general household use the added bulk of the dried product does not justify the combination type of product.

Tea extracts may be prepared in similar fashion. For preparing hot tea, there is, of course, little advantage in such a soluble product since tea-balls are so available. In the case of iced tea, however, there is a different situation, since the soluble product may be dissolved directly in cold water ready for instant use.

VEGETABLES AND OTHER PRODUCTS

Peas, whole or diced carrots, beets and many other vegetables may be freeze-dried. For ordinary purposes, however, the cost of production is prohibitive with relation to the value of the products. There are certain specialities wherein the situation is different. The "eye appeal" of a reasonable proportion of freeze-dried peas in an ordinary dehydrated combination product such as soup has commercial value. Freeze-dried peas are excellent in appearance even in dry form, and when reconstituted are indistinguishable in both appearance and flavor from the best of fresh or frozen peas.

Barker, Gane and Mapson have recorded results on the quality retained in freeze-dried peas which agrees with the author's findings.[106] They used peas previously blanched and then frozen at about $-20°C$. Drying was carried out with the peas around $-10°C$, using a $-35°C$ condenser. The final moisture content of 2.0 to 4.5 per cent was achieved, although generally a lower figure was desired.

Barker *et al.* state that the dried peas kept quite satisfactorily when stored in either air or nitrogen, although better results were obtained in the latter (with oxygen content below 1 per cent), the temperature of storage being about $15°C$. The peas are only slightly shrunken, are porous and have a low density. Rapid reconstitution is certain. Compared with frozen peas stored for the same period of time, the freeze-dried peas were of slightly better quality, color and flavor being well retained in both cases. Little ascorbic acid, if any, was lost during storage in nitrogen-packed cans for about a year, but 50 per cent or more was lost during the initial blanching operation.

Fresh strawberries, blackberries, soups, corned beef, and other meat hashes, cereals cooked in milk or cream, and tomato products offer interesting possibilities. Water, hot or cold, may be added as required. In the case of soups, the peas, carrots, and other vegeta-

Fig. 3.5. Typical freeze-dried foods: Beef, tomato juice, orange juice, peas.

bles may be added in freeze-dried form to usual dehydrated mixtures. Similarly, proportions of beef, pork, fowl, etc., may be added. Indeed, such specialty products promise to be the first full-scale application of freeze-drying in the commercial food field. Fig. 3.5 illustrates various freeze-dried vegetable products and juices.

Industrial Products

Bentonite clays and other materials have been dried with successful results in extending the surface of the colloid (U. S. Patent

No. 2,433,193). The possibilities of improving catalytic surfaces by influencing the extent and nature of the surface are of great interest.

BIBLIOGRAPHY

1. Flosdorf, E. W., and Mudd, S., "Procedure and apparatus for preservation in 'Lyophile' form of serum and other biological substances," *J. Immunol.*, 29, 389 (1935).
2. Stokes, J., Jr., Mudd, S., Roddy, R. L., Eagle, H., Flosdorf, E. W. and Lucchesi, P., *Trans. Soc. Pediatric Research, Am. J. Dis. Child.*, 48, 1428 (1934).
3. Stokes, J., Jr., McGuinness, A., and Mudd, S., *Ibid.*, 50, 535 (1935).
4. McGuinness, A., Stokes, J., Jr., and Armstrong, J. G., "Vacuum-dried human serums in the prevention and treatment of certain of the common communicable diseases: an 8-year study," *Am. J. Med. Sci.*, 205, 826–834 (1943).
5. Flosdorf, E. W., McGuinness, A. C., Kimball, A. C. and Armstrong, J. G., "Studies with *H. pertussis*. VII. Preparation and assay of hyperimmune human serum," *J. Pediatrics*, 19, 638–643 (1941).
6. McGuinness, A. C., Armstrong, J. G., and Felton, H., "Hyperimmune whooping-cough serum," *J. Pediatrics*, 24, 249–258 (1944).
7. Greaves, R. I. N., "The preservation of proteins by drying, with special reference to the production of dried human serum and plasma for transfusion," Medical Research Council, Special Report Series No. 258, 1946.
8. Flosdorf, E. W., and Mudd, S., "Blood substitutes used in transfusion." "Medical Physics," p. 116, Ed. by Otto Glasser, The Year Book Publishers, Inc., Chicago, 1944.
9. Flosdorf, E. W., Hull, L. W., and Mudd, S., "Drying by sublimation," *J. Immunol.*, 50, 21 (1945).
10. Freeman, N. E., and Wallace, W. McL., "The effect of concentrated serum on plasma volume and serum protein concentration," *Am. J. Physiology*, 124, 791 (1938).
11. Mahoney, E. B., "A study of experimental and clinical shock with special reference to its treatment by the intravenous injection of preserved plasma," *Ann. Surgery*, 108, 178 (1938).
12. Taylor, N. B., "Blood substitutes for transfusion," *Univ. Toronto Med. J.*, 19, 164 (1942).
13. Medical Research Council, Committee on traumatic shock and on blood transfusion, "The treatment of wound shock," M. R. C. War Memorandum No. 1, London, 1941.
14. Hughes, J., Mudd, S., and Strecker, E. A., "Reduction of increased intracranial pressure by concentrated solutions of human lyophile serum," *Trans. Am. Neurol. Soc.*, 62nd meeting (1936).

15. Hughes, J., Mudd, S. and Strecker, E. A., "Reduction of increased intracranial pressure by concentrated solutions of human lyophile serum," *Arch. Neuro. Psychiat.*, **39**, 1277 (1938).

16. Bond, D. D. and Wright, D. G., "Treatment of hemorrhage and traumatic shock by the intravenous use of lyophile serum," *Ann. Surg.*, **107**, 500 (1938).

17. Lozner, E. L., Lemish, S., Campbell, A. S., and Newhouser, L. R., "Preservation of normal human plasma in the liquid state. V. Clinical, chemical, and physico-chemical studies during three years of storage at room temperature." *Blood, J. Hematology*, **1**, 459 (1946).

18. Barondes, R. deR., "Powdered blood plasma and eggwhite perorally in therapy of gastrointestinal disorders," *Military Surgeon*, **101**, 306 (1947).

19. Cohn, E. J., Oncley, J. L., Strong, L. E., Hughes, W. L., Jr., and Armstrong, S. H. Jr., "Chemical, clinical, and immunological studies on the products of human plasma fractionation. I. The characterization of the protein fractions of human plasma," *J. Clin. Invest.*, **23**, 417 (1944).

20. Cohn, E. J., Strong, L. E., Hughes, W. L. Jr., Mulford, D. J., Ashworth, J. N., Melin, M. and Taylor, H. L., "Preparation and properties of serum and plasma proteins. IV. A system for the separation into fractions of the protein and lipoprotein components of biological tissues and fluids," *J. Am. Chem. Soc.*, **68**, 459 (1946).

21. Cohn, E. J., "The chemical separation and the clinical appraisal of the components of the blood," *Medicine*, **24**, 333 (1945).

22. Koop, C. E., "Plasma substitutes," *Am. J. Med. Sciences*, **213**, 233 (1947).

23. Elser, W. J., Thomas, R. A., and Steffen, G. I., "The desiccation of sera and other biological products (including micro-organisms) in the frozen state with the preservation of the original qualities of products so treated," *J. Immunol.*, **28**, 433–473 (1935).

24. Mudd, S., Flosdorf, E. W., Eagle, H., Stokes, J. Jr., and McGuinness, A. C., "The preservation and concentration of human serums for clinical use," *J. Am. Med. Assoc.*, **107**, 956–959 (1936).

24a Lahiri, D. C., "A method of improving the solubility of dehydrated concentrated horse serum immune globulins by addition of bile salt and extraction with ether," *Indian J. Medical Research*, **35**, No. 1, pp. 7–13 (1947).

25. Flosdorf, E. W., Boerner, F., Lukens, M., and Ambler, T. S., "Cryochem-preserved complement of guinea pig serum," *Am. J. Clin. Path.*, **10**, 339 (1940).

26. Boerner, F., and Lukens, M., "A simplified complement fixation technic for the serological diagnosis of syphilis," *Am. J. Clin. Path.*, **9**, 13 (1939).

27. Giordano, A. S., and Carlson, B., "Occurrence of a non-specific

substance in guinea pig serum fixed by antigens in the Wassermann test," *Am. J. Clin. Path.*, **9**, 130 (1939).

28. Rhamy, B. W., "Preservation of complement," *J. Am. Med. Assoc.*, **69**, 973 (1917).

29. Rhamy, B. W., "The development of chemical preservation of complement, especially Rhamy's sodium acetate method," *Am. J. Clin. Path.*, **4**, 35 (1940).

30. Eagle, H., "Laboratory diagnosis of syphilis," pp. 37–47, C. V. Mosby, St. Louis, 1937.

31. Ruffner, E., "Preserving of guinea-pig complement by Rhamy's sodium acetate method with 4% boric acid," *Z. Immunitatsforsch;* **60**, 166 (1928).

32. Sonnenschein, C., "Preservation of complement by Ruffner's sodium acetate and boric acid method," *Z. Immunitatsforsch;* **67**, 512 (1930).

33. Green, C. A., "Preservation of complement for the Wassermann reaction," *J. Path. Bact.*, **46**, 382 (1938).

34. Swift, H. F., "Preservation of stock cultures of bacteria by freezing and drying," *J. Exper. Med.*, **33**, 69–75 (1921).

35. Flosdorf, E. W., and Kimball, A. C., "Studies with *H. pertussis*. II. Maintenance of cultures in Phase I," *J. Bact.*, **39**, 255 (1940).

36. Flosdorf, E. W., and Mudd, S., "An improved procedure and apparatus for preservation of sera, micro-organisms and other substances: the Cryochem-process," *J. Immunol.*, **34**, 469 (1938).

37. Naylor, H. B., and Smith, P. A., "Factors affecting the viability of Serratia Marcescens during dehydration and storage," *J. Bact.*, **52**, 565 (1946).

38. Hammer, B. W., "A note on the vacuum desiccation of bacteria," *J. Med. Research*, **24**, 527–530 (1911).

39. Rogers, L. A., "The preparation of dried cultures," *J. Infectious Diseases*, **14**, 100–123 (1914).

40. Siler, J. F., and the Laboratory Staff of the Army Medical School, "Typhoid vaccine studies. Investigation of virulence and antigenic properties of selected strains of the typhoid organisms," *Am. J. Pub. Health*, **26**, 219–228 (1936).

41. Welch, H., Borman, E. K., and Mickle, F. L., "Preparation and analysis of diagnostic antipneumococcus serum," *Am. J. Pub. Health*, **29**, 35–42 (1939).

42. Appleman, M. D., and Sears, O. H., "Studies on lyophiled cultures: Lyophile storage of cultures of *Rhizobium leguminosarum*," *J. Bact.*, **52**, 209 (1946).

43. Speck, M. L., and Myers, R. P., "The viability of dried skim-milk cultures of Lactobacillus Bulgaricus as affected by the temperature of reconstitution," *J. Bact.*, **52**, 657–663 (1946).

44. Lord Stamp, "The preservation of bacteria by drying," *J. General Microbiology*, **1**, 251 (1947).

45. Reichel, J., Masucci, P., McAlpine, K. L., and Boyer, J., Unpublished work. (See Reference 46.)

46. Reichel, J., U. S. Patent Re. 20,969 (1939).

47. Shackell, L. F., "An improved method of desiccation, with some applications to biological problems," *Am. J. Physiol.*, **24**, 325–340 (1909).

48. Weiser, R. S., and Hennum, L. A., "Studies on the death of bacteria by drying. I. The influence of *in vacuo* drying from frozen state and from the liquid state on the initial mortality and storage behavior of *Escherichia coli*," p. 17, Abs. of Proceedings for the 47th General Meeting Soc. Am. Bact., May, 1947.

49. Probey, T. F., "Loss of virulence of *Treponema Pallidum* during processing of dried blood serum," *Public Health Reports,* **62**, 1199 (1947).

50. Scherp, H. W., Flosdorf, E. W., and Shaw, D. R., "Survival of the influenzal virus under various conditions," *J. Immunol.*, **34**, 447 (1938).

51. Harris, D. L., and Shackell, L. F., *J. Am. Pub. Health Assoc.*, **7**, 52 (1911).

52. Rivers, T. M., and Ward, S. M., *J. Exper. Med.*, **62**, 549 (1935).

53. Siedentopf, H. A., and Green, R. G., "Factors in the preservation of the distemper virus," *J. Infectious Diseases*, **71**, 253–259 (1942).

54. Siedentopf, H. A., U. S. Patent 2,380,339.

55. Hoffstadt, R. E., and Tripi, H. B., "A study of the survival of certain strains of viruses after lyophilization and prolonged storage," *J. Infectious Diseases*, **78**, 183–189 (1946).

56. Munce, T. W., and Reichel, J., "The preservation of hog-cholera virus by desiccation under high vacuum," *Am. J. Veterinary Research*, **4**, 270–275 (1943).

57. Wooley, J. G., "The preservation of lymphocytic choriomeningitis and St. Louis encephalitis viruses by freezing and drying *in vacuo*," *Public Health Reports*, **54**, No. 24, 1077–1079 (1939).

58. Libby, R. L., "The use of tagged antigens in immuno-chemical studies." Transactions of The New York Academy of Sciences, May, p. 248 (1947).

59. Rosebury, T., and Kabat, E. A., "Bacterial warfare, a critical analysis of the available agents, their possible military applications, and the means for protection against them," *J. Immunol.*, **56**, 7–96 (1947).

60. Smadel, J. E., Randall, R., and Warren, J., "Preparation of Japanese encephalitis vaccine," Bull. U. S. Army Medical Department, p. 963 (Nov., 1947).

61. Clutterbuck, P. W., Lovell, R., and Raistrick, H., *Biochem. J.*, **26**, 1907 (1932).

62. Chain, E., Florey, H. W., Gardner, A. D., Heatley, N. G., Jennings, M. A., Orr-Ewing, J., and Sanders, A. G., *Lancet,* **2**, 226 (1940).

63. Abraham, E. P., Chain, E., Fletcher, C. M., Gardner, A. D., Heatley, N. G., Jennings, M. A., and Florey, H. W., Lancet, 2, 177 (1941).

64. Carr, C., and Riddick, J. A., "Hygroscopicity of penicillin salts," *Ind. Eng. Chem.*, 39, 1021 (1947).

65. Welch, H., Grove, D. C., Davis, R. P., and Hunter, A. C., "The relative toxicity of six salts of penicillin," *Proc. Soc. Exp. Biol. Med.*, pp. 246–248 (1944).

66. Sherwood, T. K., Personal communication.

67. Schade, A. L., and Caroline, L., "The preparation of a polyvalent dysentery bacteriophage in a dry and stable form," *J. Bact.*, 46, 463 (1943).

68. Seibert, F. B., and DuFour, E. H., "Methods of preserving the tuberculin protein," *Am. Rev. Tuberculosis*, 41, 471 (1940).

69. Langner, P. H., Jr., and Forrester, J. S., "The disintegration of bacteria by mechanical means," *J. Immunol.*, 37, 133 (1939).

70. Forrester, J. S., and Langner, P. H. Jr., "III. Comparative reactions after intracutaneous injection of filtrates of mechanically disintegrated bacteria and of heat killed whole organism suspensions," *J. Immunol.*, 37, 141 (1939).

71. Langner, P. H. Jr., and Kern, R. A., "Studies on the immunology of hay fever," *J. Allergy*, 10, 1–14 (1938).

72. Casals, J., "Non-virulent frozen and dried antigens for complement-fixation tests with central nervous system virus infections," *Science*, 97, 337 (1943).

73. Mudd, S., "Programs for Medicine and National Health in the USSR," *Science*, 105, 306–309 (1947).

74. Hetherington, D. C., "Frozen-dried serum as a medium constituent for tissue cultures," *Proc. Soc. Experimental Biol. Med.*, 57, 196 (1944).

75. Souter, A. W., and Kark, R., "Quick's prothrombin test simplified by the use of a stable thromboplastin," *Am. J. Med. Sciences*, 200, 603 (1940).

76. Teague, D. M., Galbraith, H., Hummel, F. C., Williams, H. H., and Macy, I. G., "Effects of desiccation procedures on the chemical composition of feces, urine, and milk," *J. Lab. Clin. Med.*, 28, 343 (1942).

77. Johnston, C. G., *Surgery*, 3, 875 (1938).

78. Farr, L. E., and Hiller, A., "Preparation of dried hemoglobin without loss of activity," *Federation Proc. (Part II)*, 5, 133 (1946).

79. Drabkin, D. L., "XIV. The crystallographic and optical properties of the hemoglobin of man in comparison with those of other species," *J. Biol. Chem.*, 164, 703 (1946).

80. Drabkin, D. L., "Proceedings of the 1937 summer conference on spectroscopy and its applications," p. 94, New York (1938).

81. Westfall, R. J., Miller, O., and Westfall, I. S., "A method of drying partial protein hydrolysates and other hygroscopic materials for nutritional studies," *Science*, p. 530 (May 16, 1947).

82. Dounce, A., and Howland, J. W., "A study of crystalline beef liver. catalase dried in the frozen state," *Science,* 97, 21–23 (1943).

83. Altmann, R., "Die Elementarorganismen und ihre Beziehungen zur den Zellen," Leipzig, 1890.

84. Gersh, I., "The Altmann technique for fixation by drying while freezing," *Anat. Rec.,* 53, 309 (1932).

85. Hoerr, N. L., "Cytological studies by the Altmann-Gersh freezing-drying method. I. Recent advances in the technique," *Anat. Rec.,* 65, 293 (1936).

86. Svihla, R. D., and Osterman, E., "Growth of orchid seeds after dehydration from the frozen state," *Science,* 98, 23 (1943).

87. Wyckoff, R. W. G., "Frozen-dried preparations for the electron microscope," *Science,* 104, 36 (1946).

88. Wyckoff, R. W. G., "Electron micrographs from concentrated solutions of the tobacco mosaic virus protein," *Biochimica et Biophysica Acta,* 1, 139 (1947).

89. Mysels, K. J., "Studies of aluminum soaps. IX. Electron microscope view of lyophilized aluminum laurate," *J. Gen. Physiol.,* 30, 159–161 (1946).

90. Pease, D. C., "The disappearance of salt from glass ice during low-temperature dehydration, and its implication in electron microscopy," *Science,* 106, 543 (1947).

91. Bensley, R. R., and Gersh, I., "Studies on cell structure by the freezing-drying method. I, II," *Anat. Rec.,* 57, 205, No. 3 (1933).

92. Bensley, R. R., and Gersh, I., "Studies on cell structure by the freezing-drying method. III," *Anat. Rec.,* 57, 369. No. 4 (1933).

93. Bensley, R. R., "Studies on cell structure by the freezing-drying method. IV," *Anat. Rec.,* 58, 1, No. 1 (1933).

94. Gersh, I., and Stieglitz, E. J., "Histochemical studies on the mammalian kidney. I," *Anat. Rec.,* 58, No. 4 and Suppl. (Mar. 25, 1934).

95. Bensley, R. R., and Hoerr, N. L., "Studies on cell structure by the freezing-drying method. V," *Anat. Rec.,* 60, No. 3 (Oct. 25, 1934).

96. Bensley, R. R., and Hoerr, N. L., "Studies on cell structure by the freezing-drying method. VI," *Anat. Rec.,* 60, No. 4, and Suppl. (Nov. 25, 1934).

97. Gersh, I., and Tarr, A. M. DeL., "The so-called hyaline bodies of herring in the posterior lobe of the hypophysis," *Anat. Rec.,* 63, No. 3 (Oct. 25, 1935).

98. Goodspeed, T. H., Uber, F. M., and Avery, P., "Application of the Altmann freezing-drying technique to plant cytology. III," *Univ. Cal. Publ. Botany,* 18, No. 3, 33–44 (1935).

99. Scott, G. H., and Williams, P. S., "A simplified cryostat for the dehydration of frozen tissues," *Anat. Rec.,* 66, No. 4, 475 (Nov., 1936).

100. Scott, G. H., Personal communication.
101. Richins, C. A., "Use of the freezing-drying technique for study of vasomotor activity," *Science,* **107,** 25 (1948).
102. Burton, L. V., "High-vacuum techniques utilized for drying orange juice," *Food Ind.,* **19,** 107 (1947).
103. Sluder, J. C., Olsen, R. W., Kenyon, E. M., "A method for the production of dry powdered orange juice," *Food Tech.,* **1,** 85–94 (1947).
104. Flosdorf, E. W., U. S. Patent 2,225,627.
105. Goresline, H. E., "A discussion of bacteriological standards for dehydrated foods," *Am. J. Public Health,* **37,** 1277 (1947).
106. Barker, J., Gane, R., and Mapson, L. W., "The quality of green peas dried in the frozen state," *Food Manufacture,* **21,** 345–348 (1946).

CHAPTER 4: CHANGES IN PRODUCTS DURING DESICCATION FROM THE FROZEN STATE AND IN STORAGE

CHANGES which occur in products during desiccation may be considered on chemical, physical, and immunological bases, and on loss of viability of micro-organisms; finally, they may be considered on the basis of loss of biological activity. This chapter briefly summarizes what is more fully discussed throughout the book.

Of the various chemical species studied, proteins have received the most attention because of their importance in biological preparations. Generally, no chemical alteration detectable by ordinary methods occurs in most proteins during drying and during storage at temperatures as high as 40°C for a period of a year or more. By means of electrophoresis and photographic records of curves obtained from the various components of plasma and serum it is known that little or no change occurs. The electrophoretic patterns present a normal appearance with normal values.[1] This is in contrast with the results obtained with plasma which has been dried from the liquid state at about 40°C or lower under vacuum. Plasma may be dried through cellophane bags from the liquid state at still lower temperature.[2,3] However, the turbidity in the reconstituted product is so great that Scudder reports that it is difficult to obtain a picture. He states that there is a decrease in the albumin component, a marked change in the alpha, and possibly some change in the beta complex.

When comparing the electrophoretic patterns of plasma after

138

any type of drying, the differences which occur purely as a result of filtration through bacterial filters must be borne in mind. Scudder has shown that the electrophoretic patterns of plasma, before and after filtration, show a decrease in the fibrinogen component and an increase in the beta-globulin complex. Otherwise, there is no marked alteration. Similarly, where centrifugation is used, the temperature should not be allowed to rise appreciably, since this can produce a far greater change than that which occurs as a result of drying, regardless of the method of drying. Summarizing his electrophoretic studies, Scudder has stated that all processes which do not dry from the frozen state should be precluded, because of denaturation, where the serum or plasma is to be used as a substitute for whole blood in transfusion.

All statements concerning changes which occur after drying assume that the moisture content has been reduced to the proper level. With sensitive materials it is essential that the residual moisture be reduced to below 2 per cent and preferably below 0.5 per cent. Such products as penicillin and other biologicals are reduced in some instances to less than 0.1 per cent commercially. The effect of the final moisture content is illustrated in the case of diphtherial antitoxin by the data given in Table 3, page 47. It is evident that at a temperature as high as 37°C, the dry antitoxin has satisfactory potency even after three years, whereas in liquid form it falls off to an unsatisfactory level after six weeks. On the other hand, an incompletely dried product has poorer stability than the original liquid. With 5 to 8 per cent moisture a satisfactory potency is not maintained even as long as six weeks. Obtaining low moisture is not a problem in freeze-drying; in fact, since going to press, Makower and Nielsen in *Analytical Chemistry,* **20,** 856–8 (1948) proposed the use of freeze-drying for analyzing for moisture content of dehydrated vegetables. A large amount of water is added to a weighed dry sample. This is then subjected to freeze-drying and upon completion is dried according to standard practice in a vacuum oven or vacuum desiccator. After freeze-drying, a much faster rate of drying occurs with accurate results being obtained uniformly with such products as white and sweet potatoes, meat, and carrots.

Slow solubility of concentrated globulin preparations after freeze-drying has been discussed in Chapter 3 and needs no further comment here, except to point out that it is only the rate and not the completeness of the solubility of untreated globulin which is affected.

With the proper degree of dryness changes do not occur in other components during subsequent storage for reasonable periods of time even at relatively high temperatures. Sometimes evacuation is necessary, but not always. Fats show no chemical change during drying but undergo oxidation in storage and tend to become rancid if oxygen is not entirely excluded, even when completely and properly desiccated and kept in a moisture-free condition. Hydrolysis does not occur. Other chemical species have not been studied extensively, but in general this method of desiccation is as gentle as any and is far less likely to produce changes during drying of labile substances. Because the final moisture content can be reduced to such a low level without harm to the product, greater stability of the dry product is obtained than by any other ordinary method. Reduction to such a low moisture content by other methods usually results in loss of activity or solubility or other native characteristic, and is not practicably attainable for this reason.

The stability of ascorbic acid has been discussed in connection with fruit juices in Chapter 3. For proper preservation of citrus and tomato juices in dry form the moisture content must be below 1 per cent; otherwise, good quality in flavor is lost, as well as solubility. Similarly, unless the moisture content is below this level, there is loss of ascorbic acid after a period of some months at room temperature and above.

Physical alteration of lyophobic sols tends to occur rather readily as a result of desiccation. This accounts for the precipitation of lipoidal substances in human serum and plasma referred to previously. It occurs to a lesser degree with rabbit serum and is not noticed with horse serum. Likewise, many bacterial suspensions, unless properly treated with a protective colloidal agent such as milk, do not resuspend properly when reconstituted. Other substances, such as lyophilic protein, have remarkable properties of rapid and complete solubility, even after storage for years.

The solubility of many products is increased remarkably as a result of drying by sublimation. Most notable of these is gelatin, ordinarily dissolved in hot water only, which dissolves rapidly in cold water after drying the solution by sublimation. Other substances behave similarly.

Immunologically, little change in either serum or antigens is observed. Crystallized egg-albumin, after desiccation of aqueous solutions from the frozen state, has been kept for four and five years without detectable change in antigenic specificity. Immune sera undergo no detectable loss in titer from processing or from storage for years at room temperature. Perhaps as sensitive an index of stability as any is the complementary activity of guinea-pig serum. Proper and complete drying of this product not only results in retention of activity, but in addition the complement is maintained in stable form for a period of years.[4] In Fig. 3.1 is shown the results of five years' testing. By addition of a stabilizing solution consisting of sodium acetate and boric acid to guinea-pig serum before drying, a product is obtained which keeps well and which also maintains its stability without detectable loss of potency for a period of several days after restoration.[5] In smaller hospitals and laboratories this adds particularly to the convenience of using desiccated complement.

There is a loss of carbon dioxide during the processing of complement, but the resulting increase in pH has no effect on the complementary activity of the serum.[5,6] Restoration with acid or buffer is unnecessary. The alkalinity of reconstituted human serum or plasma does not cause reactions and it is unrelated to the turbidity of reconstituted human serum. The lyophobic lipoidal constituents are the cause of this condition but they do not render the product unfit for injection.

The turbidity does cause difficulty in carrying out precipitative reactions, as with rabbit-precipitin or in diagnostic tests for syphilis. This has been a drawback to the use of dry standardized syphilitic human sera for calibration or standardization of diagnostic test procedures. Such standard sera could facilitate the obtaining of test results from different laboratories for comparisons. The difficulty with lipoids may be overcome by double processing with intermediate Seitz filtration.[7,8] At the time of filtering the reconstituted serum after the primary drying, the titer of the serum may be adjusted by dilution to a desired point. It is then dried for the second time. The final dry, stable product accordingly has a predetermined definite titer and reconstitutes to yield a clear solution.

In the case of many viruses there is a loss in activity as a result of processing, but the final desiccated product is well stabilized and no further loss occurs during storage.[9] Viruses are in general more difficult to dry than other substances. The temperature must be maintained quite low during desiccation,[10] preferably well below $-20°C$.

The proportion of viable cells remaining in cultures of bacteria after desiccation from the frozen state is as little as 5 per cent, but the surviving cells keep well. The survival percentage may be materially increased by using a protective protein, such as milk.[11] Elser, Thomas, and Steffen[7] have reported phenomenally long periods of storage of dry, viable cells. H. *influenzae* has been kept for four years and H. *pertussis* for ten years,[11] even though both are organisms with which difficulty often is encountered in preservation. *Treponema pallidum* and spermatozoa do not survive drying.

The biological activity of many other substances, such as enzymes,[6] penicillin, certain hormones, vitamins and other labile substances, is maintained without loss both during drying and subsequent storage. Biological activity as well as viability of microorganisms is a far more sensitive index of the delicate nature of freeze-drying than any method of chemical assay for chemical components. With such little alteration in activity and viability it is clear that little chemical and physical change occurs during or after freeze-drying.

The foregoing discussion assumes proper control of the conditions of freeze-drying. If for any reason a portion of the material undergoing desiccation rises above its melting point so that fusing occurs, deterioration may result. Not only may the solubility of such portions be greatly reduced, but chemical change and reduction in biological activity are likely to take place. In a word, it is imperative to guard against slipshod technique during drying in order to realize the full benefit of freeze-drying.

BIBLIOGRAPHY

1. Scudder, J., "Electrophoretic patterns of serum and plasma," "Blood Substitutes and Blood Transfusion," pp. 126–139, Charles C. Thomas, Springfield, Ill., 1942.
2. Thalhimer, W., "A simple, inexpensive method for drying serum in the frozen state in cellophane bags," *Proc. Soc. Exper. Biol. Med.*, **41**, 233 (1939).
3. Hartman, F. W., "Use of cellophane cylinders for desiccating blood plasma. A rapid, economical and bacteriologically safe method," *J. Am. Med. Assoc.*, **115**, 1989–1990 (1940).
4. Flosdorf, E. W., Boerner, F., Lukens, M., and Ambler, T. S., "Cryo-chem-preserved complement of guinea-pig serum," *Am. J. Clin. Path.*, **10**, 339–344 (1940).
5. Boerner, F., Flosdorf, E. W., and Lukens, M., "Stabilization of high vacuum-dried guinea-pig complement before drying and after restoration with water," *Am. J. Clin. Path.*, **11**, 122–127 (1941).
6. Flosdorf, E. W., and Mudd, S., "Procedure and apparatus for preservation in 'lyophile' form of serum and other biological substances," *J. Immunol.*, **29**, 389–425 (1935).
7. Elser, W. J., Thomas, R. A., and Steffen, G. I., "The desiccation of sera and other biological products (including micro-organisms) in the frozen state with the preservation of the original qualities of products so treated," *J. Immunol.*, **28**, 433–473 (1935).
8. Mudd, S., Flosdorf, E. W., Eagle, H., Stokes, J., Jr., and McGuinness, A. C., "The preservation and concentration of human serums for clinical use," *J. Am. Med. Assoc.*, **107**, 956–959 (1936).
9. Scherp, H. W., Flosdorf, E. W., and Shaw, D. R., "Survival of the influenzal virus under various conditions," *J. Immunol.*, **34**, 447–454 (1938).
10. Flosdorf, E. W., and Mudd, S., "An improved procedure and apparatus for preservation of sera, micro-organisms and other substances—the Cryochem-process," *J. Immunol.*, **34**, 469–490 (1938).
11. Flosdorf, E. W., and Kimball, A. C., "Studies with *H. pertussis*. II. Maintenance of cultures in phase I," *J. Bact.*, **39**, 255–261 (1940).

CHAPTER 5: EQUIPMENT USED FOR

MEDICAL PRODUCTS

TYPES OF SUITABLE CONTAINERS

WHEN freeze-drying was first applied to medical products intended for injection much consideration had to be given to the problem of suitable containers. Not only must the product be dried under conditions which permit asepsis to be maintained, but the containers must be sealed in such a fashion as to prevent ingress of moisture to the dried product. This requires a vapor-proof final package. Furthermore, the container must be readily usable by the physician for dissolving the product aseptically and placing it in a syringe for injection.

The original procedure set up to meet the foregoing requirements was one of sealing the containers under the original processing vacuum by fusing off a "Pyrex" glass exhaust tube with a flame.[1] To facilitate this operation the filled containers were dried by placing them on a manifold of the type described in a later section in this chapter. These types of containers are still used, but in limited numbers commercially. The procedure has considerable merit, nevertheless, in biological laboratories for research.

A rubber stopper in the container was the means established to afford convenient and aseptic use of the product by the physician with syringe and needle. Typical containers of this type are illustrated in Fig. 5.1. To permit sufficiently rapid and unrestricted flow of vapors from the containers during drying, the exhaust tubes necessarily must be of large internal diameter. To seal such

144

containers under vacuum, therefore, the exhaust tubes originally were specified to be of "Pyrex" glass.[1] Unless the large glass exhaust tube is heated rapidly and pulled out rapidly when soft, the glass will suck in, with loss of vacuum in the container. Only

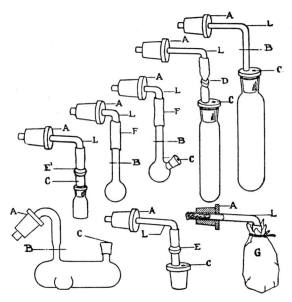

Fig. 5.1. Types of Containers and Exhaust Assemblies
A, manifold stoppers; B, point at which glass is sealed off; C, thin membrane section of container stopper through which syringe needle is plunged, for introducing water at time of use; D, rubber tube-stopper with metal ring clamp shut off; E, rubber tube-stopper with metal ring clamp open; E[1], miniature rubber tube-stopper with metal ring clamp open; F, rubber tubing connection; G, sterilized exhaust assembly with cotton plug in tube, L, and paper wrapping around container stopper; L, glass exhaust tube.

"Pyrex" glass will withstand the temperature shock of this rapid heating and of rapid cooling without annealing. The seal is made with a Hoke oxygen torch fitted with a specially designed crossfire attachment having very fine tips (Fig. 5.2). By careful slow and even heating of the tube on all sides at once, while pulling on the glass, an excellent seal is easily made with "Pyrex" exhaust tubes up to 5 mm internal diameter (Fig. 5.3).

When using the rubber tube stopper, annealed brass sleeves must be firmly squeezed with pliers which close with flat and parallel jaw surfaces and have handles about eight inches long. This operation may be performed better by using a special hand seal press which employs compound lever action to exert a high pressure. The sleeve should be squeezed down about 8 mm from the flat part of the stopper (Figs. 5.1 and 5.3). The vacuum pump should be run continuously up to this point. It is then turned off

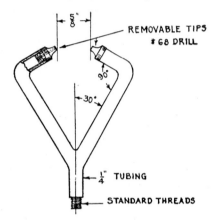

Fig. 5.2. Cross-Fire Attachment for Standard Hoke Hand Torch.

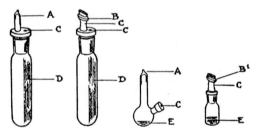

Fig. 5.3. Sealed Containers
A, glass sealed with flame; B, rubber tube-stopper after metal clamp is closed and rubber is severed with scissors; B¹, miniature rubber tube-stopper closed and severed as B; C, thin membrane section of container stopper through which syringe needle is plunged for introducing water at time of use; D, desiccated serum in amounts of 5 to 50 ml.; E, desiccated virus, bacteria, vaccine, etc., in amounts of 0.1 to 1.0 ml.

and air admitted to the apparatus. The containers sealed under the original vacuum are then removed by cutting the rubber tube with scissors next to the clamp.

A later modification in the procedure makes it possible to use the same containers constructed of ordinary soft glass. This not only reduces the cost of the container, but eliminates the need for use of oxygen in the flame for sealing. Such containers are illustrated in Fig. 5.4. The lower tube carries a stopper of standard

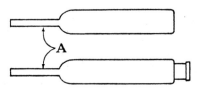

Fig. 5.4. Types of Containers
A = where sealing tube is constricted for final sealing.

vaccine type. At the end of the process, if asepsis is not necessary, air is slowly admitted into the apparatus from the pump-side of the desiccant chamber or cold condenser, and becomes dry before it comes into contact with the dried biologic. One by one the containers are removed from the apparatus, the exhaust tubes constricted at point A, and a secondary vacuum is drawn by direct attachment to a vacuum pump. Direct attachment is made to effect rapid evacuation; evidence indicates that for ordinary biologics a vacuum of a few millimeters is satisfactory.

If asepsis is to be preserved the sealing operation is modified slightly. For this purpose, Fig. 5.5 shows how the containers are attached to the apparatus. In Fig. 5.6 is shown the method of assembling the container with the connector tubes, as well as the arrangement of the parts for preliminary sterilization. During the desiccative process asepsis is maintained, as in the case with use of "Pyrex" containers. An "S" connector is used somewhat more conveniently, however, than the original "L" type of connector tube. At the end of the process, to maintain asepsis, the individual stopcocks on the manifold outlets are turned off, one by one. After a given stopcock is turned off, the rubber connector "R" attached to the container (Fig. 5.5), is punctured at the point "P" by the needle of a specially prepared syringe barrel (Fig. 5.7). Dry, sterile air is thereby slowly admitted; the exhaust tubes of the containers are then constricted immediately; the containers are re-evacuated and sealed as soon as possible as described above. In

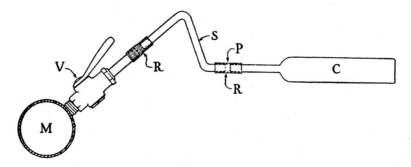

Fig. 5.5. Container Attached to Manifold
M = cross section of manifold. V = stopcock. R = rubber connector sleeve. C = container. S = "S" connector tube. P = point of puncture with air-dryer and sterilizer (Figure 5.7).

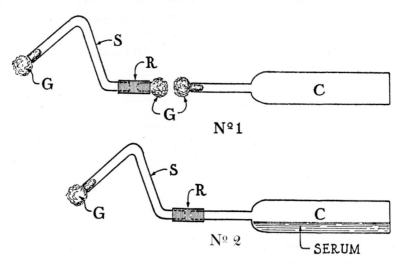

Fig. 5.6. Filled Sterile Container Assembly
S = "S" connector tube. G = cotton plug. R = rubber connector sleeve. C = container—No. 1 is as sterilized before filling container; No. 2 is as filled container and accessories are assembled before attachment to manifold as shown in Figure 5.5.

this way the more difficult technique of sealing exhaust tubes of "Pyrex" glass under "original" vacuum is circumvented and asepsis is still maintained.

The air-dryer and sterilizer is made ready by heating in the usual bacteriological hot air oven at 200°C for a half-hour. It may be made ready for use again with the next set of containers by re-heating for a half-hour at 200°C, which procedure not only steri-lizes it but regenerates the calcium sulfate. The two ends should be kept closed with sterile rubber stoppers when it is not in use.

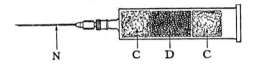

N   C   D   C

Fig. 5.7. Air-Dryer and Sterilizer
Syringe barrel with needle "N" attached to it and filled with cotton "C" and calcium sulfate "D."

For preservation of cultures flint-glass test tubes 6–7 mm O.D. which have been constricted before the desiccation of the cultures may be used. This is possible because of the small volume of material to be dried, 0.05 ml being an optimum quantity. One-half of this should be a suitable protein, such as sterile skim milk, serum, inactivated serum, gelatin, etc.; the other half may be the culture as grown, or as concentrated by centrifugation. The technique used with drying cultures is discussed on p. 210.

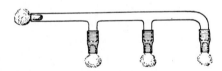

Fig. 5.8. "L" Triple Connector for Culture Containers.

Tubes suitable for the preservation of bacterial and viral sus-pensions are 95 mm in length and 7 mm in outside diameter. Before desiccation these tubes are constricted, the outside diameter being reduced to about 3 mm for a longitudinal distance of about 10 to 15 mm. Capillary pipettes are necessary for filling them, whether the containers are filled before or after constricting. After drying, these containers may then be sealed under the original vacuum with a hand-torch similar to that described previously, using air in the torch in place of oyxgen. Two or three such containers may be processed from a single manifold outlet by use of suitable glass connector tubes (cf. Fig. 5.8).

Later it was found that rubber stoppers, even when coated with cement, do not adequately withhold water vapor from the product. Potency of active products was found to decrease suddenly and unexpectedly, and solubility was lost. It was discovered that over a long period of time, particularly under adverse tropical conditions of temperature and humidity, the permeability of the rubber stopper to water vapor soon raised the moisture content of the "dry" product to a level above that required for stability.[2] It was shown that using ordinary high temperature incubators for determining the duration of potency with rubber stoppered containers gave misleading results because of the low relative humidity set up in the hot incubator. By controlling the humidity at these high temperatures in the incubators so that they would be comparable to tropical conditions, entirely different experimental results were obtained. It was further shown that synthetic rubber, such as neoprene, produced little difference in the final result. Fig. 5.9 shows the increase in moisture which results from storage for six months under various conditions of temperature, both with the humidity uncontrolled and controlled at 100 per cent. Fig. 5.10 illustrates corresponding results after 12 months of storage. All the determinations were made upon the contents of evacuated containers. These results were obtained with horse serum in 10-ml amounts and are representative of what is to be expected with other biologicals dispensed in small amounts, such as penicillin. These should not be stored with rubber stoppers for more than a few months under warm, moist atmospheric conditions.

The amount of moisture passing through the rubber stopper, as theoretically would be expected, was found to be the same under conditions of 100 per cent relative humidity as when the containers were stored under water at the same temperature. Although 12 different compounds of rubber and neoprene were tested, the variation of the different compounds from the average curves as shown was less than 8 per cent, indicating the hopelessness of using the materials for stoppers that were then available.

The quantity of water vapor passing through a given size stopper was found to be fairly constant in amounts of serum from

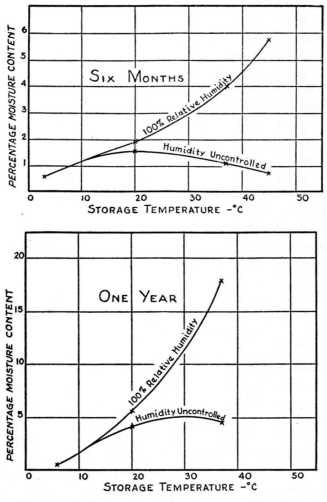

Figs. 5.9 and 5.10. Increase in moisture content of 10 ml. amounts of dried horse serum in rubber stoppered bottles—typical of other biologicals such as penicillin and convalescent plasma and serum. Relative humidity when uncontrolled in the incubators becomes very low at the higher temperatures.

1 ml up to 500 ml. This is because the determining factor was the surface area and thickness of the thin membrane in the stopper and because the product within the containers, at around 10 per cent moisture, still has low vapor pressure and considerable affinity for water vapor. For this reason, on a percentile basis, the effect of storage is less pronounced with respect to increase in moisture content in terms of dry solids when the amount of total solids in the container is large, as for example with plasma. This is in contrast with the condition which exists when smaller quantities are used, as in cultures, guinea-pig complement, penicillin and other highly active substances. In these the *percentile* increase of moisture in the solids is much more rapid as a result of the fixed amount of moisture entering the container.

For example, compare a 10-ml amount of serum with a 300-ml amount of plasma. If, under certain conditions of warm, moist storage, the 10-ml of serum will take up to 8 per cent moisture content, the 300-ml amount of plasma will have its moisture content increased only by one-thirtieth of this, or by about 0.27 per cent. The reason is that there are thirty times as much solid matter by weight in the plasma container as in the small serum container, yet the amount of moisture permeating the stopper is the same. On the other hand, with penicillin, where the amount of solids may be only one-fifth as great as in the 10-ml quantity of serum, the moisture content could go as high as 40 per cent. A similar situation exists in the case of other biological materials put up in small quantities, such as viral vaccines, guinea-pig complement, and the like. The moisture entering the container is to a major degree a result of permeability and not just a result of moisture dissolved in the rubber.* Otherwise, the increase in moisture content would not be dependent upon the relative humidity of the outside atmosphere as demonstrated,[2] and as discussed above. The manner in which the increase in moisture resulting from the storage of rubber-stoppered vials is reflected in loss of potency is illustrated

---

* In the case of rubber stoppers used to close bottles dried in a chamber where the stoppers are not necessarily dried along with the product, as they are in use of manifolds,[1] the sterile stoppers after autoclaving must be dried by other means. This may be done by use of a vacuum oven, at approximately 28 inches and 80 to 110°C, or by other suitable drying means.

in Table 1.[3] With products less stable than diphtherial antitoxin, the effect is even more marked. The humidity "uncontrolled" is that resulting from warming of the air in ordinary incubators at 37 and 45°C under the usual seasonal conditions near Philadelphia. The contrast obtained in tests at relative humidity of 100 per cent is striking.

TABLE 1

LOSS IN POTENCY OF DIPHTHERIAL ANTITOXIN HORSE-GLOBULIN

Stored 45 weeks in Rubber-stoppered Vials. Initial Moisture Content −0.5%

Temperature	Relative Humidity	Potency
(° C)	(%)	(units per ml)
Original	—	850
20	uncontrolled	850
20	100	800
37	uncontrolled (low)	800
37	100	750
45	uncontrolled (very low)	800
45	100	450

As a result of these findings, two general types of containers have been proposed to meet requirements for the exclusion of water vapor and for convenience in handling by the clinician. The one comprises the ordinary rubber-stoppered glass container enclosed within a hermetically sealed outer metallic container such as a tube or can. This was first put into practical operation in 1939 and described the following year on the basis of the several years' laboratory tests under various conditions.[4] This is the type of container which was adopted and used successfully in the United States and Canada for blood plasma and blood serum for the Armed Forces during World War II, because it was considered best for products of this type.[5] It is suitable for penicillin. It has also been used successfully with convalescent serum for about ten years at the Philadelphia Serum Exchange at the Children's Hospital. In the latter case, the size of package is small, accommodating 10 to 25 ml of serum, also vacuum packing is unnecessary. For these conditions a hermetically closed collapsible metal tube is admirably suited for exclusion of moisture.

Another container, well adapted to blood plasma and particularly desirable for many types of products, including penicillin, is one which involves a rubber stopper sealed within the stem of

Fig. 5.11. Containers for permanent exclusion of moisture from dried products. Container on extreme left is a collapsible metal tube with a special hermetic seal. The next to the right makes use of a vacuum sealed tin can. The two containers on the right utilize a special all-glass container carrying a rubber stopper seated within the hermetically sealed stem.

an all-glass hermetically sealed ampoule.[6] The high cost has limited use of this container to more expensive products and those which are stored for long periods. Examples of these various containers are illustrated in Fig. 5.11.

It is important to consider the experimental procedure which may be followed in obtaining data such as the foregoing. This early work was carried out at the University of Pennsylvania with the co-operation of Sharp and Dohme, Inc. and the West Company, Philadelphia. Rubber and neoprene were each compounded with different types of filler and made into stoppers. At that time, other synthetic rubbers were not readily available.[2] The neoprene mixtures were prepared according to formulas determined after consultation between the West Company and E. I. Du Pont de Nemours & Company, Inc., Wilmington, Delaware. The various compositions are shown in Table 2.

TABLE 2

COMPOSITION OF STOCKS*

(Parts per hundred)

	100	66F	39B	127 †	75G	96	141	141A	141B	142	143	144
Rubber.......	95	51	45	61	0	33.5	36.1	36.1	35.1	0	32.5	66
Neoprene......	0	0	0	0	51	0	0	0	0	81.3	0	0
Sulfur, accelerator, etc.....	5	2.5	2	1	0.5	3.63	11.19	14.19	15.19	2.42	3.63	4
Barium sulfate.	0	40	0	34	0	56.25	0	0	0	0	54.25	0
Clays.........	0	0	46	0	16	0	44.71	44.71	44.71	12.21	0	0
Vulcanized rape seed oil.....	0	0	0	0	0	5.62	4	4	4	0	5.62	0
Paraffin.......	0	0	0	0	0	1	0	0	0	0	1	0
Resin.........	0	0	0	0	0	0	4	1	1	4.07	0	0
Gutta percha...	0	0	0	0	0	0	0	0	0	0	3	30
Other fillers....	0	6.5	7	4	32.5	0	0	0	0	0	0	0
Degree of hardness........	soft	soft	very hard	hard	hard	soft	very hard	hard	soft ‡	soft	soft	soft

* Information supplied by The West Co.
† Fast cure
‡ Too soft to use

Laboratory storage of serum at elevated temperatures (37 to 50°C) in Philadelphia, where the normal indoor temperature is 20 to 30°C and the relative humidity varies from 20 to 90 per cent, gives rise to a variety of conditions, usually fairly dry at the higher incubator temperature. The conditions are dry also at artificially elevated temperatures even in the summer when the outside air is at a high relative humidity.

To meet the wider range referred to above, the tests were carried out under two sets of conditions of relative humidity. The first was under the varying conditions produced by the seasons in controlled-temperature vaults, and will be referred to as "normal relative humidity." The second was close to saturation. The "saturated" condition was established by placing large numbers of containers in large sealed jars; the bottoms of the jars were covered with a thin layer of water. Jars were placed at three temperature ranges, 20 to 30° (underground vault), 36 to 38°, and 45 to 50°C. At the "normal" humidities storage was carried out at 2 to 4°C, in addition to the above three temperature conditions. The actual "normal" relative humidities, as measured by wet bulb depression, are shown in Table 3. In addition a number of containers were stored

TABLE 3

VARIATION OF RELATIVE HUMIDITY WITH TEMPERATURE UNDER THE CONTROLLED "NORMAL" CONDITIONS OF THE INVESTIGATION

Temperature	Relative Humidity
(° C)	(%)
2– 4	50–70
20–23	50–90
36–38	20–37
45–50	8–15

under water at 37°C. In all this work 25-ml containers were used. Preliminary experiments were carried out with necks of different dimensions to determine the optimal relation of the size of the neck to size of stopper.

For air permeation a large number of stoppered empty 25-ml glass containers were evacuated and then sealed under vacuum. The air leakage was determined during storage, initially at weekly intervals, later at monthly intervals, as follows. Water from a syringe was allowed to be drawn into the container by the remaining vacuum; the volume of water thus drawn in was recorded. The container was then opened, and the volume of water necessary to fill it completely was measured. From these values was computed the "percentage of vacuum remaining." This procedure eliminates errors in computation from slight variations of container size. Two containers were opened at each interval, and the average readings obtained after these intervals were plotted against the duration of storage; the curves plotted were all smooth, indicating gradual and progressive reproducible changes.

In determining the permeation of moisture the same style of container was used on 10 ml of normal horse serum which had been dried on a manifold-type of equipment, as will be described in a succeeding section. At the end of the process the containers were sealed *in vacuo*. Containers were opened at intervals in order to make moisture determinations by the method of Flosdorf and Webster.[7] The results have been plotted in Fig. 5.12.

The stoppers used are illustrated in Fig. 5.13 and are of the following description: No. 57, a stopper with a hole, for the glass exhaust tube which is sealed by fusion, and a thin membrane section for piercing with a syringe needle. No. 137, the same as No. 57 except that it carries an integral rubber tubular extension, to be sealed with a metal clamp, instead of the hole for glass tube. This rubber tubular extension provides a considerable area of thin rubber which offers little resistance to permeation. No. 72, the same as the No. 137 except that it has no special thin membrane section for piercing with a syringe needle. The tubular extension below the metal clamp is used for this purpose. No. 73, the same as No. 72 with the exception of lesser dimensions for smaller containers with small necks.

Leakage through the clamped end of the No. 137 stoppers (and other tubular types), had it occurred, would have invalidated conclusions concerning permeation; such leakage, however, has been found to be negligible. This was determined by coating with Picein cement: first, the end of the cut tubular extension up to and including the clamp; second, the entire tubular extension; and third, the entire stopper. The results are tabulated in Table 4. Permeation is appreciably retarded only when the entire tubular extension is coated, and further retardation is not appreciable even if the entire stopper is coated. Furthermore, when the metal clamps are removed from the uncemented tubular extensions after a period of several weeks, it is found that the rubber and neoprene tubing has been tightly sealed. Any small error that might be introduced in this way in comparing the various gums is negligible because all the gums have had the same treatment.

The tests with small ampoules have shown that the bodies of the stoppers which were pierced with a syringe needle have given

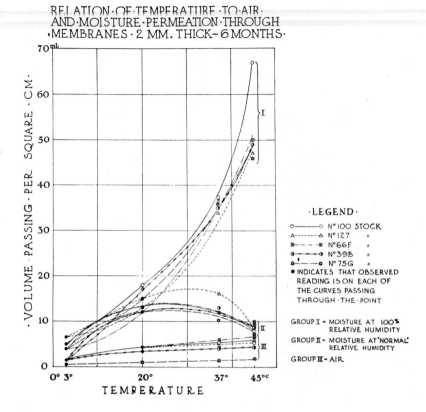

RELATION·OF·TEMPERATURE·TO·AIR·
AND·MOISTURE·PERMEATION·THROUGH
·MEMBRANES·2 MM. THICK~6 MONTHS·

Fig. 5.12. Air and moisture permeation through rubber. Concerning the air and water vapor pressure differentials, see data for No. 72 stopper in Tables 5 and 8 and footnote, page 160. The fact that at the higher temperature, particularly in the case of air, the differential is less would make the curves steeper were they corrected to a constant differential. Inasmuch as the quantity of air and moisture which has undergone permeation has been so nearly the same in the case of all the stocks (nearly constant residual moisture content of the horse serum and percentage vacuum remaining after any given time interval), the differentials may be taken as changing at about the same rate for all the stocks. Therefore the data as obtained furnish directly a satisfactory basis for comparison. At 0° the air pressure differential is approximately constant at 752 to 8 mm. or 99 to 1.

a further indication of the tendency of rubber to seal itself. The results show that the compression of the rubber within the necks of the containers is sufficient to seal the hole and maintain the vacuum during the storage period as well as though the stoppers had never been pierced.

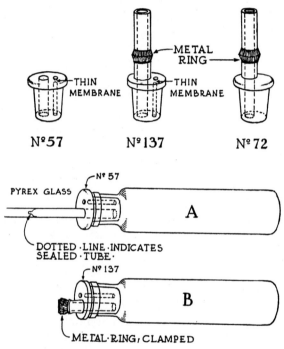

Fig. 5.13. Containers and Stoppers
A. Glass sealing tubes through stopper No. 57. B. Integral rubber tubing extension on stopper No. 137 is sealed by the metal ring clamp.

Since the leakage through the cut end of the extensions on the stoppers is at most relatively small, the permeation through a unit area of rubber 2 mm thick may be calculated as a first approximation. The amount of moisture and air passing through the body of the No. 137 stopper has been determined with stopper No. 57, and in this way the permeation through the tubular rubber extension of the No. 137 can be calculated. The actual volumes of water, calculated as vapor at standard conditions (760 mm Hg and

273°A), passing through a unit area of the tubular extension of certain of the stocks, have been plotted in Fig. 5.12 and compared with air permeation. These results cover a six-month period under varying conditions of storage. The curves show that the permeation of air is definitely less than that of moisture under all conditions, with all the rubber stocks and with neoprene. The degree of permeation to moisture is dependent on the relative humidity and on the temperature. At saturation the temperature coefficient of permeation to moisture is exceedingly high.

The permeation of air and moisture through the stocks not included in Fig. 5.12 falls in every case within the limits of that for the two extremes illustrated. It is evident, therefore, that the composition of the stocks does influence the permeation, but not to the extent that might have been expected. Furthermore, the effect of changing from rubber to neoprene is of even smaller magnitude than changing the other components, except in the case of air permeation. These observations are not inconsistent with the results of Starkweather and Walker,[8] who showed considerable influence of other ingredients, particularly rosin (as in No. 142 stock), upon the water absorption of neoprene. They demonstrated that the absorption is rapid in the initial stages. In experiments, where a large differential in vapor tension on the two sides of the membranes is being maintained,* it is not inconsistent to obtain similar rates of permeation, even though within certain narrow limits the equilibrium concentration of water within the membrane varies.

In the case of air, neoprene exhibits greater resistance to permeation than any of the rubber mixtures. Of the two neoprene mixtures, No. 750 was superior; No. 100, having only pure gum, sulphur, and accelerator, became considerably less resistant to moisture at higher temperatures.

A very interesting observation was that serum in containers stored under water at 37°C did not increase in moisture content

---

* Although no determinations of vapor pressure have been made, the hygroscopic effect of the Lyophile normal horse-serum is evident by the observation that its moisture content will be increased by as much as 1 per cent of its weight in one minute when exposed directly to a relative humidity of 68 per cent at 25°C. (Reference 7). This rate may be taken as a qualitative indication of low vapor pressure.

any faster than samples stored in air at 37°C and 100 per cent relative humidity. In other words a relative humidity of 100 per cent caused as rapid a permeation of moisture as storage under water, which theoretically would be expected.

TABLE 4

AIR LEAKAGE THROUGH TUBE-STOPPERS STORED AT 3°C

Vacuum Remaining

| Stopper* | Storage Period Months | None (%) | Picein Cement | | Entire Stopper (%) |
			Tips Only (%)	Tips and Tubes (%)	
No. 73†	2	66	69	81	81
No. 73†	4	55	53	63	65
No. 137	4	87	..	94	...

* No. 66F stock.

† The containers into which stoppers No. 73 were inserted are 2 ml in volume. This increases the proportional loss in vacuum which is due to air dissolved in the rubber.

It was observed that the neoprene mixtures lost their elasticity upon storage. The holes under the thin membranes collapsed after a few months of compression within the necks of the container. One container stored under water for six months drew 6 ml of water in around the edges of the neoprene stopper (No. 75G). This was the only instance of such an occurrence.

As an indication of the relative effectiveness of the two styles of stopper, the actual percentage of vacuum remaining in the containers after six months of storage is given in Table 5, and the moisture content of the serum in Table 6. Data have been included only for No. 66F, which the author believes to be generally the best stopper. The latter decision is based on general workability, lack of cracking, freedom from small holes, etc., inasmuch as several mixtures gave similar results in the tests on air and moisture permeability. The permeation over a period of 12 months is shown in Tables 7 and 8.

It is evident that under controlled conditions of storage in a refrigerator, the No. 57 stopper appears to be satisfactory for pro-

TABLE 5

VACUUM REMAINING IN RUBBER-STOPPERED LYOPHILE SERUM CONTAINERS AFTER SIX MONTHS OF STORAGE*

	No. 66F Stock			
	Vacuum Remaining			
Stopper	*2 to 4°C*	*20°C*	*37°C*	*45°C*
No.	*(%)*	*(%)*	*(%)*	*(%)*
57......................	98	97	94	93
72......................	8.5	62	43	25

* The air pressure differential on the two sides of the membrane at any given time is obtainable directly from the table by subtracting the corresponding percentage from 100; the ratio of the remainder to 100 is the differential.

TABLE 6

THE MOISTURE CONTENT OF LYOPHILE NORMAL HORSE SERUM AFTER SIX MONTHS OF STORAGE*

	2 to 4°C	*20°C*		*37°C*		*45°C*	
Stopper †	*NRH*‡	*NRH*	*100% RH*§	*NRH*	*100% RH*	*NRH*	*100% RH*
No.	*(%)*	*(%)*	*(%)*	*(%)*	*(%)*	*(%)*	*(%)*
57....	0.9	1.4	1.4	1.3	3.7	1.8	4.4
72....	1.5	4.0	5.0	4.1	11.1	3.9	14.1

* Concerning the water vapor differential on the two sides of the membrane, see footnote on page 160.
† No. 66F stock.
‡ NRH = "normal" relative humidity.
§ RH = relative humidity.

tection of biologics for one or two years. Whether or not the stopper is satisfactory for conditions of shipment depends upon the length of time under adverse conditions. For periods of a few weeks, under very adverse conditions, the permeation of air and moisture through the No. 57 stopper does not seem to be too serious. Tests on duration of potency have indicated that a residual moisture content of 2 per cent may be tolerated, but that an upper limit of 1 per cent is better. Initial moisture must be reduced well below this to allow for some increase. For greatly extended periods of storage, especially under adverse conditions, an all-glass container is preferable, although its use by the physician is not so simple.

TABLE 7

EFFECT OF TIME ON MOISTURE DIFFUSION INTO RUBBER-STOPPERED LYOPHILE SERUM CONTAINERS

			No. 66F Stock Residual Moisture					
Stopper No.	Temperature (°C)	Humidity	Original (%)	2 Weeks (%)	1 Month (%)	2 Months (%)	6 Months (%)	12 Months (%)
57	2 to 4	N.R.H.	0.5	..	..	0.8	0.9	1.3
	37	N.R.H.	0.5	..	..	1.2	1.3	2.1
	37	100 RH	0.5	1.0	1.6	2.0	3.7	6.0
	37	under water	0.5	0.9	1.8	1.9	3.1	6.1
72	2 to 4	N.R.H.	0.5	..	..	..	1.5	2.3
	37	N.R.H.	0.5	..	..	1.9	4.1	4.4
	37	100 RH	0.5	2.5	4.1	6.5	11.1	17.0
	37	under water	0.5	3.0	4.9	6.5	12.5	17.4

TABLE 8

EFFECT OF TIME ON AIR DIFFUSION INTO RUBBER-STOPPERED LYOPHILE SERUM CONTAINERS

		No. 66F Stock Vacuum Remaining					
Stopper No.	Temperature (°C)	2 Weeks (%)	1 Month (%)	2 Months (%)	4 Months (%)	6 Months (%)	12 Months (%)
57	2 to 4	99	99	99	99	98	96
	37	99	99	98	95	94	92
72	2 to 4	98	96	94	91	85	65
	37	93	85	77	56	43	17

The No. 72 stopper is satisfactory as a temporary seal if the storage is under refrigeration and not in excess of six months. The stopper is unsatisfactory for conditions ordinarily met in shipment. A well compounded rubber mixture appears to be fully as satisfactory for sealing dry biologics as one of neoprene.

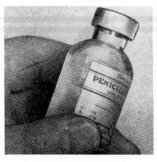
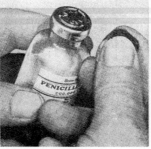
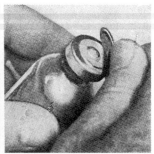

Fig. 5.14. A low-cost, rubber stoppered penicillin container which has the stopper protected by an aluminum seal and cap.

Fig. 5.15. Here the cap is removed, exposing the aluminum seal and tear tab.

Fig. 5.16. Seal disc is lifted to expose the rubber stopper which may be pierced with a hypodermic needle to make the solution and to withdraw it.

Initially, penicillin was dispensed in all-glass ampoules. Since about 1944, however, the all-glass ampoules have been given up by almost all manufacturers. Also, since that time, the price of penicillin has been greatly reduced and, in an effort to hold this at a minimum, competition has forced the elimination of the more expensive flame-sealed ampoule in most instances. An ordinary molded type of bottle or vial is used (some bottles prepared from tubing). Then an ordinary rubber stopper is used as a closure, and is protected by means of an aluminum metal cap. This type of container and its use are illustrated in Figs. 5.14, 5.15, and 5.16. More recently, this same kind of closure is being applied to containers used for other products including freeze-dried blood plasma. Most certainly with plasma, satisfactory results can be obtained and the large tin can eliminated for all ordinary peace-time conditions of storage.

PRE-FREEZING

For carrying out the freeze-drying process, the product to be dried must be frozen. Pre-freezing may be accomplished by means of external cooling or by vacuum evaporation to induce "self-freezing." In early applications of freeze-drying the former procedure was used with the aid of a bath of Dry Ice in alcohol, methyl "Cellosolve," or other solvents.[1] The physical shape and position in which the products are frozen in the container are highly important. The layer of frozen material should be kept as thin as possible consistent within a container not unreasonably large. The evaporating area should be kept as large as possible. In general, a volume of product not in excess of about 50 per cent of the size of the bottle should be used. During the war the volume of blood plasma was raised to 75 per cent of the capacity of the bottle, but this was a special case. The military advantage of the smallest possible package under war conditions is worth the premium in the added processing cost due to thick layers and small evaporating surface.

There are four general shapes or positions in which products usually are frozen: (1) "flat" freezing, in which the bottles or vials are placed on their sides for freezing; (2) "slant" freezing, in which the bottle is raised slightly at the neck or mouth end to prevent the product from running out of the container before freezing is completed; (3) "plug" freezing, in which bottles are allowed to stand upright with the material frozen on the bottom; (4) "shell" freezing, used in cases where any one of the three preceding methods would result in too thick a layer or too small an evaporating surface. This is generally necessary where relatively large volumes are dried per container, as with blood plasma, in which a single unit consists of 300 ml. The containers are rotated in the freezing bath so that the frozen material assumes the form of a partial or complete shell around the inner periphery of the container. This is particularly advantageous when the product cannot be dried within 24 hours unless the layer is made thinner by "shelling." When dealing with smaller amounts per container, in which drying is readily completed within a 24-hour cycle without shelling, the added manipulation and labor are normally unjustified. The possible exception to the last statement is that since the solubility of products dried from shell-frozen form is more rapid, because of greater exposed surface, there is an advantage in shell-freezing those which have poorer solubility, *e.g.*, concentrated globulins. With small amounts per container, shell freeze increases handling problems to avoid thawing during loading.

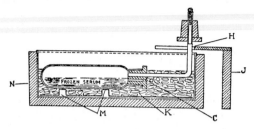

Fig. 5.17. Freezing Bath End Section
N, insulation of felt or rock-wool; M, false bottom support for containers; K, Dry-ice in Methyl Cellosolve; J, support for containers and for rocking the containers during initial freezing of serum; H, end of slots into which the L exhaust tubes fit; C, thin membrane.

In Fig. 5.17 is illustrated an early type of freezing pan used in freeze-drying.[1] Provision was made for "rocking" the containers while being "flat" frozen. This formed a hollowed groove along the longitudinal axis of frozen material, resulting in increased evaporating surface and a thinner layer. Fig. 5.18 is a photograph of an actual pan of this type.

Fig. 5.18. Freezing Pan.

Where products are dried on a manifold exposed to room air, the shape of the container must bear a definite relation to the amount of product and the form in which it is frozen. Drying on an external manifold affords the major means of controlling the temperature of the product during drying.[1] The evaporating surface area must be adjusted so that it gives a satisfactory ratio with respect to the surface of product adjacent to the glass wall of the container. At the latter surface, heat is absorbed from the atmosphere, which counterbalances the loss in latent heat of sublimation upon evaporation of the ice. The more nearly the ratio of these surfaces approaches unity, the greater the factor of safety with regard to thawing during desiccation with exposure of the container to warm room air, although a value as high as 2.0 is satisfactory (assuming optimal conditions otherwise). The amount of evaporating surface should be proportioned to the volume of the product in a ratio of at least 1 to 2 sq cm area per ml of serum.

When drying is carried on within vacuum chambers, the amount of heat reaching the bottled product is more readily controlled. In such instances this ratio becomes less critical. For rapid drying cycles, a major deviation from these ratios cannot be allowed.

When small volumes, particularly those under 1.0 ml per container, are being dried there is danger of thawing before the containers are all attached to the manifold and evacuation carried out. Consequently there is an advantage in placing a freezing bath around the containers after attachment to the manifold. After evacuation has been completed the freezing liquid should be removed so that drying may be accelerated by warm air.

"Shell" freezing may be carried out by hand rotation of the bottles in a freezing bath for small-scale purposes. A small shelling machine, typical of those used for large production, is illustrated in Fig. 5.19. The bottles are rotated mechanically and the bath is chilled with "Freon" refrigeration. Warren[9] has described a relatively simple type of shell-freezing unit suitable for smaller size ampoules. This is illustrated in Fig. 5.20, showing front and side views. The entire aluminum rotor is mechanically rotated, the lower portion being immersed in a Dry Ice-chilled liquid bath.

Greaves in 1942[10] described a novel method of shell-freezing by spinning. This has become known as "spin-freezing," although the physical shape of the product is about the same as that obtained by rotation in a low temperature liquid bath as just described. Greaves stated that spin-freezing gives a product which after desiccation has somewhat superior qualities of reconstitution. The method was applied successfully during the war in some parts of Canada and the U. S. and in England for plasma production.

Fig. 5.19. A typical Shelling Machine.

Blood serum or plasma in 400-cc amounts per container is spun with the bottle on its vertical axis at a speed of 900 rpm in a cold room maintained at $-18°C$. Under these conditions, a cone is forced down through the bottle, which finally produces a hollow core along the longitudinal axis. The liquid forms a shell on the inner periphery of the bottle, where it freezes, thus exposing a maximum surface for evaporation during the drying process, together with a minimum depth of frozen material in the particular bottle used (Figs. 5.21 and 5.22). Under these conditions, the product freezes as small crystals and it is this property to which Greaves attributes the reported superior solubility. Similarly, spinning within a vacuum drying chamber (Fig. 5.23) permits shell-freezing by vacuum alone and without a preliminary degassing step (to be discussed later).

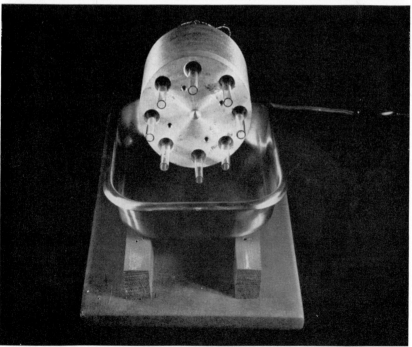

Fig. 5.20. Warren Shell-freezer for Small Ampoules.

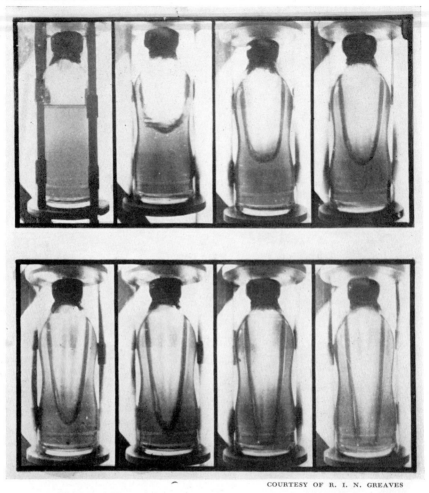

Fig. 5.21. Stages in the Development of the Cones during Spin-freezing. This series of photographs was taken with an interval of approximately 4 seconds between each exposure.

Inasmuch as any one of these types of machines for shell-freezing (except the last) requires operation for a good many hours before a sufficient number of bottles is accumulated to charge a drying chamber, a cold-storage room is necessary. The bottles are placed in this room until the proper number has been accumulated. The temperature of storage for most products should be below

Fig. 5.22. Vertical Spin-freezers in the Freezing Room of the Large Drying Plant. This cold room is maintained at −18°C. by a current of air which is kept circulating over the brine coils; these are behind the diaphragm seen at the far end of the room. There are three spinners, each of which can take 36 M.R.C. transfusion bottles, a total load of 108 bottles per run of two hours.

−25°C. Just how low a temperature is required depends upon conditions existing in a particular plant, particularly with regard to the length of time the containers are exposed to temperatures above freezing during the transfer to the drying chambers and during evacuation.

With products that are externally pre-frozen in smaller amounts per container, it is necessary to obtain full vacuum in the drying chambers quickly to prevent thawing. Particularly with products like penicillin, dispensed in amounts of about 1 ml per container, it is advantageous to chill the drying chambers to sub-freezing temperature to avoid thawing before evacuation. The temperature of the dryers may then be raised at a controlled rate to secure a maximum rate of drying and low final moisture.

By using chambers which may be chilled to sub-freezing temperatures it is possible to carry out actual freezing directly within the chambers. This may be done in all cases except where the product must be shell-frozen, unless spun by Greaves' vacuum-spinning device. Many plants operate on this basis, thereby avoiding the handling during freezing in outside liquid baths or cold rooms, transferring to freeze-storage vaults and then moving the materials again to drying chambers. Furthermore, all danger of thawing before evacuation is eliminated.

As indicated, products may be self-frozen by rapid vacuum evacuation. If solutions containing protein are placed under high vacuum, they immediately froth. Products in small individual containers will bubble out of the exhaust tube in an uncontrolled manner. Similarly, products in larger pans are difficult to keep under control. For this reason, for a long time it was considered impractical to employ self-freezing, particularly in the final container.

Fig. 5.23. One of the Heater Heads for the Final Pilot Plant, after its Conversion for Centrifugal Vacuum Spin-freezing

This head is for centrifugal vacuum spin-freezing 225 bottles, each containing 10 ml. of fluid. It consists of three aluminum discs on a central shaft which is rotated at 1,450 revs./min. by the electric motor under the top cover. Each disc has 75 holes drilled in it at an angle of 7° from the vertical. The cast-iron slip rings and Morgenite brushes for the resistance thermometer can be seen at the top of the shaft. Beneath each disc are the heater spirals and radiant heat screens.

The above-mentioned condition may be overcome by preliminary degassing, or spinning as discussed. Degassing is accomplished by evacuating slowly to the point where frothing just begins to occur. Reduction in pressure is then stopped. By allowing the system to remain under this partial vacuum for a half-hour to an hour, the gases can be sufficiently removed. The degassing may be accelerated by further progressive lowering of the pressure as quickly as possible, after some degassing has occurred. At no time should the pressure be reduced to the point where the material froths out through the necks or exhaust tubes. During this operation there is a slight evaporation of moisture sufficient to keep the materials in a cooled condition. The pressure may be controlled either by placing a stopcock or valve in the pump line, which can be shut off, or by placing a small-bore "T" connection in the pump line with a stopcock on the "T." The latter device enables the operator to admit some air to the pump to control the pressure.

When degassing is completed, the pump is allowed to evacuate the system to the limit of its capacity. When the pressure falls to the range of 2.5 to 1.0 mm Hg frothing will not occur, but almost immediate freezing will take place and drying from the frozen state will proceed. In other words, in the absence of the usual dissolved gases, boiling does not take place, even though the pressure is now below the point where boiling ordinarily should occur for the given temperature of the product. Usually the temperature of the substance falls for a time a few degrees below its freezing point so that it is simultaneously superheated and supercooled. Freezing will then set in with the suddenness characteristic of that encountered with supercooled solutions, in a manner similar to the sudden crystallization of supersaturated solutions. Tapping the containers tends to initiate the freezing in the supercooled solutions, but it is usually unnecessary.

In this manner the advantages of rapid freezing are achieved without the use of refrigerants. After initial freezing, the temperature, of course, returns to the freezing point, but when freezing is complete and as sublimation proceeds, it falls to the range of -10 to $-20°C$. From then on, the thermal drying curve follows that of products externally pre-frozen.

Inasmuch as there is some desiccation from the liquid state, the final appearance of a serum product is a highly porous mass covered with a glossy, amorphous, amber-like film. Solubility of most products is excellent, and in the case of certain ones, superior solubility characteristics are produced. With other materials, such as certain viruses and heavy suspensions of semi-solid masses like bacterial centrifugates, external pre-freezing is necessary.

As mentioned, Greaves has proposed the use of centrifugal force during self-freezing as a substitute for preliminary degassing. Greaves states that a bubble is most vulnerable at its birth and that for this reason a small antagonistic force is sufficient to inhibit bubble formation.[11] He reports that a speed of 1450 rpm with the normal radius of 1 inch is sufficient to inhibit the formation of bubbles in liquids under vacuum, although under these conditions existent bubbles were not destroyed. Protein solutions may be subjected to high vacuum while spinning, with uniform results and without bubble formation. (See Fig. 5.23.)

An advantage of this type of freezing is that when spinning occurs on the vertical axis of the bottle, a cone is forced down through the liquid, thus distributing the liquid on the inside periphery of the bottle during freezing, with results similar to those obtained when spin-freezing on a horizontal axis in a cold vault. The disadvantage is the mechanical complexity of the apparatus for spinning at these speeds under vacuum. A similar method has been worked out by Dr. George H. Brown of the Radio Corporation of America Laboratories in Princeton, New Jersey, for avoiding the frothing of penicillin during drying of the *liquid* at around *room temperature*.[12] However, under these conditions, the height of the vacuum is not nearly so critical and the mechanical problems are less severe.

CHAMBERS AND MANIFOLDS FOR CONTAINERS

There are two major differences in operation between manifolds and drying chambers. First is the manner of vacuum sealing, which means that the type of container which may be used is different; when using manifolds a special connection must be made with each individual container. Second is the difference in the method of heating. Before the art was developed along modern lines, the product was kept in refrigerators and every effort was made to keep it cold externally. Accordingly, while working to keep the product frozen, heat was withheld from the containers so that improper drying and unsatisfactory results were obtained. In 1935, a manifold-type of equipment came into use[1] whereby heat was abstracted from the atmosphere by the individual containers of product being dried. These containers at the end of drying were then sealed under original vacuum and the entire process carried out with maintenance of sterility. Products dried in this fashion have less than 1 per cent moisture.

The manifolds and the connectors for attaching the containers to the manifold were designed to permit high-speed attachment after removing the containers from the freezing bath. Inasmuch as these connections had to be tight for high vacuum to be maintained without using excessively large pumps, great care was necessary in construction. A simple laboratory type of construction using all-glass is illustrated in Fig. 5.24, having been designed by the author for general laboratory work[1] and for a number of years it was the only type used. In Fig. 5.25 is illustrated a larger type of apparatus of metal construction built under the author's direction for hospital use.[1] Fig. 5.26 shows an apparatus of this type for small commercial operation, the one illustrated being the first commercial freeze-drying installation in the world actually used to produce market packages of a product suitable for parenteral use. Human convalescent serum was dried in large amounts.

The type of manifold used when containers had soft glass exhaust tubes for sealing, as discussed in the preceding section, has been referred to in connection with Fig. 5.5. Fig. 5.27 illustrates the type of equipment embodying such a manifold.

Heckly has described the same type of manifold[13] but has it placed in a vertical position. This seems to have no particular advantage, for if products are to be frozen by covering with Dry Ice after attachment to the manifold, more complex manipulation results. In general, glass equipment should be avoided if possible.

Wyckoff and Lagsdin[14] describe the so-called "pig." This embodies an internal Dry Ice condenser which is vacuum-insulated. Containers are arranged on the outer periphery of the apparatus, as illustrated in Fig. 5.28. The upper portion of the figure illustrates a "pig" with 30-cc ampoules for penicillin and the lower "pig" illustrates 750-cc bottles containing 500 ml of blood plasma. An ad-

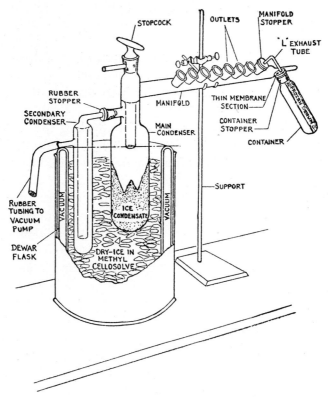

Fig. 5.24. Miniature Glass Apparatus.

vantage of this type of equipment is the proximity of the cold surface of the condenser to the outlets of the containers. This advantage is more apparent than real because the neck of the bottles or ampoules is one limiting factor. After the vapors have emerged from this restriction it is simple enough to provide a vapor line sufficiently large to carry the vapors without appreciable increase in pressure. Also, the condensing surface is small, so that when large quantities of blood plasma are dried it is necessary to insu-

Fig. 5.25. Large Metal Apparatus.

Fig. 5.26. Small commercial-scale equipment built at University of Pennsylvania in 1935 and installed at Sharp & Dohme, Inc. (1).

late the containers with bags, as illustrated, in order to retard the rate of application of heat from the atmosphere. A major disadvantage is the small capacity of the condenser for Dry Ice, which

Fig. 5.27. Cryochem type of equipment for desiccating from the frozen state. A regenerable desiccant comprising mostly calcium sulfate (Drierite) with a small quantity of Silica Gel (for a small amount of vapors other than water) contained in baskets within the white tank. The manifold is shown with outlets to which individual containers for drying are attached. Pre-freezing is readily carried out by spreading cracked dry-ice over them, supported on trays. Dry Ice is removed after evacuation. At the end of drying, the glass tubes attaching the containers to these outlets are sealed by fusion with a flame.

necessitates recharging every hour or so. Toward the end of drying, the temperature of the entire room is raised to hasten the completion of drying.

By various means it is possible to control the temperature of the product through the rate of supplying heat to individual containers on a manifold, which, while less simple, is effective. The

Fig. 5.28. Wyckoff and Lagsdin "pigs." Upper illustration shows 30 cc. ampoules of penicillin. Lower illustration shows 750 cc. bottles containing two units of blood plasma each.

Fig. 5.29. A series of drying chambers used in production of penicillin in a plant having four drying chambers of this size. About 1,000,000 doses of penicillin may be freeze-dried every 24 hours.

temperature of the entire room may be controlled, beginning first at a low point (below 0°C) and then by increasing temperatures as drying proceeds. Where it is not readily possible to control the temperature of the entire room, an electric fan may be used to circulate the air heated by electric light bulbs or other means over the containers. Infrared lights may be arranged to direct radiation at the containers.

Liquid baths will provide the closest control and the necessary calories can be introduced more rapidly at a lower temperature. This affords less danger of overheating dried portions of products in the containers toward the completion of the drying. At the outset, the temperature is held below freezing; but above that desired for the material being dried and as drying proceeds, the temperature of the bath is gradually raised. The temperature of the bath soon can be set at the maximum to which it is safe to take the final dried product, and just as fast drying can be procured as is obtained with dry higher temperature sources, such as hot air or infrared radiation. The baths accomplish this at the lower temperature because of better transfer of heat through the direct contact of the container walls with the liquid. Although the period of drying is reduced to a minimum, baths are more complicated to operate and do not necessarily reduce the cost of equipment or of operation. In production where cost becomes a major consideration it is advisable to use drying chambers rather than manifolds.

The major advantage of a manifold is in its greater flexibility for use with a wide variety of products requiring containers of different sizes. A multiplicity of products and types of containers may be run simultaneously. It is simple to maintain sterility and carry out steps in various research problems and other applications of freeze-drying with a minimum of equipment. However, for large-scale production, vacuum shelf dryers have proved very satisfactory and are the most widely used type of equipment in commercial freeze-drying in the United States and Canada today. Electrical sources of heat, such as resistance heaters, induction heating, high-frequency fields, dielectric heating, infrared light and other forms of energy may be utilized. Baths may be used under the same conditions as discussed above with manifolds. Then, however, oils of low vapor pressure at the temperatures encoun-

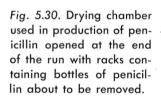

Fig. 5.30. Drying chamber used in production of penicillin opened at the end of the run with racks containing bottles of penicillin about to be removed.

tered must be employed to avoid evaporation in the vacuum drying chamber. So far, circulation of hot fluids through the shelves and jackets of the drying chambers has been used most. In order that drying may proceed uniformly, it is essential that the hot-water system be properly designed for even distribution of heat to all portions of the chamber so that all containers will dry at the same rate. Electrically heated shelves may be used, but there must be good reason in any given case to justify this type of direct heating because there is a greater problem in securing even distribution. Also, at the completion of the drying of one batch, a longer time is required for chilling the chamber before loading the next batch. With liquid-heated shelves, cold liquid is readily circulated to shorten the time between batches—an important consideration in commercial operation.

When the chambers are chilled to a sub-freezing temperature for pre-freezing, a non-aqueous fluid must be circulated instead of water. This must not have too great a viscosity at the lower temperatures encountered, especially in the heat exchanger or cooler where the fluid itself is chilled by Dry Ice, "Freon," or ammonia. It is also preferable for the fluid to be noninflammable and it must, of course, have a boiling point above the highest temperature to which it is necessary to take the products during drying. Trichloroethylene has been found to be practical for this purpose, although mixtures of glycol and water as well as other fluids have also been used.

Fig. 5.29 illustrates a series of such drying chambers in use in the production of penicillin. Fig. 5.30 shows a chamber with the door open and the product ready to be unloaded. The vials of penicillin are held within the racks. The stainless steel lid used for purposes of sterility is arranged with adequate passageways for escape of vapors in a downward direction, completely protecting the product from contamination by particles falling into the racks. The chambers are heavily insulated since they may be carried to temperatures of $-40°C$. At the end of drying, the temperature is increased to as high as $65°C$.

These drying chambers are usually so designed that they will withstand 15 pounds internal steam pressure for sterilization. At

Fig. 5.31. The Experimental Drying Plant.

The desiccator is made from glass cylinders, and the refrigeration unit is a small SO_2 unit. The lowest temperatures obtained with this plant were around $-20°C$., but the results obtained showed that the principle was sound and enabled the preliminary experiments on automatic heat control to be carried out successfully.

COURTESY OF R. I. N. GREAVES

Fig. 5.32. The Original Pilot Plant.

The SO_2 compressor has been replaced by a 3-cylinder "Hallmark" methylchloride machine giving a temperature below $-40°C$. with a heat exchange of 250 watts. This machine could dry 5 litres at a time from a 25-litre bottle.

COURTESY OF R. I. N. GREAVES

Fig. 5.33. One of the Heater Heads for the Final Pilot Plant.
This head is made to accommodate 35 M.R.C. transfusion bottles, each of which will hold 400 ml. of serum or plasma vertically spun-frozen round its inside periphery.

COURTESY OF R. I. N. GREAVES

Fig. 5.34. The Large Drying Plant.
The instrument panel showing the recording galvanometers and heat control circuits.

COURTESY OF R. I. N. GREAVES

the end of a drying period, the vacuum may be released with dry and sterile air or nitrogen. This is arranged very simply by placing on the inside of the chamber a container charged with cotton and a suitable desiccant. Upon opening the vacuum break valve, all air entering the chamber must pass through this dry-air sterilizer. Regenerable chemicals, such as calcium sulfate or silica gel, should be selected, so that when the sterilizer is removed for heating in the oven for resterilization, the desiccant will be regenerated at the same time. Chambers and other equipment used by Greaves in England for serum and plasma during the war are illustrated in Figs. 5.31 through 5.38.

SIZE OF VACUUM AND VAPOR LINES

When either chambers or manifolds are used, the size of the vapor line to the condenser for carrying the water vapor is of utmost importance to permit rapid drying. The following are certain useful equations derived by Normand of Carbide & Carbon Chemicals Corporation[15] as rule-of-thumb relations based on Knudsen's equation.* These relations are applicable for determining the proper diameter and length of round pipe within an accuracy of 10 per cent. Conductance of the pipe is determined first and after this the net pumping speed is determined.

The formula for determining the pumping speed varies with the range of pressures encountered. These are as follows and conductance is expressed as cfm.

(1) *Diffusion pump range,* where there is molecular flow and when pressure in microns multiplied by diameter in inches is less than 7 and when the length in feet is greater than the diameter in inches:

$$C = 13 \, \frac{D^3 \, \text{(inches)}}{L \, \text{(feet)}}$$

In the special case when length in feet is less than the diameter in inches, there is a condition approximating an aperture. In this

---

$$* \; Q = 4/3\sqrt{2\pi} \; \sqrt{\frac{R'T}{M}} \frac{R^3}{L} \, (p_1 - p_2)$$

case the conductance is obtained by multiplying the cross-sectional area of the pipe in square inches by 150.

(2) In the *intermediate range* we have the condition where pressure multiplied by diameter is greater than 7 and less than 220.

$$C = 0.5 \ \frac{D^4}{L} \ P + 13 \ \frac{D^3}{L} \ \frac{(1 + .64 \ PD)}{(1 + .79 \ PD)}$$

(3) For pressures in the *range of mechanical pumps* and where pressure times diameter is greater than 200 the following applies. This is the range of viscous (laminar) flow.

$$C = 0.5 \ \frac{D^4}{L} \ P$$

In freeze-drying equation (3) is applicable. This relation is important because the net pumping speed which must next be determined depends upon the conductance of the piping itself, as well as on the speed of the vacuum pump. The relation between the speed of the pump and conductance of the piping in determination of the net pumping speed is as follows:

$$\text{Net pumping speed} = \frac{1}{S^L} = \frac{1}{S \ (\text{pump})} + \frac{1}{C}$$

The above conductances are based on pumping air. The conductance will be nearly 50 per cent greater in the case of water vapor because of the smaller molecules.

To illustrate use of the above formula, let us calculate an example in determining the conductance of a pipe 5 inches in diameter and 156 feet long at an average pressure of 100 microns. Also, we shall determine the net pumping speed obtainable with such a pipe when using a pump having a speed of 200 cfm.

$$C = 0.5 \ \frac{(5^4)}{(156)} \ 100 = 0.5 \ \frac{(625)}{(156)} \ 100$$

$$C = 200 \ \text{cfm.}$$

$$\frac{1}{S^L} = \frac{1}{200} + \frac{1}{200} = \frac{2}{200}$$

$$S^L = 100 \ \text{cfm.}$$

In other words, the long pipe has a conductance of 200 cfm. and the net pumping speed obtained with a vacuum pump having a capacity of 200 cfm. is only 100 cfm.

If a pump with twice the speed, *i.e.* 400 cfm., is used the net pumping speed obtained through the long pipe will be increased to only 133 cfm. as illustrated below:

$$\frac{1}{S^L} = \frac{1}{400} + \frac{1}{200} = \frac{3}{400}$$

$$S^L = 133 \text{ cfm.}$$

A similar calculation may be made for the water vapor itself being evaporated from the frozen product. It is necessary to consider the thickness of layer and whether the material is frozen flat, in plugs, shell-frozen, or frozen in droplets. This has been discussed earlier in this chapter and the peak rate of evaporation must be determined in terms of liters of material per hour from each drying chamber, bottle, or the like for a given vapor line, tubing, or bottle neck. This, of course, must be converted to volume of vapor for given pressure and temperature. This peak rate varies not only with conditions of freezing just mentioned, but also with the product itself, and careful experimental data must be obtained on which to base any calculations which are to be used in design of production equipment. Of course in small-scale experimental equipment, it is easy to make the lines large enough on the basis of previous experience to cover almost any product. In design of production equipment, however, this is likely to be too costly, and a calculation should be made. As an example, in removal of 4 kg of moisture per hour by sublimation under peak load conditions at 300 microns, a vapor line ten feet long is calculated to require a diameter of eight inches, assuming no restrictions by valves.

A further factor involves angles in the line, and the effect of this is debatable. A good average condition seems to be that one right-angle elbow in the system may be considered as equivalent to a length of pipe equal to its diameter. Similarly, valves must be chosen which offer as little restriction as possible. For example, Globe valves restrict the flow of vapor quite considerably and should not be used in lines where high velocities are desired. Globe

Fig. 5.35. The Large
Drying Plant.
Loading a primary
chamber with frozen
material. The control
bottle with its thermo-
couple can be seen in
the foreground.

COURTESY OF R. I. N.
GREAVES

valves are suitable as vacuum breaks, provided that they are so installed that the packing is not on the vacuum side. In this way, only
when the valve is open for release of the vacuum is the packing
connected in the system, and then it does not matter if there is
leakage. Gate valves are suitable for use in vapor or vacuum lines
as far as offering no restriction is concerned. However, they offer
the serious problem of maintenance in preventing leakage through
the packing. Lubricated plug valves, diaphragm valves, or rubber-
seated flange-type valves are preferable (ordinary plug-type valves
or petcocks are not satisfactory).

PRESSURE DROP

Sometimes it is necessary to determine the extent of pressure
drop through a slit or other type of aperture in the system. For ex-

ample, side walls are sometimes arranged on each drying shelf, up to the shelf above, for containing materials in direct contact with the heating surface. At front and back, the wall is cut down to allow a ¼-inch slit for escape of vapors. If the total combined length of the two slits is 120 inches, there are 30 sq in of cross-sectional area for escape of vapors.

To determine the pressure drop through the slit, it is necessary to determine the velocity of vapor flow. This depends upon the pounds of water to be evaporated and the pressure, the latter being determined by the temperature at which the product is to be dried. That is, the pounds must be converted to volume of vapor at some given pressure such as 1 mm. Let us assume a rate of flow of 20 cu ft per second. The 30 sq in of slit area is about 0.21 sq ft, so dividing the cubic feet by square feet we obtain a velocity of nearly 100 ft/second.

Fig. 5.36. The Large Drying Plant. Transferring dried material from the primary to the secondary chambers.

COURTESY OF R. I. N. GREAVES

The following relation will afford calculations of the pressure drop:

$$v = C\sqrt{2gh}$$

v is the velocity, C a constant, g is acceleration due to gravity, and h is pressure drop in terms of feet of the vapor. To convert this last to absolute pressure, it must be multiplied by the density of the vapor, which in the present example would be the weight of one cubic foot of the vapor at 1 mm Hg pressure, *i.e.*, 0.000066 lb/cu ft.

C is the coefficient of contraction of the vapors passing through the orifice and we may assume 0.65 as reasonable. On this basis, microns of Hg pressure drops are obtained as follows:

$$100 = 0.65\sqrt{(2)\ (32)\ h}$$

$$\text{microns} = h \times \text{density} \times 1000$$

$$\text{microns} = h\ (0.000066)\ (1000) = 9$$

So we see that the drop in pressure through the slit is negligible. If the degree of contraction were less then the assumption of

Fig. 5.37. The Large Drying Plant.
General view of the desiccator room, showing the secondary desiccators in the foreground and the primary desiccators with the loading staging in the background. The heater heads from the two chambers which are defrosting are raised.

COURTESY OF R. I. N. GREAVES

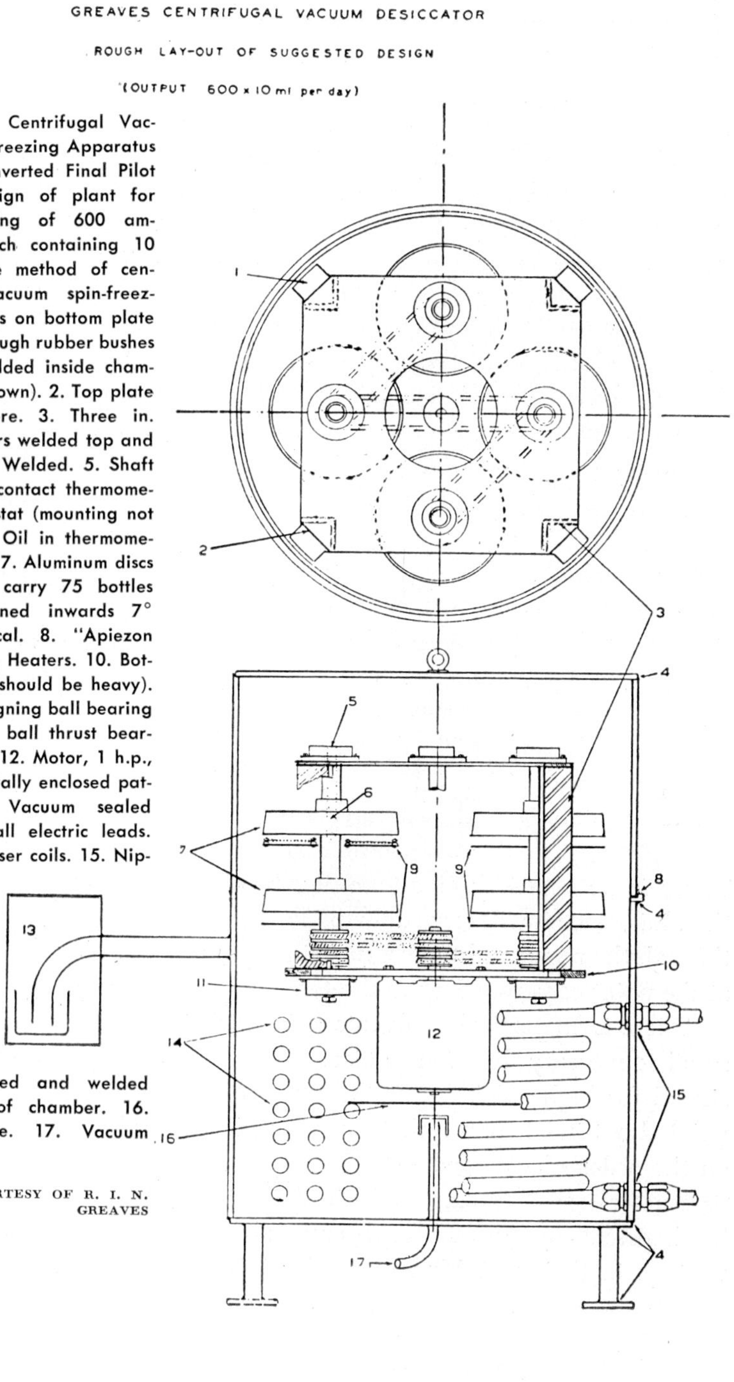
GREAVES CENTRIFUGAL VACUUM DESICCATOR
ROUGH LAY-OUT OF SUGGESTED DESIGN
(OUTPUT 600 x 10 ml per day)
1
2
3
4
5
6
7
8
9
10
11
12
13
14
15
16
17

Fig. 5.38. Centrifugal Vacuum Spin-freezing Apparatus in the Converted Final Pilot Plant. Design of plant for daily drying of 600 ampoules, each containing 10 ml. by the method of centrifugal vacuum spin-freezing. 1. Lugs on bottom plate bolted through rubber bushes to lugs welded inside chamber (not shown). 2. Top plate cut off here. 3. Three in. angle pillars welded top and bottom. 4. Welded. 5. Shaft bored for contact thermometer thermostat (mounting not shown). 6. Oil in thermometer pocket. 7. Aluminum discs drilled to carry 75 bottles each, inclined inwards 7° from vertical. 8. "Apiezon Q" seal. 9. Heaters. 10. Bottom plate (should be heavy). 11. Self-aligning ball bearing with single ball thrust bearing below. 12. Motor, 1 h.p., 3-phase, totally enclosed pattern. 13. Vacuum sealed entry for all electric leads. 14. Condenser coils. 15. Nipples, screwed and welded into wall of chamber. 16. Baffle plate. 17. Vacuum outlet.

COURTESY OF R. I. N. GREAVES

$C = 0.65$, in other words approaching unity, the drop would be even less.

EVACUATION

Since drying by sublimation is a high-vacuum process, it is necessary to consider the means for pumping both non-condensable gases and water vapor. As to non-condensable gases, air must be exhausted from the system initially, and air leaking into the vacuum system must be continually removed. Also, gases dissolved in the product need to be pumped out of the equipment as fast as they are released. Removal of water vapor *in vacuo* will be discussed in the next section; discussion here will be confined to the initial evacuation of air and handling of leakage into the vacuum system.

Mechanical oil-sealed high-vacuum pumps of the rotary type are by far the most widely used. Not only must air be well removed to make the process operative, but it is important that the residual amounts of air be reduced to as low a level as possible so that condensers and desiccant, whichever is used, will have maximum efficiency. For example, when using a low-temperature condenser, if the temperature of the surface of the ice on the condenser is −40°C, the vapor pressure of the ice will be 90 microns. Water vapor at a pressure of 90 microns will then pass through the vacuum pump and will sweep residual air with it. For this reason, whatever pump is used must have a high capacity at the pressure corresponding to the temperature of the ice on the condenser. There is no necessity of attempting to obtain a higher vacuum than this, since it will serve only to increase the flow of water vapor through the pump and the pressure in any event will only equalize at the point corresponding to the temperature of the condenser.

There is no particular advantage in using booster pumps, such as oil or mercury diffusion or ejector boosters, unless they are designed for high efficiency at the pressure just indicated. It was pointed out in Chapter 2 that since temperatures of condenser ice on the order of −30 and −40°C usually are sufficiently low, the pressure range of interest is from about 100 to 300 microns. Unless boosters are designed for this range of pressure, there is no advantage in their use. Modern mechanical vacuum pumps of the rotary type have high efficiency in this range of vacuum. This is illustrated in Fig. 5.39. In some instances, lower temperature and higher vacuum may be necessary.

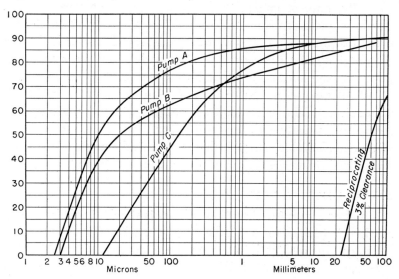

Fig. 5.39. Efficiency of various mechanical oil-sealed rotary vacuum pumps, A, B and C at high vacuum compared with reciprocating type.

When using all-welded steel construction for condensers, vacuum chambers, and vapor and vacuum lines, and plug-type, diaphragm-type or other suitable high-vacuum valves, very tight vacuum systems can be achieved. With such construction, a satisfactory rate of evacuation and a satisfactory vacuum can be maintained during operation using 1 cu ft of rotary vacuum pump displacement per minute for every cubic foot of space under vacuum. The vacuum-pumping capacity for rotary mechanical pumps of several thousand cubic feet per minute presents no problem today; therefore adequate capacity for any ordinary installation used for medical products is available.

The foregoing capacity is for drying chambers with bottles of relatively large capacity such as those for blood plasma, or loaded with penicillin or other products in correspondingly small amounts in chambers chilled to sub-freezing temperature. In either case,

evacuation within five minutes usually is sufficiently fast. If penicillin in 1-cc amounts is being dried and if the chambers are not
chilled, usually evacuation within one or two minutes is essential.
Then the ratio of cubic displacement to space to be evacuated
should be increased from 1 to 1 up to 5 to 1, or even 10 to 1. However, this presents no serious problem, inasmuch as this high ratio
of pumping capacity need be applied to chambers during evacuation only, and because the chambers are evacuated one by one.

When greater capacity than this is required, as in the food field,
steam ejectors with either four or five stages with one or more intercondensers, usually with barometric legs, may be used for removal
of non-condensable gases. Either mechanical pumps or separate
"roughing" steam ejectors may be used for evacuation.

LEAK DETECTION

In glass apparatus, detection of leaks is simple. High-frequency
spark coil testers are available on the market for operation on
ordinary 110-volt light circuits. In the micron and low-millimeter
ranges, when the coil is held near or adjacent to the glass, a discharge is given. The color of the discharge varies with the pressure,
but this is not a sensitive quantitative indicator and cannot be used
as a substitute for a McLeod Gage in accurate measurement of the
pressure. At higher pressures, no discharge is given and similarly
in pressures below the micron range no discharge is obtained and
a so-called "cold vacuum" has been reached. In locating leaks, the
tester is moved along the various points of the glass apparatus and
when the tip of the coil becomes close to the leak, a spark discharge
will be seen to jump directly to the leak itself and simultaneously
the color of the discharge within the glass apparatus changes. Care
must be taken, however, not to punch holes in weak points at glass
joints in the apparatus if the discharge coil is a powerful one.

The same system may be used for testing vacuum-tightness of
finally sealed ampoules. In this case, the best procedure is to allow
the sealed ampoules to stand for a day or two. In the event that the
leak is a small one, it may take more than a few minutes for the
vaccum to be discharged and by waiting for a few days, containers
with small leaks as well as large ones are located.

In metal equipment, the same system may be used with modification. A glass tube with a sealed-in metal connection is attached by one means or another, such as with rubber tubing, to some connection on the apparatus. Preferably, this should be near or in the vacuum pump line. By use of a spark coil a discharge is set up in this tube. Then acetone, trichloroethylene, or other fluid is sprayed or painted around the various suspected joints in the equipment. If the leak is large enough, this will be drawn into the apparatus and change the color of the discharge at the detector tube. This method is generally not as suitable as others.

Similarly, the above organic fluids will change the reading of an electrical gage such as one of the Pirani type. The reading will be made better if the leak is a small one and is momentarily closed off; in the case of a large leak, the reading will be made worse if a large quantity of the fluid is drawn into the vacuum system and evaporated. However, this method also lacks sensitivity.

First of all in the metal systems there frequently are valves or other means of segregating the equipment into sections. This should be done and rates of leakage determined without the vacuum pump running, in order to isolate the portion of the equipment where the leak or leaks are located. When the particular section has been found, paint the suspected joints with a good grade of red crankcase paint such as Sherwin Williams No. 1246 or G. E. No. 1201-B Glyptol or equivalent. Not only would the vacuum gage record an improvement in pressure when the leaky surface is coated with paint, but as the paint dries the leak is stopped. If for any reason it is undesirable to rely on the paint, other suitable means should be used for correcting leakage, such as welding, soldering, or the like. Rubber tubing and gaskets may be checked by use of castor oil.

At vacuums higher than the micron range, the mass spectrometer was used with great success in the war-time development of atomic energy equipment. This same equipment may also be used at higher pressures by connecting it through a valve to the equipment to be tested. In other words, the testing apparatus itself operates under the usual highest vacuum. Helium gas is played over the suspected points in the equipment; at the point where leakage occurs, it is drawn into the equipment and over into the mass spectrometer, where it will be rapidly detected provided the pumping speed in cfm. is some 50 times greater than the volume of the system in cubic feet.

As a practical matter, only the method using the mass spectrometer is to be recommended for the sub-micron range of pressures, but in the micron range encountered in freeze-drying, the paint brush provides the simplest method, even though it may be frowned upon by expert physicists accustomed to a small fraction of a micron. With an organic volatile solvent, either of the two methods above may be used, but generally it will be found more laborious. Incidentally, a non-inflammable solvent such as trichloroethylene in many cases is to be preferred to one like acetone, although trichloroethylene is somewhat of a health hazard under prolonged exposure.

Another method for testing leaks is to evacuate the system, shut off the vacuum pump and fill with "Freon" to about 3 lbs pressure. By use of an acetylene torch around suspected points, the change in the color of the flame to green will show the leaks. Inasmuch as "Freon" is fairly expensive, it is well to have the leak localized beforehand into a particular section by the standard practice of determining leak rates in the several isolated sections. After locating the leak, the system should be thoroughly aired to prevent "Freon" from getting to the vacuum pump oil.

The General Electric Co. has recently offered a detector for halogen—containing compounds and the device gives excellent results with freeze-drying equipment. Carbon tetrachloride may be used instead of "Freon," and if so, a dish of it is placed in the equipment, all doors, rubber connectors, etc. clamped tight and about 5 psi air pressure set up. The G.E. detector may then be used, but question any supposed leaks around door gaskets, etc., which internal pressure will tend to force open.

REMOVING MOISTURE IN VACUO

"Dry Ice" condensation: pigs. Fig. 5.40 illustrates an early and simple type of Dry Ice condenser.[1] The condensers are kept at approximately $-78°C$ by immersion in a bath of Dry Ice sus-

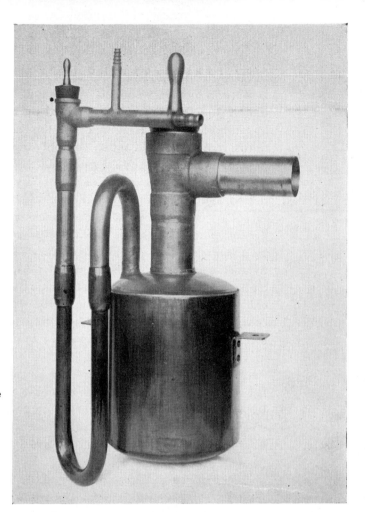

Fig. 5.40. Condensers of large metal apparatus.

pended in a suitable organic liquid in an insulated container. Of the various liquids tried for suspending the Dry Ice (acetone, ethanol, ether, "deodorized" kerosene, trichloroethylene, numerous butyl and amyl compounds), methyl "Cellosolve" (the methyl ether of ethylene glycol) has been found most satisfactory. This liquid has a sufficiently low melting point and viscosity, has no offensive odor or known health hazard, is of reasonable cost and has a relatively high flash point. Alcohol and deodorized kerosene provide a second choice.

In small sizes, the construction of a metal condenser is similar to that of glass (see Fig. 5.24). There are, however, a few points of difference in operation. The flat top of the main condenser is adjusted about an inch below the mouth of the vacuum jar and the

Dry Ice in methyl "Cellosolve" is brought to within ¼ or ½ inch of the flat top. No stopcock is provided for admission of air to the apparatus at the end of a run; one of the manifold stoppers is withdrawn from a manifold outlet. To empty the condensers, the rubber joint between the manifold and main condenser and the rubber tubing pump connection at the secondary condenser are disconnected. Before chilling down the condensers for the next run the secondary condenser must be completely empty; otherwise, it may become plugged with ice. The intake tube from the manifold into the main condenser should extend from ½ to 1 inch below the flat top on the inside of the metal condenser. All the rubber connections on the metal condensers should be made before the condensers are chilled and they should then never be disturbed while they are cold; otherwise, small pieces of ice condensed from the atmosphere collect on the metal around the frozen rubber parts and leaks are inevitable.

In the case of glass condensers, if any of the condensate thaws between runs, a condenser bath should not be repacked with Dry Ice until they have been emptied. Otherwise, the freezing of the condensate as a solid block would break the glass, which is in contrast with the manner in which the icelayer builds up when condensed from the vapor phase.

For apparatus illustrated in Fig. 5.25, a condenser of the type illustrated in Fig. 5.40 is used. The main condenser consists of a cylinder of copper with a copper bottom, convex outward, and a dome-shaped top of stainless steel. From the stainless steel dome projects a secondary condenser of copper tubing with stainless steel inlet and outlet. Both condensers are fitted with plugged outlets through which the condensate, when thawed, may be removed by siphoning. The purpose of the stainless steel dome is to prevent freezing over of the vapor inlet to the condenser. It is because stainless steel is a poorer conductor of heat than copper that the copper sidewalls are at a lower temperature and can collect all the condensed ice. Unless this type of construction is used, inner deflector baffles are required, but these are likely to cause more difficulty by freezing and clogging than the type of construction just discussed.

Fig. 5.41. Large Dry-Ice type condenser operating with chamber-type equipment.

A still larger condenser of this Dry Ice type used rather extensively through World War II is illustrated in Fig. 5.41. More recently, an improved type of Dry Ice condenser has been developed which utilizes the vacuum in the system to insulate the bath. The bath is located in the center, as illustrated in Fig. 5.42. A photograph of such an installation is illustrated in Fig. 5.43.

These condensers also permit the use of large blocks of Dry Ice, so that extensive chopping is not necessary. The so-called Wyckoff-Lagsdin "pigs" consist of essentially this same type of condenser with individual container outlet connectors (open nipples) spread around the outer periphery of the outside wall of the condenser.[14] Drying with this type of equipment has the same disadvantages as the use of a manifold, both from the point of view of the many vacuum-tight connections which must be made, and satisfactory control of heat. Jacobs[16] described apparatus identical with that of the Wyckoff-Lagsdin "pig," except that glass construction was used with outlets like the original ones with the glass manifold.[1]

Heckly has described a glass type of Dry Ice condenser[13] essentially the same in principle as that illustrated in Fig. 5.24. The secondary condenser, however, is a piece of glass tubing placed internally within the main condenser and for this reason serves no useful purpose. The temperature of the secondary condenser is just

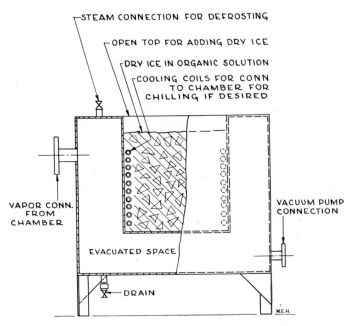

Fig. 5.42. Later type commercial Dry-Ice condenser.

as high as that of the main condenser and could be dispensed with by use of suitable baffle. Indeed, as has been shown with the condensers in commercial operation during the war of the type illustrated in Fig. 5.42, if the main condenser is of proper construction, no secondary condenser need be provided. The Heckly condenser has the advantage of utilizing more or less standard glass parts, but the several rubber stopper connections are subject to leaks. The major disadvantage is in the fragility of glass parts, and today little or no commercially manufactured equipment is used which is not of metal construction. Usually the value of the products being dried is so high that danger of losing them justifies the added cost of metal equipment.

Condensation with Mechanical Refrigeration: Fixed and Moving Surfaces. When using Dry Ice condensers, even though the Dry Ice bath may be maintained at −78°C, the temperature of the surface of the ice as condensed may be considerably above this temperature. There are three reasons for this: (1) the conductivity of heat across the layer of ice already condensed; (2) the "skin effect" of heat transfer as the ice condenses on the ice surface, from the ice to metal and from metal to the cold bath; and (3) the usual relatively small surface of condensation. When utilizing Dry Ice, these factors are not serious because of its low temperature. When using mechanical refrigeration, on the other hand, the lower the temperature at which the BTU's of condensation must be removed, the greater the amount of mechanical refrigeration necessary, because compressors have a lower tonnage output at the lower the

Fig. 5.43. Modern small-scale Dry-Ice type of plant.

temperature. By using condensers of large area, all the ice may be condensed as a relatively thin film. The loss in conductivity across the ice layer is reduced to a minimum. Because of the large area of condensation there is less temperature drop, since fewer BTU's must be absorbed per square foot of surface. On this basis ammonia or "Freon" temperatures as high as −35°C are suitable[1,17] and compressors of reasonable size are adequate.

Defrosting of such condensers may be carried out quickly by cold-water sprays, steam, or hot fluid passed through the coils which provide the surface for condensation. Defrosting is all the more rapid since the layer of condensate is thin. By using two or more condensers in parallel the operation may be continuous, one condenser at a time being taken out for defrosting.

Scraper type of condensers with blades much like those of a lawnmower have been used;[18] in these the layer of ice is kept thin by continual scraping, with discharge of fine ice into a receptacle. These condensers have the advantage of maintaining a thin layer of ice. Because of mechanical problems the extent of surface is usually made small and there is less efficiency than with an extended fixed surface. Also, mechanical problems such as the freezing of scraper blades, tightness of stuffing boxes and the like, are not encountered with fixed surface.[19] Experience has proved that the moving type of condenser requires greater tonnage of refrigeration for operation. On the other hand, the scraper type has been made to work well, and if satisfactory vacuum locks can be used for removal of the scraped ice, a *single* condenser may be used for continuous operation, although this usually is not done.

Wetted Wall Condensation. Hygroscopic liquids at reduced temperature may be used for condensation by being allowed to flow around the walls or along tubes in a vacuum condenser, or the liquid may be sprayed to a chamber. Such liquids as glycol at temperatures of about 0°C or slightly lower have suitably low vapor pressures.[20] The fluid is then removed from the vacuum system, heated for regeneration, and reinjected to the vacuum system. Continuous operation may be carried out in this fashion. Hickman[21] proposed spraying cold salt solutions like calcium chloride.

Chemical Desiccating Agents. Equipment utilizing a regenerable chemical desiccant has been found inexpensive and convenient in operation, particularly in smaller capacities. The initial cost of equipment, however, when very large volumes must be processed (as in preparing blood plasma, etc.) is higher than that of other types. This is partly because of the size of the desiccant chambers, which must maintain the vacuum, and partly because of the equipment for periodic regeneration of the desiccant. Furthermore, the routine regeneration of literally tons of desiccant makes this type of equipment less convenient to operate in large-scale production. For small-scale operation in hospitals and laboratories, consisting of less than a few liters per batch, the Cryochem procedure is simplest and provides the lowest-cost equipment. This is especially so if dry-air oven sterilizers are available for use in regeneration. Equipment utilizing built-in regenerators is used successfully. A small machine of this type is illustrated in Fig. 5.44. Fig. 5.45 shows the interior of this chamber. The vessels containing the product are kept within the refrigerated zone, which may also be heated by thermostatically controlled electrical heaters around the coils (not visible in photograph). Alternatively, electric shelves may be used, the desiccant being below this area. This combination unit has the advantage that the heat of reaction of the water vapor with the desiccant tends to be transferred to the containers where heat is required for sublimation. This self-regenerating type of equipment is particularly advantageous in out-of-the-way areas where Dry Ice is unavailable and where the capacity requirements do not justify larger scale mechanically refrigerated condenser units. A number of these units have been operating for as long as ten years in Africa and elsewhere. Cryochem equipment with calcium sulfate as desiccant has been used by the Food and Drug Administration in test work and standardization of penicillin.[22]

Calcium sulfate has been the most widely used chemical desiccant for freeze-drying and has proved particularly satisfactory. Its theoretical capacity for water vapor to form the hemi-hydrate is 6.6 per cent. Generally, in computing capacity, however, it is safer to allow 6 per cent, since regeneration is not always complete.

Also, not more than about one-quarter of this capacity should be used in drying a single batch because, unless special precautions are taken to cool the calcium sulfate, its temperature rises during

Fig. 5.44. Single chamber-type of 4-liter Cryochem apparatus with built-in regenerator and with refrigeration unit in combination for freezing and drying within the upper part of the chamber.

reaction with water vapor to the point that too high a vapor pressure is reached. Because of the vacuum conditions, and since calcium sulfate itself is a poor conductor of heat, the heat of reaction is not rapidly dissipated. Magnesium perchlorate has also been used successfully, but because of the greater difficulty in regeneration it has not met with as great favor, particularly since the lower vapor pressure it exhibits is not normally required in freeze-drying. The non-regenerability of calcium chloride as well as its deliquescent character render it more expensive and less convenient to use. Sulfuric acid for obvious reasons is not well suited to this purpose.

Fig. 5.45. Interior of single chamber-type of Cryo-chem apparatus showing refrigeration coils and sterility rack for suporting containers.

Physical Adsorbents: Adtevac. Silica gel, alumina and other physical adsorbents may be used. These generally have a greater saturation capacity for water vapor than chemical desiccants like calcium sulfate. However, at vapor pressures sufficiently low for freeze-drying, the capacity for these is less than half that of calcium sulfate. Silica gel as an adsorbent has a vapor pressure which increases with every small increment in moisture adsorbed. This is in contrast with chemical desiccants which form fixed chemical hydrates, these having a constant low vapor pressure until saturated. This increased vapor pressure of adsorbents is particularly disadvantageous in a vacuum desiccation process, because at the end of the drying cycle the vapor pressure of the adsorbent is at a maximum when it should be at a minimum. This can be prevented by changing to fresh desiccant at the end of a cycle. Hill and Pfeiffer described so-called "Adtevac" equipment utilizing adsorbents in which the capacity of silica gel is increased by placing it in mechanically refrigerated cannisters.[23]

Direct Pumping with Mechanical Pumps and with Multi-Stage Steam Ejectors. Direct pumping equipment is fundamentally one of the simplest forms of drying equipment available. The same pumping system removes both water vapor and non-condensable gases. The equipment has, automatically, a tremendous capacity for initial evacuation (except in case of steam ejectors) and adequate capacity for water vapor during drying. Further, toward the end of drying, when the requirements for pumping water vapor are reduced, the pressure automatically becomes lower in the vacuum system to aid in reducing the residual content of moisture in the product to a minimum level.

Direct pumping may be carried out by means of either an ejector pump or an oil-sealed rotary pump. In the latter case, the pump must be equipped for continuously removing water from the oil of the vacuum pump, as by a centrifugal clarifier.[24] A multi-stage steam ejector with interstage-condensers is suitable and is widely used in large-scale operation,[24] in which case a separate "roughing" ejector for evacuation is needed. Evacuation jets have different design characteristics from the pumping jets. Combinations of these or of other accessory means, such as oil diffusion or oil ejector pumps, may be used. In any event, the volume occupied by the water vapor under conditions of such a high vacuum is tremendous. The pumps used must have an exceedingly high volumetric capacity under these conditions (see Table 9).

Upon casual consideration, it might appear that an ordinary oil-sealed mechanical rotary pump would have insufficient capacity because of its lower efficiency under conditions of high vacuum. However, inasmuch as the water vapor is condensed on the high-pressure side of the rotary pump, at a pressure equal to the vapor pressure of water at the temperature at which the pump is

TABLE 9

VOLUME OF WATER VAPOR UNDER HIGH VACUUM CONDITIONS

Absolute Pressure		Cu Ft/lb (26°C)
mm	*microns*	
5.0	5000	3,420
1.0	1000	17,100
0.5	500	34,200
0.25	250	68,400
0.01	10	1,710,000
0.001	1	17,100,000

1 lb of steam at atmospheric pressure (760 mm) and 100°C occupies 26.8 cu ft

operating, the pump is able to operate against a back-pressure which is much below atmospheric. This is generally about 125 mm Hg. In effect, this approximates a second stage for the pump, so that under actual conditions of pumping water vapor, a single-stage oil-sealed rotary pump will maintain its efficiency close to 100 per cent at 200 microns.

Even so, the capacity of any mechanical pump within practical limits is such that in the larger scale of operation, a jet-type ejector is preferred. In employing a steam ejector, either a four- or five-stage ejector may be used. The greater the number of intercondensers, the higher the efficiency in the utilization of steam. The value of this type of equipment compared with low-temperature condensation must be based on the availability and relative costs of steam and cooling water compared with electrical power for the refrigeration compressors. In any event, large quantities of steam and cooling water are required for steam ejectors. By-product facilities for these may be available at certain locations and the cost of operation then becomes more favorable.

MISCELLANEOUS TYPES OF EQUIPMENT

Elser, Thomas and Steffen[25] have suggested a variety of types of equipment. None of these, however, makes provision for rapid and controlled introduction of heat as it is now used. Also, in recent years other forms and variations of laboratory equipment have been suggested, such as that of Wells, involving use of a laboratory glass desiccator,[26] and that of Folsom[27] utilizing a single glass vessel for plasma attached to a single condenser of exactly the same type used with a manifold.[1] Cooper and Grabill[28] have described a modified Cryochem apparatus[29] in which a standard 3-necked "Pyrex" Woulff bottle of 2-liter capacity is used to hold the desiccant. Heckly[13] has also described a condenser and manifold apparatus essentially the same as originally used,[1] except that the manifold is placed in a vertical position and the secondary condenser has been eliminated, as discussed earlier in this chapter. Bauer and Pickels[30] and Smadel, Randall and Warren[31] have described apparatus with vertical manifolds too; their purpose is to arrange the containers on the manifolds in a freezer unit similar to an ice-cream storage cabinet. Then the vapors from the manifold are carried through a connecting line at the top to a standard Dry Ice condenser.[1] This type of equipment provides external means of controlling temperature of the product below freezing during the early stages of drying, and then by turning off the refrigeration the temperature can be increased gradually by means of a hot-air blast into the cabinet. This apparatus has been used in drying delicate viruses. Similar results should be obtainable with chamber type of equipment in which the temperature may be controlled similarly at any desired point from about $-40°C$ to as high as required.

Bradish, Brain, and McFarlane[32] and Bradish[33] have also reported on the use of chamber equipment in which the temperature of the shelves is regulated by the flow of ethyl alcohol at low or relatively high temperature. Just above the shelves supporting the trays of material being dried, either in bulk or in ampoules, there is a cold plate maintained at a temperature as low as $-80°C$. This acts as a condenser and avoids the use of a vapor line. The theoretical aspects of this have been discussed in Chapter 2. Although there is some question as to the theoretical justification, in certain instances this type of installation possesses merit and has been used in the United States as well as in England. Similar variations have been described by many others. Goodspeed and Uber[34] have developed a type of freeze-drying apparatus for carrying out the Altmann technique for plant cytology. Here again, however, no provision was made for rapid and controlled conditions of heating. Other similar equipment has been described by various investigators for carrying out the Altmann technique discussed under "Histology and Cytology" in Chapter 3. Frobisher, Parson, Pai and Hakim[35] described another glass desiccator apparatus of a rather inefficient type for preserving stock cultures. An ordinary mercury manometer is suggested as a means of reading the pressure, so that there is no means of knowing whether the proper degree of vacuum in the micron range has been obtained for carrying out freeze-drying. Apparently the method and apparatus do not give very satisfactory results because the authors state that some species like pathogenic *Neisseria* and *Hemophilus* did not survive long under the conditions described, whereas we know that these organisms are readily enough kept in viable form for many years following proper freeze-drying.

COSTS

In 1935, with Dry Ice at the lowest available price, two cents per pound, it was estimated[1] that the cost of Dry Ice consumed in processing was about eight cents for each 25 ml of serum under the best operating conditions. This would amount to about one dollar per 300 ml dose of blood plasma. No attempt was made to estimate the other costs involved, but it is obvious that these would have been tremendous. Today this has been reduced to much below the earlier figure. The electricity used for operation of refrigeration compressors is almost negligible in comparison with the eight cents formerly required for Dry Ice. For the 300-ml dose of blood plasma, these power costs, both for freezing and for refrigeration of the condenser, amount to only about five cents; therefore, the major cost is one of labor and that is not great. Inasmuch as medical products must be dispensed in individual bottles, and packaged in any event, these operations should not be included as part of the cost of freeze-drying. It will generally be found that freeze-drying today adds but little to the cost of most medical products. Inasmuch as the major item of expense involves factors of overhead, labor, amortization of the equipment, and the like, no fixed figures may be given, as they vary with local conditions from plant to plant. The cost of other operations, such as filtration of serum, centrifugation of blood plasma, etc., is higher than that of freeze-drying operation *per se.*

TYPICAL LABORATORY PROCEDURE

Naturally, the exact procedure must be adapted to the type of equipment being used. During the past few years, as has been seen above, there have been so many variations and minor modifications published that it would be futile to attempt to describe them all. The following may be taken as typical of procedure followed with what has been perhaps the most widely used form of laboratory equipment.

Further, even with the same general type of equipment there will be some modification in procedure depending upon the specific product being dried and also the volume in which it is dried. This typical procedure will be described in terms of drying of cultures of bacteria and viruses. In view of the comprehensive discussion of the various factors given in this chapter the procedure described can readily enough be adapted to any specific form of apparatus and to almost any type of product.

In the 1935 type of equipment[1] illustrated in Fig. 5.46, the metal condenser is contained within the large thermos bottle containing Dry Ice in methyl "Cellosolve." The vacuum pump is shown at the left. The containers and the exhaust tube assembly with rubber stoppers are sterilized according to usual bacteriological practice before filling and freezing. Prefreezing in the various types of containers is carried out in the Dry Ice freezing bath. These containers, Nos. 1, 2, 3, 4 and 5, are shown attached to the manifold after freezing. Also, the 95 x 7 mm flint glass test tubes described on p. 149 may be used. See Chapter 3 for culture menstrum.

Controlled heating of the culture during drying is made simple and automatic because the rate of sublimation of water vapor is regulated by the surface conditions set up in freezing. That is, the material is initially frozen in containers of proper size and shape,

Fig. 5.46. Dry-Ice equipment for virus research.

in such a way as to give the correct relationship of the evaporating surface of the frozen culture to the surface adjacent to the glass, through which atmospheric heat is transferred to the frozen solid. The evaporating surface must be large in relation to the surface of glass exposed to the atmosphere through which heat is being supplied. That is the reason for placing the bottles on their sides for freezing. By gentle rocking back and forth a thin layer frozen on the inner wall of the container provides a large evaporating surface. Alternatively, by rotating the bottles during freezing in a properly shaped bath, the culture may be "shell frozen" around the entire inner periphery of the glass containers. There should be no bubbling or melting of the preparation during the early stages of drying or at any other time. As discussed above, the actual temperature needed for a particular culture during drying depends entirely upon the type of preparation. This must be determined experimentally. Proper provision for the escape of water vapor from the container to the condenser is provided by having tubes of adequate diameter.

The culture in its containers is brought to a very low temperature before attaching to the manifold. Attachment of the containers to the manifold must be rapid. Vacuum is quickly drawn by the pump to avoid thawing by permitting rapid sublimation to take place as soon as possible. (The apparatus should be sufficiently tight to the vacuum pump to produce about 50 to 100 microns on

Fig. 5.47. Small Canadian installation for blood plasma. Two small drying chambers on the left were the first used in World War II as described in Chapter 1 before being incorporated in the expanded plant as illustrated. Large mechanically-refrigerated condenser is shown suspended from the ceiling in the foreground.

"blank suction" without culture being dried, *i.e.,* tested beforehand). If the 95 x 7 mm tubes are used, it is best to place a freezing bath around them after attachment to the manifold until evacuation to at least 400.

Drying must be continued until the final moisture content has been reduced to less than 1.0 per cent and preferably below 0.5 per cent. During the early stages of drying, frost collects from the atmosphere on the outer walls of the containers. After the ice within the frozen culture preparation has almost completely sublimed, the temperature automatically starts to rise. At the same time the frost on the outside walls of the container will disappear and be replaced by liquid condensation. This indicates a temperature above 0°C, but below that of the room. Finally, the temperature of the culture reaches that of the room and all condensation on the outer walls of the container disappears. The total length of time to reach this point should be noted and then about half that number of hours additional should be allowed for reduction to proper final level of moisture content.

In the case of cultures, to avoid contamination it is desirable to seal the exhaust tubes of the container under original vacuum by fusion of the glass with a flame. "Pyrex" glass is specified because of its low thermal coefficient of expansion; that is, it will withstand the temperature shock of sudden heating so that the glass may be drawn to a capillary and finally sealed by fusion. As a glass-blower will recognize, it is not possible to allow slow heating of the glass followed by slow cooling, as is customary in glass blowing, because of the large size of the glass tube holding vacuum; it would be "sucked in" to form a hole which would allow air to leak in.

After initial attachment of the sterile containers, the direction of flow of all air and vapors is outward from the containers into the manifold, and this flow is rapid. Because of the shape of the exhaust tubes as illustrated (Fig. 5.1 and 5.5), with all glass and rubber parts up to the manifold having been previously sterilized,

Fig. 5.48. Part of a row of 20 drying chambers at Sharp & Dohme which represents the largest medical freeze-drying installation in the world. Chamber doors open in the sterile area, all refrigeration and mechanical equipment being located in adjacent machine room.

Fig. 5.49. Part of equipment and 11 condensers for operation of the drying plant illustrated in Figure 48.

it is not possible for any contamination to occur by gravity from the manifold itself. Therefore the manifold itself need not be sterilized in normal operation. Finally, by sealing under original vacuum the cultures are obtained in final form without contamination.

Where Dry Ice is not available, the Cryochem type of equipment mentioned above is used, as illustrated in Fig. 5.27. The specially prepared calcium sulfate is supported in special perforated trays containing the desiccant in a bed about 2 or 3 inches deep in each tray. The trays must be supported with proper separations between them to allow easy access of water vapor to the desiccant. Theoretical stoichiometric capacity of the desiccant for water vapor is 6.6 per cent by weight to form the hemi-hydrate. In practice about 6 per cent is utilized. Per single batch not over one-quarter of this amount, *i.e.*, 1.5 per cent is utilized because of the temperature conditions within the desiccant, that is, it is warmed by the heat of reaction with water vapor. However, four such maximum batches or more of smaller size may be dried before regeneration is necessary.

For regeneration of the calcium sulfate, heating in an ordinary oven like a bacteriological dry wall sterilizer is carried out. The oven should be operated at a temperature of 180 to 200°C. When the desiccant itself reaches 150°C, regeneration is complete, but it should be checked by moisture analysis to be certain that it is below about 0.2 or 0.3 per cent. The desiccant is initially prepared from gypsum in the same manner and is available commercially.

With this apparatus the same type of manifold and containers may be used as was discussed with Dry Ice equipment above. In the illustration, however, valves are shown on each outlet which facilitates operation as previously discussed (including the use of non-"Pyrex" type of glassware for materials other than cultures).

BIBLIOGRAPHY

1. Flosdorf, E. W., and Mudd, S., "Procedure and apparatus for preservation in 'lyophile' form of serum and other biological substances," *J. Immunol.*, 29, 389 (1935).
2. Flosdorf, E. W., and Webster, G. W., "Neoprene and rubber stoppers for lyophile serum containers," *India Rubber World*, 98, 33–37 (1938).
3. Flosdorf, E. W., Data obtained in collaboration with Mr. G. Willard Webster of Sharpe & Dohme, Inc.
4. Flosdorf, E. W., Boerner, F., Lukens, M., and Ambler, T. S., "Cryochem-preserved complement of guinea-pig serum," *Am. J. Clin. Path.*, 10, 339–344 (1940).
5. Strumia, M. M., Newhouser, L. R., Kendrick, D. B., Jr., and McGraw, J. J., "Development of equipment for administration of dried plasma in the armed forces," *War Medicine*, 2, 102–113 (1942).
6. Reichel, J., U. S. Patent No. 2,290,355 and No. 2,324,237 (1942).
7. Flosdorf, E. W., and Webster, G. W., "The determination of residual moisture in dry biological substances," *J. Biol. Chem.*, 121, 353 (1937).
8. Starkweather, H. W., and Walker, H. W., *Ind. Eng. Chem.*, 29, 1380 (1937).
9. Warren, J., "A machine for shell-freezing biological materials in small glass ampoules," *Proc. Soc. Exper. Biol. Med.*, 66, 381 (1947).
10. Greaves, R. I. N., "The freezing of human serum and plasma in Medical Research Council transfusion bottles, before drying by sublimation from the frozen state," *J. Hygiene*, 41, 489–495 (1942).

11. Greaves, R. I. N., "Centrifugal vacuum freezing," *Nature*, **153**, 485 (1944).

12. Brown, G. H., Bierwirth, R. A., and Hoyler, C. N., "Radio-frequency dehydration of penicillin solution," *Proc. Inst. Radio Engineers*, p. 58w (Feb., 1946).

13. Heckly, R. J., "A simple lyophilizing apparatus for laboratory use," *J. Immunol.*, **54**, 91–95 (1947).

14. Wyckoff, R. W. G., and Lagsdin, J. B., "A simple outfit for drying plasma from the frozen state," *Am. J. Clin. Path.*, 8, Tech. Sect. 10–16 (1944).

15. Normand, C. E., Paper presented on "Design of high vacuum systems" at the Cambridge High Vacuum Symposium, October 31, 1947; *Ind. Eng. Chem.*, **40**, 783–787 (1948).

16. Jacobs, H. R., "An improved lyophilizing apparatus for small-scale operations," *Quarterly Bull., Northwestern Univ. Med. School, Chicago*, **21**, No. 2, p. 156 (1947).

17. Flosdorf, E. W., Hull, L. W., and Mudd, S., "Drying by sublimation," *J. Immunol.*, **50**, 21–54 (1945).

18. Morse, R. S., "High vacuum technology," *Ind. Eng. Chem.*, **39**, 1064 (1947).

19. Kendrick, D. B., "Refrigeration applications for blood plasma and biologicals," *Refrigerating Engineers*, **47**, 33–39 (1944).

20. Sherwood, T. K. (M.I.T.), Personal communication, 1944.

21. Hickman, K. C. D., U. S. Patent No. 2,402,401 (1946).

22. Welch, H., Grove, D. C., Davis, R. P., and Hunter, A. C., "The relative toxicity of six salts of penicillin," *Proc. Soc., Exp. Biol. Med.*, pp. 246–248 (1944).

23. Hill, J. M., and Pfeiffer, D. C., "A new and economical desiccating process particularly suitable for the preparation of concentrated plasma or serum for intravenous use: the Adtevac process," *Ann. Int. Med.*, **14**, 201 (1940).

24. Flosdorf, E. W., Stokes, F. J., and Mudd, S., "The Desivac process for drying from the frozen state," *J. Am. Med. Assoc.*, **115**, 1095–1097 (1940); U. S. Patent No. 2,345,548 (1944).

25. Elser, W. J., Thomas, R. A., and Steffen, G. I., "The desiccation of sera and other biological products (including microorganisms) in the frozen state with the preservation of the original qualities of products so treated," *J. Immunol.*, **28**, 433 (1935).

26. Wells, A. H., "A simple, inexpensive apparatus for high vacuum desiccation with a review of its laboratory uses," *Am. J. Clin. Path.*, **13**, No. 1 (Jan., 1943).

27. Folsom, T. R., "A method for drying clinically useful quantities of plasma and serum: The unit desiccator," in "Blood Substitutes and Blood Transfusion," pp. 49–63, C. C. Thomas, Springfield, Ill., 1942.

28. Cooper, M. L., and Grabill, F. J., "A simplified apparatus for the preservation of bacterial cultures in the dried state," *J. Lab. Clin. Med.*, **25**, 184–188 (1939).

29. Flosdorf, E. W., and Mudd, S., "An improved procedure and apparatus for preservation of sera, microorganisms and other substances: the Cryochem process," *J. Immunol.*, **34**, 469–490 (1938).

30. Bauer, J. H., and Pickels, E. G., "Apparatus for freezing and drying virus in large quantities under uniform conditions," *J. Exp. Med.*, **71**, 83–88 (1940).

31. Smadel, J. E., Randall, R., and Warren, J., "Preparations of Japanese encephalitis vaccine," *Bull. U. S. Army Med. Dept.*, **7**, 963 (1947).

32. Bradish, C. J., Brain, C. M., and McFarlane, A. S., "Vacuum sublimation of ice in bulk," *Nature*, **159**, 28 (1947).

33. Bradish, C. J., "Freeze-drying," *Chem. Products*, (July–August, 1947).

34. Goodspeed, T. H., and Uber, F. M., "Application of the Altmann freezing-drying technique to plant cytology. II. Character of the fixation," *Univ. Calif. Pub. Botany*, **18**, 23–32 (1935).

35. Frobisher, M., Jr., Parsons, E. I., Pai, S. E., and Hakim, S., "A simplified method for the preservation of bacteria by desiccation in vacuo," *J. Lab. Clin. Med.*, **32**, 1008 (1947).

CHAPTER 6: EQUIPMENT FOR FOODS

BATCH OPERATION

LARGE drying chambers similar to that illustrated in Fig. 6.1 may be used. In larger sizes it is more advantageous to construct these chambers as large cylinders because of lower cost. For the same amount of space, cylindrical construction is cheaper than rectangular, but there is more waste space in the former.

It is preferable to place products in direct contact with the shelves during drying so that better heat transfer is obtained. From metering tanks these shelves may be loaded automatically so that there is little labor in this operation.

Hot water is circulated through the hollow shelves and jacket under controlled conditions, as discussed in Chapter 2. At the end of drying, the product may be broken up with a long knife or hoe-like blades and removed. The shelves are tilted and with vibration allow the product to be easily unloaded. It is usually placed in drums which can be sealed and transferred to a packaging room. Other automatic means are available, these varying with the particular products.

Raw meat, shell-fish, and other solids are preferably frozen in trays which are then transferred to the dryer shelves. These same trays are removed after drying which simplifies unloading in the case of such products. With products like oysters and clams considerable care must be given to the unloading operation to avoid breakage of the dry, friable mass.

A plant to produce about three tons of dry orange crystals per day from unconcentrated juice would require 12 vacuum chambers of this type. If cylindrical, the diameter is 9 ft and the length 12 ft. The chamber must be constructed entirely of stainless steel. Both ends of the drying chamber are arranged with quick-opening doors which are held tight during the drying operation by means of swinging I-bolts to pull the door into a seat of heavy rubber

Fig. 6.1. Chamber for meat.

gasket. Actually, after the equipment is under vacuum, the pressure of the atmosphere is sufficient to seal the door and hold it tight. The I-bolts serve to pull the door in evenly at the time of closing in order to obtain a tight enough seal to start evacuation. After the vacuum has been reduced a few inches the atmosphere does the rest.

In such large dryers the doors are supported on jib cranes and are well balanced. Mounting is arranged so that the doors can be readily opened and swung out of the way for unloading. It is necessary to construct the jackets and hollow shelves to withstand the vacuum operation since there is pressure within the jackets and shelves. Suitable manifolds are provided to carry the heat exchange fluid into the jackets and shelves.

Burton[1] has described another type of batch dryer which utilizes the warm water-jacketed walls of a vertical and cylindrical tank. In this case the juice is sprayed onto the wall for self-freezing under the influence of a vacuum of 500 to 700 microns. The thickness of the layer is adjusted for a six-hour drying cycle and automatic means are used for discharging the product, such as by scraping with blades which are permanently installed. The product is then discharged in customary fashion to a vacuum can at the bottom of the dryer which may be transported on a dolly arrangement to a packaging room where the relative humidity has been reduced to 20 per cent. In this particular case, the concentrate is dried; this has been prepared by vacuum evaporation in the range of 10 to 15 mm by passing through a series of 13 such concentrators. The preconcentrating part of the equipment is continuous, but the final drying is of more or less standard means.

A battery of mechanical pumps or multi-stage large steam ejectors is used for evacuation. In the latter case, a separate ejector is necessary, usually three or four stages for "roughing." This has different design characteristics from that used for holding high vacuum. The latter is usually four or five stages. The reason for the two ejectors is that during the "roughing" operation, large quantities of air are removed, which means that the first and second stages must be of high capacity. Steam requirements are large. During the holding operation, while drying is taking place, as there is not much air going through the ejector these stages can be made considerably smaller, saving in cost of steam. The advantage of mechanical pumps lies in the fact that the same equipment can be used both for roughing and for holding high vacuum. This means less standby equipment. The limitation in use of mechanical pumps is reached when the multiplicity of individual pumps is too great for convenience of maintenance.

For removal of water vapor, either a steam ejector or mechanically refrigerated condensers are used, as discussed in Chapter 2. If steam ejectors are used, the design characteristics must be for the same vacuum range as in low temperature condensation. Therefore, the ejectors used in direct pumping compare with those used for holding high vacuum only, in conjunction with a refrigerated condenser. Naturally, however, when the ejector is pumping all the water vapor as well as air and other non-condensables, the third and fourth stages must be considerably larger, but the first and second are the same. To determine size simply requires calculation of the weight of water vapor to be pumped at various pressures based on drying rates, as mentioned in Chapter 2.

If mechanically refrigerated condensers are used, they may be welded directly to the drying chambers. This is preferable to the use of vapor lines, since large valves are not used. This makes it possible to secure unrestricted flow of vapor more readily.

The low-temperature condensers in large sizes needed for foods are refrigerated with ammonia, using compound compression. The condensers may be either of the multiple extended and fixed-surface type to give continuous condensation (similar to those for medical products) or they may be of the scraper type,[2] which also lend themselves to continuous operation. With the latter type, the same considerations apply as with medical products with regard to the lower ammonia temperature which must be maintained. The maintenance problems and higher initial cost also must be balanced against the use of multiple extended surface of the fixed type, in which one condenser out of a series is always in the de-frosting part of the cycle. With the scraper type standby equipment is necessary, so there is some idle investment too. The selection of the type of condensers to be used must be based on these relative advantages and disadvantages.

In the case of the orange-juice plant discussed above, ammonia refrigeration would require the installation of about 1200 electrical horsepower. Except on initial pull-down, the actual consumption would be about two-thirds of this amount.

CONTINUOUS OPERATION

In large-scale industrial production, continuous operation is considered to be the ultimate goal. The reasons for this are several, from elimination of storage of quantities of raw product between batches on an uneven flow (such as in juicing operations for orange juice), to allowing packaging operations to proceed with uniformity and reduction of labor.

In drying by sublimation, however, continuously operating equipment involves more than ordinary problems in mechanical engineering. Generally speaking, stuffing boxes and other moving parts under high vacuum provide difficulties in maintenance. Leaks in any high-vacuum system of this sort spell death to smooth operation. Every cubic foot of air which leaks into the system expands to nearly 2,000 cu ft at high vacuum, and all this must be exhausted at once by the pumps. Such moving parts must be avoided, if possible. A virtually continuous flow can be achieved in what might be termed "batch cycling," and this avoids such problems.

By use of a number of dryers operating in sequence on a cycle which permits loading and unloading on a nearly continuous basis, the first two of the above advantages in continuous operation are met. By providing automatic filling of the drying chambers prior to freezing and drying, together with mechanical means for unloading, labor is reduced to a low point, lower than in fully continuous operation if maintenance is considered.

The reliability and simplicity in mechanical operation of the high-vacuum equipment used in batch cycling offer the strongest challenge to any piece of equipment which introduces precarious mechanics. In addition, this type of equipment greatly simplifies the problem of rapid introduction of heat into the frozen material without harm to it.

On the other hand, with further mechanical progress, undoubtedly a satisfactory continuous machine will be developed. There have been several attempts, and eventually it is to be expected that such equipment may come to be used, at least for certain products (some, like oysters, will provide more serious mechanical obstacles for continuous handling). Morse[2] has described bellows-type and grease-type seals suitable for such equipment.

With liquid products like orange juice, the juice or concentrate may be sprayed into tall towers under high vacuum. The particles will self-freeze and puff and fall to the bottom of the chamber. Because of the flow of vapors at high velocity the fall of the finely divided particles is sufficiently retarded that drying can be completed by the time the powder reaches the bottom of the tower, with proper supply of heat. Greaves[3] described attempts at spray drying from the frozen state, but found no satisfactory solution to the various problems, particularly that of supplying the heat of sublimation in the required time.

Also, continuous drying on drums as well as on belts has been tried.[4] The product may be sprayed onto these moving surfaces, or it may be brushed on by some type of feed device such as an overflow pipe with proper spreader blade. With a belt-operated machine the product needs to be taken through a number of heated zones. When drying concentrate it is necessary to chill the final dried product to a certain extent before unloading because of its plastic nature at higher temperatures used at the end of freeze-drying. This same consideration, of course, applies to batch drying; but with a continuously operating belt a final cooler zone is provided for the purpose. Heat may be applied by means or radiation from steam-heated platens or by means of infrared lamps. The latter represents higher operating cost, as electricity costs more than coal or steam used direct. In fact, the cost of electricity used in infrared lamps may be as great as that of carrying out all the remainder of the freeze-drying operations. The same problems exist in the case of a drum and are even harder to meet.

Any one of these three types of continuous machine must have an arrangement for discharging the material. Since the product is dry and flowable, it may be carried along by various known means, such as by vibrating screens or on belts. The product must be carried into a vacuum-lock chamber from which it is carried to the packaging room.

With either one of these types of continuous equipment, the same vacuum-pumping means, low-temperature condensers and other equipment for removal of air and water vapor would be used as with the batch operation. The same capacity would be required for the same daily output, i.e., there would be no saving as the result of continuous operation in power or machine costs for removal of water vapor and for evacuation.

Tumbling types of equipment have also been suggested, and these could be used with frozen meat particles and with granulated frozen juices and extracts. Because of the plastic condition of many juices and extracts, however, lower drying temperatures would have to be used to avoid sticking of particles, and this would increase the cost. With products like meat, there would be considerable breakage of the small particles and the reconstituted final product would not be as satisfactory. With products like eggs, in which a non-plastic powder is obtained, this type of equipment is highly satisfactory. Hormel[5] has described a machine of this general type in which the rotating drum consists of a basket-like material. As it dries the product falls through the holes and is taken out of the zone of infrared radiation. It remains in the heated zone only as long as the ice phase is present, but when dry it becomes friable and falls through the screen. This affords a convenient means for carrying pre-frozen products through a hot zone with continuous removal into a vacuum-lock chamber.

PACKAGING

It is just as necessary to withhold moisture from foods which have been dried by sublimation as it is from medical products. Until now, only packages made of metal or glass have been found to meet the necessary requirements. Small tin cans are very satisfactory. Extruded tubes of tin or aluminum with proper type of hermetic seal have been found quite satisfactory for certain products such as fruit juices and coffee extracts after testing over a period of years. Aluminum foil is satisfactory and is well suited for single-serving packages.

Air-conditioning must be used during the packaging operation, with adequate reduction in humidity to prevent excessive absorption of moisture. The temperature and humidity of the air must both be controlled in relation to the vapor pressure of the product and the temperature at which it is being packaged, to minimize increase in moisture content of the product. This does not mean that the vapor pressure in the air must be below that of the product, but it must be near enough so that during the time required for packaging the product will not pick up excessive moisture.

Many products are entirely stable when sealed under air, provided practically all moisture is excluded. Foods containing fats or lipoids must be sealed either under vacuum or in inert gas because oxidation proceeds even in the absence of moisture. Tin cans and jars with proper seals may be readily used for vacuum packaging. There is no reason why even foil packages could not be used for sealing *in vacuo,* but equipment for this purpose is still in the developmental stage.

Other small packages have been tested, but none except those of metal or glass have been found suitable. Cellophane, "Pliofilm," and various types of waterproof papers have been found insufficiently vaporproof for this purpose. In the case of some foods, however, there may be reason to combine certain of these other materials with metal foil.

COSTS

The cost of drying by sublimation naturally varies with the product in question, the solids content, temperatures required during drying, amount of handling, and the like. With products of relatively high value, such as orange juice, goat's milk and meat, the cost of drying is low in relation to the combined cost of the raw material and the cost of preserving by other methods which do not yield a high quality product. The drying of oysters which yield friable solids entails higher handling cost.

The approximate cost of drying ordinary products may be determined on the basis of an approximate cost per pound of water to be removed. That is to say, the differences in drying most liquid food products which have been considered are not great enough to involve a wide variation in power costs per pound of water to be removed, so that preliminary costs may be based on the actual percentage of water. There are exceptions to this in products which, when highly concentrated, become plastic solids at freezing temperature. These offer greater cost per pound of water to be removed. Also, the relative degree of porosity, as in the case with protein solutions versus solutions high in sugar content, affects the relative ease of removal of water, this often being as much on the basis of temperature as anything else. Until there has been extensive commercial drying of foods by sublimation accurate cost figures will not be available.

In Table 1 is given an estimate on the cost of production of meat based on its final dry weight. It must be borne in mind that this is purely an estimate and conditions would naturally vary from plant to plant, but the table will serve as a guide to the factors which must be considered. To these costs must be added that of the raw meat and its preparation for drying as well as the cost of cans used in packaging. Only productive overhead as applied to the drying operation *per se* has been included. This item, too, would naturally vary with local conditions.

TABLE 1
PRODUCTION OF RAW GROUND BEEF:—TYPICAL ESTIMATE OF TOTAL COST ON A PRODUCTION SCALE (1941)

	Cost per pound of dehydrated raw meat
Labor and power for drying	$0.08
Labor for packaging	.01
Amortization of drying equipment	.03
Interest, overhead, and royalty	.10
Total cost of drying per pound of dry° meat	$0.22

° Will be approximately four cents per pound of fresh meat.

TABLE 2
ORANGE CRYSTAL DRYING PLANT: ESTIMATE OF TYPICAL PRODUCTION COSTS (1941)

Daily capacity	
Juice	48,000 lbs.
Crystals°	4,800 lbs.
Seasonal capacity†	
Crystals	720,000 lbs.
Cost of producing 1 lb. of crystals, from straight juice	
Labor, estimated at $1.50 per hour	$0.02
Water	0.001
Steam	0.006
Electricity	0.09
Total‡	$0.117

° The daily capacity in terms of crystals could be quadrupled by the use of a good concentrate.
† The seasonal capacity is based on 5 months' operation. It can be increased 8 times by holding frozen concentrate for 12 months' operation.
‡ Add cost of packaging in No. 2½ cans.

In Table 2 is shown a similar typical itemization of the costs directly involved in drying orange juice. Table 3 gives a schedule of the total cost of making the final product, including packaging as for institutional, restaurant or military uses. Most of the items in Table 3 are for other than drying and naturally will vary with individual plants, particularly overhead, as well as with cost and type of fruit in any given season. In general, the power cost of removal of water from foods on a large commercial scale is on the order of two to four cents per pound of water. All these estimates are based on the 1941 price level.

TABLE 3

PRODUCTION OF ORANGE JUICE CRYSTALS BY SUBLIMATION DRYING: TYPICAL ESTIMATE OF TOTAL COST (1941)

This is based on a daily capacity of 24 tons of juice, which would require about 1,000 boxes of fruit daily. Figures represent use of straight juice for 5 months' operation.

	Cost per lb. crystals
Drying	
Production, labor and power from Table 2	$0.117
Juice, figured at $2.50 per box of fruit delivered, 13 per cent solids, yielding 5 lbs. of crystals per box	0.50
Extraction	0.04
Stabilizer*	0.023
Labor for packaging	0.01
Amortization	
Drying equipment (5 yrs.)	0.065
Production plant	0.10
Container cost, using No. 2½ cans for 12½ oz. of crystals, and carton cost for 48 cans per case	0.056
Interest, overhead and royalty	0.156
Total cost per pound of finished product	$1.067

* Not required with the juice of all fruit, but in many cases a superior product may be obtained by the use of a stabilizer.

BIBLIOGRAPHY

1. Burton, L. V., "High-vacuum techniques utilized for drying orange juice," *Food Ind.,* **19,** 107 (1947).
2. Morse, R. S., "High-vacuum technology," *Ind. Eng. Chem.,* **39,** 1064 (1947).
3. Greaves, R. I. N., "The preservation of proteins by drying. With special reference to the production of dried human serum and plasma for transfusion," Medical Research Council, Special Report Series No. 258, 1946.
4. Sluder, J. C., Olsen, R. W., and Kenyon, E. M., "A method for the production of dry powdered orange juice," *Food Tech.,* **1,** 85–94 (1947).
5. Hormel, J. C., U. S. Patent 2,388,917.

APPENDIX I
List of U. S. Patents

Re 20,969: Reichel

1,970,956: Elser

2,085,391: Reichel

2,085,392: Reichel

2,099,659: Reichel

2,149,304: Masucci

2,163,996: Flosdorf

2,166,074: Reichel

2,176,004: Reichel

2,176,041: Pittenger

2,176,042: Pittenger

2,198,752: Barr

2,199,815: Flosdorf

2,199,816: Flosdorf

2,199,817: Flosdorf

2,215,265: Flosdorf

2,225,627: Flosdorf

2,225,774: Flosdorf

2,283,867: Flosdorf and Stokes, Jr.

2,290,355: Reichel

2,292,447: Irwin, Jr.

2,324,237: Reichel

2,340,102: Barr

2,345,548: Flosdorf and Stokes, Sr.

2,352,581: Winkler

2,353,985: Barr

2,353,986: Barr

2,354,200: Cutler

2,372,181: Barr

2,372,182: Barr

2,372,352: Barr

2,374,232: Pfeiffer and Hill

2,380,036: Flosdorf

2,380,339: Siedentopf

2,388,134: Flosdorf, Westin and Stokes, Jr.

2,388,917: Hormel

2,389,452: Patterson

2,396,561: Flosdorf

2,400,748: Flosdorf

2,402,401: Hickman

2,406,682: Hayes and Humes

2,411,152: Folsom

2,431,496: Natelson and Weiss

2,433,193: Bechtner

2,433,905: Hughes, Jr.

2,435,503: Levinson *et al.*

2,435,854: Taylor

2,436,693: Hickman

2,437,060: Williams and Deutsch

2,438,150: Cutler

2,441,730: Strumia

2,444,124: Wedler

2,445,120: Levinson *et al.*

2,453,033: Patterson

2,459,329: Levinson *et al.*

2,460,197: H. L. Smith, Jr.

2,471,677: Flosdorf

2,471,678: Flosdorf

APPENDIX II
Sherwood's Studies with Penicillin

The following information has been received as a personal communication from Professor T. K. Sherwood of the Massachusetts Institute of Technology, based on early war-time investigation, and is included with his permission. Although penicillin of type described is no longer produced and crystalline penicillin is not freeze-dried, the work is of interest as related to general principles of freeze-drying.

One of the first considerations of Sherwood was the matter of transfer of heat to the containers. "The bottles have an inside diameter of approximately 2.8 cm. and the original ice thickness with a 10 cc charge is about 1.8 cm. The ice has a thermal conductivity of roughly 0.0054 g cal/(sec) (sq cm) (°C/cm), so that the heat flux through the original ice thickness with a 20°C temperature difference is 1300 g cal/hr, corresponding to a rate of vaporization of 1.9 g/hr. This checks the initial slopes of totalled curves sufficiently closely to suggest that heat transfer up through the ice is the controlling factor. The vertical glass wall has a cross section of only 31% of that of the ice and the conductivity of glass is roughly but one-third of that of ice, so conduction up through the glass walls should be small. The heat conduction up through the ice cannot be calculated simply, because the bottles unfortunately have concave bottoms, and contact with the plate occurs only at the rim. Radiation from plate to the bottom ice-surface tends to make the heat input to the bottom more uniform than if heat were transferred only by contact at the rim, but if the plate is at 20°C and the ice at 0°C the rate of radiation corresponds to only about 0.13 g/hr ice evaporated. Radiation at these temperatures, even to the side walls of the bottle, can be only a minor factor. This last conclusion is born out by the fact that the rate of vaporization of the icy ball is very low.

"In spite of the close check of rate of heat conduction through the ice and initial rates of vaporization, there appear to be several reasons to believe that this heat conduction cannot be the only factor. The most obvious is the fact that the rate of vaporization *decreases* as the ice layer becomes thinner. A second reason is the relatively small variation in average rate in Runs 1, 2 and 3, in which the initial ice thickness varied three-fold. Actually, the lowest rates were obtained with the smallest initial ice thickness. Finally, in Run 31 a high rate was obtained with an ampoule in which the ice was frozen on the walls, in which case the vertical heat conduction rate could have been very small."

The next consideration of Sherwood's investigations was the matter of vapor diffusion. "Convection currents above the ice in the bottle must be very small at the low operating pressure, so the possibility suggests itself that the controlling rate may be the rate of molecular diffusion in the gas space over the charge. This appears to be ruled out by the fact that the rate was not greatly increased by cutting off the top of the bottle.

"The fluffy residual salt deposit presents a resistance to vapor removal from the ice surface beneath; it may be considered either as a layer offering resistance to molecular diffusion of water vapor or as offering frictional resistance to vapor passage because of the high volumetric vapor rates and small passages in the form of pores. Since this resistance increases progressively as the charge evaporates, it might seem, at first thought, to explain the decreasing rate and the high rates obtained with shell-frozen charges. As pointed out previously, however, the vaporization of frozen distilled water proceeds at roughly the same rate as in the case of the salt solutions, so the salt residue cannot be a controlling factor."

Sherwood then arrived at an elementary theory of drying from serum bottles, this being based on the consideration that the rate of heat input is proportional to the temperature difference between the source of heat and the evaporating surface, and that the rate is also proportional to the pressure difference between the evaporating surface and the condenser."

(In determining the pressure of water vapor only in the vacuum system, Sherwood used the icy ball referred to on page 230. This is discussed on page 61.)

$$"R = K_1\,(T_p - T_i) = K_2\,(P_i{}^2 - P_c{}^2)$$

where R = rate of drying, g/hr

T_p = temperature of plate, or heat source, °C

T_i = temperature of evaporating surface, °C

P_i = vapor pressure at evaporating surface, mm

P_c = vapor pressure at condenser, mm

"Here K_1 is the conductance of the heat path from plate to ice surface, and K_2 is the flow coefficient for vapor passage through the porous residue on the ice surface, out of the bottle, and through the vapor lines to the condenser.

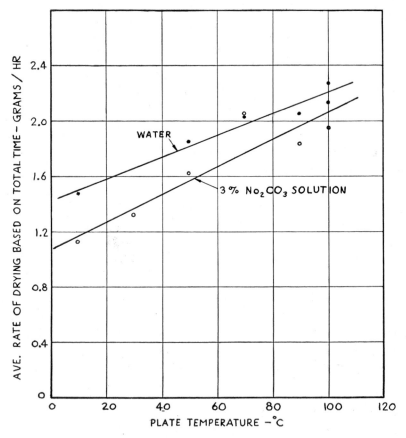

Fig. 1. Effect of temperature of plate supporting serum bottle. Total pressure 95 to 100 microns.

"Thermocouples in the bottles indicate that with the plate 30°C T_i is about −30°C for water ice and −10°C for the frozen carbonate solution. From the data of Fig. 1, K_1 is found to be 0.028 for water and 0.034 for carbonate. This indicates that the resistances of the thermal path are similar for the two. The corresponding values of K_2, however, are 20.4 for water and 0.36 for carbonate. This difference is presumably due to the bulky porous residue in the case of the carbonate, since this residue may be expected to offer a considerable resistance to vapor removal. Because of this residue, the ice temperature rises from −30 to −10°C, and the vapor pressure is increased from 285 to 1940 microns. The temperature difference is reduced from 60°C to 40°C and the rate is decreased roughly in this ratio. The large increase in vapor pressure and the slightly reduced rate offset the added resistance to vapor removal presented by the porous residue on the evaporating surface. This explains why a large added resistance to vapor removal can have only a small influence on the rate of drying at constant total pressure."

Sherwood has stated that the theory he outlined is not complete. It cannot explain the quantitative effect of plate temperature unless K_1 is assumed to decrease with T_p, which he thinks hardly seems reasonable. It seems clear, however, that the ultimate theory must be based on the concept of thermal and vapor flow resistances in series, with an overall driving force represented by the difference between the temperature of the heat source and the pressure in the condenser.

SUMMARY OF SHERWOOD'S FINDINGS

"For the drying of 10 cc of sodium penicillin solution (10,000 O.u./cc) frozen vertically at −70°C in the standard 25 cc. serum bottle and in contact with a horizontal, heated plate, a general summary of the results is as follows:

"1. The factors affecting the transfer of heat from the drier plate to the plane of vaporization determine the overall length of drying cycle. The factors affecting the flow of water vapor from the plane of vaporization to the drier chamber exert a negligible effect upon total drying time.

"2. The most important factor affecting the transfer of heat is the resistance to heat flow offered by the insulating layer of dry penicillin which forms as the drying progresses.

"3. The structure assumed by the dry penicillin is dependent upon the impurities associated with the penicillin and the drier pressure. In the general case for a given penicillin the structure resulting from a pressure of 10 microns requires from 3 to 4 times as long to dry to 1 per cent moisture as does the structure obtained at 200 microns.

"4. Plate temperatures as high as 100°C may be used without a detectable loss in potency.

"5. For any given structure, the time of drying for a 100°C plate is about 40 per cent less than for a 40°C (104°F) plate. This value is also affected somewhat by drier pressure.

"6. The presence of moderate amounts of organic solvents does not appear to influence the rate of drying or the appearance of the product.

"Results obtained under experimental conditions other than those tested above are summarized as follows:

"7. Initial liquid volumes of 5 cc (20,000 O.u./cc) require about 75 per cent as much time for drying as do 10 cc. Volumes less than 5 cc do not result in any appreciable shortening of the drying cycle.

"8. Initial liquid volumes less than 4 to 5 cc usually yield poor structures with some melting and foaming.

"9. Drying times are from 10 to 25 per cent less when the serum bottles are surrounded by a loosely fitting metallic collar attached to the plate than when the plate alone is used.

"10. For certain penicillins, the temperature of freezing affects the final structure, and thus the length of drying cycle.

"In the course of the work over 300 samples of various material were dried. In order that the results of all runs might be more or less comparable, the general experimental procedure was maintained the same wherever possible and is described below. Modification of this procedure will be discussed in the following sections of this report.

"*Apparatus.* The evacuated drier chambers consisted essentially of a bell jar mounted on a horizontal steel plate. Directly beneath the plate was a single-tube, vertical condenser, cooled by a bath of Dry Ice and methyl "Cellosolve." The vacuum was produced by mechanical and/or oil diffusion vacuum pumps. The pressure in the bell jar and the pressure of the gas leaving the condenser were measured with a McLeod gauge. Water vapor was excluded from the gauge by a low-temperature trap.

"The bottles containing the material to be dried were placed upon a horizontal copper plate supported within the bell jar. The temperature of the plate was measured by means of a thermocouple attached to the top surface. An electrical coil suspended beneath the plate furnished the heat for the drying. In order that the pressure in the bell jar might be maintained at any desired level, a controlled air leak was introduced just before the vacuum pump.

"*Operating Procedure.* In the majority of the runs, 10 cc of the solution to be dried were frozen in the standard 25-cc. serum bottles, in either a Dry Ice-methyl "Cellosolve" or an ice-salt bath. Before each run the copper plate was cooled to approximately $-30°C$ ($-22°F$) with Dry Ice. The pump and condenser capacity of the system was such that the pressure within the bell jar could be reduced to any desired value within 20 to 30 minutes. As soon as the desired pressure was attained, it was held at this level by use of the controlled air leak. By means of variable resistances in series with the heating coil, the temperature of the plate was then raised to the desired value. The rate of temperature increase was governed by the properties of the material being dried. In cases where the material exhibited a tendency to melt and foam caution was used in raising the plate temperature; however, in most cases from 20 to 30 minutes were required to reach the desired temperature.

"Final moisture contents were obtained in the standard manner over P_2O_5 for 72 hours.

"Since the major portion of experimental work done on this project involved the desiccation of 10 cc of frozen sodium penicillin solution from the standard 25-cc serum bottle on a horizontal plate, the following discussion will necessarily be restricted to these results. Many of the conclusions, however, may be extrapolated to other conditions which are now being used industrially. In many of these cases, such as drying from liquid volumes less than 10 ccs. and the use of heat sources other than a flat plate, sufficient data were obtained to indicate the effect of these variables.

"*General Considerations.* The various factors affecting the rate of drying of penicillin from the frozen state may be divided into two classes, those involved with the transfer of heat from its source to the surface of the ice where the vaporization is taking place and those affecting the rate of vapor flow from this surface to the condenser. For any flow process there exists a general relationship that the rate of flow, *i.e.*, the quantity flowing per unit of time, is directly proportional to the overall driving force causing the flow and inversely proportional to the resistance offered by the path through which the transfer takes place. In the case of the flow of heat under consideration, the driving force is the overall temperature difference between the source of heat in the drier and the point of vaporization, and the resistance is made up of such factors as the contact resistance between the source of heat and the surface of the bottle, the conductivity of the glass, the contact resistance between the glass and the solid within the bottle, and the conductivity of the solid from this point of contact to the plane of vaporization. The driving force for the flow of water vapor may be considered to be the difference between the pressure of the water vapor at the point of vaporization and the pressure of the water vapor in the condenser. The resistance to the flow of vapor is a function of the porosity of the dry penicillin which may exist between the surface of the ice and the free space in the bottle, the orifice effect of the neck of the bottle, and the size, shape, and construction of the drier chamber and the connecting lines to the condenser. While the overall rate of drying is actually affected by all of these factors, their relative effect may vary to such an extent that some may be considered as negligible.

"*FACTOR CONTROLLING THE RATE OF DRYING.* Before discussing the importance of each of the above factors, it is of interest to describe the various phases which may be observed during the drying of a penicillin sample. Since the solution expands somewhat on freezing, the resulting plug of ice presses quite firmly against the walls of the bottle. The first vaporization, therefore, takes place from the top surface of the ice. As the drying proceeds, the plane of vaporization recedes not only from the top, but also in from the sides. Depending upon the characteristics of the penicillin sample under consideration, the resulting layer of dry material may, in the general case, behave in either of two ways. It may maintain itself as a plug of roughly the same volume of the original ice, or at least the same general shape in case shrinkage occurs; or it may crumble as it dries to a powder which occupies only a small fraction of the original ice volume. In the first case and during the latter stages of drying, the plane of vaporization not only recedes from the top and sides, but also from the bottom, so that the last bit of ice to be removed exists as a small ball completely surrounded by a porous insulating layer of the dried material. In the latter case the residual ice is more or less visible until it is completely removed.

"On the basis of these observations it is apparent that the path resistance to both the flow of heat and the flow of water vapor changes as the drying progresses. Where a porous plug is formed, the heat must be transferred in through this material, and the resulting vapor must diffuse out, in either case the desired transfer of heat or vapor being retarded. The transfer of heat is further complicated where shrinkage of the plug occurs by the resulting free space between the plug and the walls of the bottle. Where disintegration occurs during drying, these effects are also of consequence, although not to as great a degree.

"In the early stages of the experimental work, an effort was made where possible to determine the relative effect of each of the above factors which were considered to have any influence upon either the transfer of heat or the flow of water vapor. The complete details of this work which were carried out in this laboratory have not been publshed; however, the general conclusion may be reached that by and large the factors affecting the transfer of heat control the rate of drying. In the light of the fact that this conclusion is based primarily upon data obtained from laboratory equipment, the above statement must be restricted to the flow of water vapor from the point of vaporization to the drier chamber. It is possible that the flow resistance from the drier to the condenser might be of sufficient magnitude to limit the rate of drying.

"The significance of the fact that the factors affecting the transfer of heat control the rate of drying (subject to the limitations pointed out above) may be clarified by considering the analogy to the evaporation of water by boiling from an open pan. Regardless of the rate of heat input the temperature of the water does not vary to any great extent from that value corresponding to a vapor pressure of one atmosphere, i.e., 212°F, at normal barometric pressure. If the temperature of the source of heat is doubled the rate of heat transfer controls the rate of evaporation. If, however, the water is confined in a chamber open to the atmosphere through only a small orifice, as the rate of heat transfer is increased, the pressure within the chamber must increase in order to force the greater quantity of water vapor through the orifice. Due to this increase in pressure, the temperature of water will necessarily rise to a new value as fixed by the chamber pressure. If the temperature of the heat source is now doubled, for example, the overall temperature difference and also the rate of evaporation are not doubled; consequently, the flow of vapor from the system has influenced the rate of evaporation. If the orifice is small enough, its resistance to vapor flow can control the process completely.

"*Experimental Evidence.* From thermocouples frozen in the plug of the frozen solutions, it was determined over a wide range of drying condition (pressures and temperatures) that the surface of the vaporization is at a temperature very nearly equal to that ice would have to exert a vapor pressure of water equal to the total pressure in the drier chamber. This represents a condition similar to the case of water boiling in an open pan where the water temperature is fixed by the pressure of the atmosphere above the pan. If, for example, the pressure drop across the neck of the bottle had been appreciable, the surface temperature of the ice would have increased because of the higher pressure within the bottle. Actually both by calculation and by experimental work it was determined that the pressure drop at the bottle neck is negligible.

"In the light of the above considerations as well as other data which will not be repeated here, the conclusion that the factors affecting the transfer of heat control the rate of drying from 25-cc serum bottles seems well justified.

"RESULTS AND DISCUSSION. The following section concerns principally the results obtained on the drying characteristics of various commercial penicillin samples.

"The experimental procedure outlined in a previous section of this report was followed in most of the work. In cases where modifications were used, the specific details will be discussed together with the results. Also included in this section are brief discussions on the use of McLeod gauges and on the possibility of absorbing water vapor in a suitable solvent at low pressures as a means of eliminating the refrigeration now used in the present condensers.

"Definitions of Structures. Since the structure obtained during drying has been found to be the factor of the most influence in controlling the overall length of drying cycle, the following arbitrary definitions will serve to describe each of the general forms of structure obtained and will be used in the subsequent discussion.

"Type A. The final dried penicillin occupies nearly the original volume of the frozen solution. The plug as well as its cross-section are continuous and have a pith-like appearance. When shaken the sample breaks easily into a fluffy material resembling flakey snow, occupying about the same volume as the original solid plug. The color of this type is always the lightest shade obtainable from any given sample of penicillin and has the fastest rate of solution.

"Type B. Any intermediate form between Type A and Type C. Structures approaching Type C are characterized by an increasing amount of shrinkage in the residual plug of penicillin, together with disintegration to a powder around the edges and at various points throughout the plug. The solid mass is not continuous, but is more sponge-like in appearance. A cone of solid at the center, in height nearly equal to that of the original frozen solution, is often the last to disintegrate. The plug can be broken with little difficulty to a powder form which lacks the fluffy characteristics of that obtained from the Type A. Colors are intermediate between Types A and C.

"Type C. The penicillin disintegrates as the drying progresses and the final material exists as a course powder of about 20 50 mesh in the bottom of the bottle, occupying about one-twentieth of the volume of the original solution. In color this type is always much darker than either A or B for tiny pellets of fused material are usually present.

"Type D. A miscellaneous classification including those structures obtained when melting and/or foaming occur during the drying operation. Several forms of this type were obtained, the most common having the following general descriptions: (a) foam-like, (b) coral-like, (c) a plug resembling solid molasses, or (d) a combination of any of these and either Types A or B. The colors of this type are generally dark, and the time of solution of the dried material may be as long as a minute.

"*Effect of Impurities.* Under any given conditions of drying, the impurities associated with the penicillin determine the type of structure which will result. With any given penicillin the structure varies principally with the drier pressure. Type A structures requiring lower pressures than any other type. During the course of this work tests were made on eight commercial samples of sodium penicillin of varying purity (O.u./mg T.S.) and the results as regards the interrelationship of impurities, structure, and pressure have been summarized in Table 1. In order that the exact effect of impurities on structure might be understood more fully, the drying characteristics of crystalline sodium penicillin were also determined. If the behavior of the crystalline material is taken as a basis, the data show that the operating pressure which must be realized if, for example, a Type A structure is to be obtained is a function not only of the quantity of impurities present, but also to a minor extent their composition. No information was obtained as to the nature of the impurity (or impurities) which cause the variation in structure; moreover, a study of the basic recovery processes used by each of the eight producers indicated no correlation between the method of recovery and the final structure. No conclusion is justified, therefore, except that the impurities present control the structure formation, which, as will be discussed later, controls the length of drying cycle. Except for Type D structures, plate temperature was found to have negligible influence upon structure formation.

Other varibles which have a minor effect upon structure will be discussed in subsequent sections.

TABLE 1

EFFECT OF DRIER PRESSURE UPON FINAL STRUCTURES
FOR VARIOUS PENICILLIN (SODIUM)

Penicillin	O.u./mg.	Pressure	in	Microns		
		5	50	100	200	400
1 (cryst.)	1620	A	A	A	A	
2	800	A	A	A	A	C
3	750	A			C	
4	450	A	B	B	C	
5	430	A			C	
6	250	A				
7	170	A	A		D	
8	370	B + D	D	D	D	
9	250	B + D	D			

Drying conditions:
Volume: 5–10 cc in 25-cc serum bottle
Freezing temp = −70°C

"It should be pointed out that structure formation is reversible, that is, if a Type C structure resulting from a run at 200 microns is redissolved and then dried at 5 microns, an A structure will be obtained. The Type C structure can then be reformed by again redissolving and drying at 200 microns. In other words, the appearance of the penicillin can be altered by the drying conditions employed; however, it is understood that the potency and therapeutic value of the penicillin are independent of structure, and the fact that in many industrial cases structures other than A are obtained is not considered serious.

"The cause of the melting and foaming inherent with Penicillins No. 8 and 9 is also obscure, other than that it is due to impurities. The extent of this difficulty was reduced by the use of low drier pressures and might possibly have been eliminated had it been possible to maintain plate temperatures below 0°C; however, such a procedure would necessitate drying cycles greater than thirty hours. It is possible that as the drying progresses, a low-melting eutectic is formed at the interface between the dry material and the remaining ice-penicillin and impurity mass, although approximate eutectic determinations indicate that about $-20°C$ ($-4°F$) is the minimum melting point possible. Since the temperature of the ice interface, even at a drier pressure of 200 microns, is lower than $-30°C$, no conclusion is justified. There is also the possibility that one or more of the impurities may in itself have a low melting point, but because of the complex nature of the impurities, no definite information was obtained.

"Melting and foaming or at least some sacrifice in the appearance of the product can result because of too high plate temperatures over the period during which the drier pressure is being reduced to the operating level (*i.e.*, evacuation). Until a pressure is reached at which the cooling effect of vaporization is sufficient to maintain the frozen state of the solution, the plate temperature should be maintained at a level less than the melting point of the solution. For most penicillins, $-6°C$ ($21°F$) appears to be satisfactory, although lower temperatures are recommended.

"*Effect of Structure.* The overall length of drying cycle to obtain a residual moisture content of 1 per cent has been found to be essentially dependent upon the following variables and in the following manner: the impurities present fix the structure which will be obtained, the structure together with the plate temperature and the pressure then controlling the rate of heat transfer to the ice surface and thus the rate of vaporization. The factual basis for these conclusions is presented in Table 2, which is a summary of data obtained from over 300 drying runs. Attention is called to the specific drying conditions used; other modifications in procedure will be discussed in later sections of this report. In most cases in obtaining these data the drier pressure and the plate temperature listed were attained within thirty minutes and were then maintained constant for the duration of the run.

"Since in no case did Type B structures occur with drier pressures less than 50 microns, nor Type C at less than 100 microns, drying times for these structures at lower pressures are not available. Moreover, it is believed that these structures will not be formed at pressure lower than those stated in each case. Drying times for Type D structures fell within no definite limits, although in most cases the times were of the order of those required for Type

B and C structures. There were also indications that where considerable fusion occurred, the removal of the last traces of water was retarded by this type of structure.

TABLE 2

TOTAL DRYING TIME AS A FUNCTION OF STRUCTURE, PRESSURE, AND TEMPERATURE

Structure	Plate Temp.	Pressure	in	Microns	
		5	20	50	100–200
Type A	40°C	30 hrs.	24 hrs.	22 hrs.	14–22 hrs.
	100	20	12–15	10–14	12
Type B	40			18–20	8–13
	100			10–12	4–8
Type C	40				8–10
	100				4–8

Drying conditions:
Volume: 10 cc in 25-cc serum bottle
Freezing temperature: −70°C
Final moisture content: 1 wt. per cent
Heat source: Horizontal copper plate

"Since the length of drying cycle for pressures between 100 and 200 microns did not correlate well with the absolute pressure, the data over this range have been included under one heading. In other words for a Type A structure and a 40°C (104°F) plate, the drying time might be 22 hours at both 100 and 200 microns, or again 14 hours for both pressures. Because the definitions of structure are necessarily broad and since the effect of structure upon drying time is so pronounced, the wide limits of from 14 to 22 hours are indicative of the precision of the data and the method of correlation.

"*Effect of Pressure.* In view of the profound effect of pressure upon structure formation (Table 1) and the controlling influence of structure upon the length of drying cycle (Table 2), two basic effects of pressure should be noted. Based upon the conclusion that the factors affecting the transfer of heat, *e.g.*, structure, etc., are those contributing to the overall control of the rate of drying, these effects of pressure will be considered in the light of their possible influence upon heat transmission.

"In the case at hand, the rate of heat transfer is proportional to the overall temperature difference between the plate and the surface of the ice and inversely proportional to the resistance to heat transfer offered by the path through which the heat must flow. As will be pointed out, both of these are affected by pressure. Since it has been noted that the surface temperature of the ice during drying is approximately that which ice would have to exert a vapor pressure of water equal to the total pressure in the drier, the effect of pressure is obvious. For a constant plate temperature, therefore, the overall temperature difference increases as the pressure decreases. Although this would imply that the rate of heat transfer should increase as the pressure is lowered, the effect of pressure upon the path resistance is an opposite one, and apparently is of greater magnitude. The fact that the drying time for a Type A structure is much greater than for Type C indicates that for a Type A structure the insulating layer of dry penicillin which surrounds the residual ice as the drying progresses offers considerable resistance to the flow of heat. It is known that the resistance to heat transfer of a porous material increases as the apparent density decreases, heat being transferred by radiation and gas convection as well as by conduction through the solid itself. Since Type A structures have very low apparent densities, the amount of heat transferred by direct conduction is probably small. The heat transferred by convection would vary with the pressure, *i.e.*, in a perfect vacuum the heat transferred by gas conduction would be zero, and for a given structure and overall temperature difference, the radiant heat transfer would be constant. Although the relative magnitude of each type of heat transmission is not known, it appears that gas convection through the pores of the dry penicillin is important and to some extent is a function of pressure. The net effect of pressure for a given structure and plate temperature is indicated in Table 2.

Constant vs. Variable Pressure. Most of the data already presented were obtained from runs where the drier pressure was maintained at a constant level for the entire cycle by means of a controlled air leak on the low pressure side of the vacuum pumps. The possibility presented itself, however, that for certain penicillins it would be of advantage to start the drying cycle at a low pressure to prevent melting and if possible to form a Type A structure and to raise the pressure to over 2,000 microns at the end to obtain the higher rates of drying. Such a procedure was tried for several penicillins, and it was found that the length of the drying cycle might be reduced as much as 20 per cent; however, the delicate control necessary indicates that the idea may not be applicable to industrial driers. It was found that the pressure should not be raised until the net moisture content of the sample is such that no melting and foaming will occur. Since all the bottles in a full-scale drier apparently do not dry at the same rate, no simple means of determining the safe point to raise the pressure is evident other than trial-and-error. Pressures as high as 400 to 500 microns could probably be used without the danger of melting; however, the advantages gained is less than for pressures as high as 2,000 microns, and the problem of determining the proper point in the cycle to increase the pressure is still present.

"In this regard the question arises as to the pressure necessary to remove the last traces of water (to less than 1 per cent). Within the scope of this work, no case was found where pressures less than 200 microns were required. In one instance three out of four Type A samples were dried to a negligible water content in 11 hours with a plate temperature of 40°C (104°F) and a drier pressure for the last three hours of the cycle of 2200 microns.

"The control of pressure in the industrial driers has in most cases been limited to the regulation of plate temperatures, which at the end of a cycle has little effect. Whether or not a controlled air leak to the vacuum pumps would be feasible is not known; however, in some cases the use of high pressures, especially at the end of a cycle, may be of advantage, and some means of pressure regulation should be developed.

"As regards the maintenance of low pressures, where the condenser and/or the vacuum pump capacity are adequate, no difficulty is encountered other than air leakage. Where the vacuum capacity is limited, and in the absence of leaks, either reduced loads to the drier or low plate temperatures are necessary to maintain the desired low pressure.

"*Effect of Temperature. 1. On Potency.* It has been concluded that plate temperatures as high as 100°C (212°F) could be used without a detectable loss in potency. Additional data have been obtained which also bear out this conclusion, even in cases where melting and foaming occur. The data in Table 3 are for a penicillin which gave Type D structures under the conditions used, considerable foaming having occurred during the drying. From these it is further concluded that plate temperatures approaching 100°C give no loss in potency within the accuracy of the assay, regardless of the type of structure which is formed.

TABLE 3

Run No.	Plate Temp.	Potency Before Drying	O.u./mg.T.S. After Drying
1	100°C	366	350
2	130°C	366	105

Drier Pressure—200 microns
Sample Volume—5 cc
Time of Drying—20 hrs.
Final Moisture—negligible

"*On Rate of Drying.* Based upon the previous conclusions that the rate of heat transfer controls the length of drying cycle, for any given structure, *i.e.*, for a constant resistance to heat transfer, the length of drying cycle should be inversely proportional to the overall temperature difference between the plate and the surface of vaporization. By making such an analysis of the data in Table 2, this assumption was found to be true within the precision of the data. The equation presented in earlier reports (Nos. 4, 5, and 6) has proved adequate for predicting overall drying times for 10 cc of solution and Type A structures; however, it is not applicable to any other conditions. Similar equations could be developed for each set of conditions and structures, but it is felt that Table 2 will better indicate the effect of structure, pressure, and plate temperature upon the length of drying cycle.

"*Effect of Freezing Temperature.* This variable has been subjected to extensive experimental investigation but will not be discussed here. The general conclusion, however, is that for certain penicillins the rate and temperature of freezing can effect the final structure of the penicillin and, therefore, the rate of drying. Of the various samples tested, only Penicillin No. 2 (Table 1) was affected by freezing temperature; however, this variable may become of more interest as the purity of other products is improved.

"*Effect of Concentration of Initial Solution. 1. On Structure.* In tests on several penicillins it was found that initial concentrations higher than 40,000 O.u./cc in general gave poor structures, usually a very hard cake. At very high concentrations (80,000–100,000 O.u./cc) Type D structures were usually obtained, regardless of the structure resulting from lower concentration for the same penicillin under similar drying conditions. As would be expected, the color of the final product becomes darker as the initial concentration increases.

"*On Rate of Drying.* It has been found that the length of drying cycle is almost independent of the amount of solution charged to the bottle. Five ccs. of solution were found to require about 75 per cent of the time of drying of 10 ccs. and any volume less than 5 cc resulted in no shortening of the cycle. Drying times for volumes of 5 cc and less are presented in Table 4. The fact that

TABLE 4

Peni-cillin No. (Table 1)	O.u./cc	Pressure (microns)	Plate Temp. (°C)	Time of Drying (hrs)	Final Moisture (%)
4	100,000	45	40	19	0.8
	33,000	"	"	"	0.4
	20,000	"	"	"	0.1
8	100,000	6	"	20	0.6
	50,000	"	"	"	1.0
	33,000	"	"	"	0.6
	20,000	"	"	"	0.4

1 cc appears to dry no more rapidly than 5 cc may be due in part to the one-fifth reduction of contact area between the ice plug and the wall of the bottle. There are also indications that the removal of the last traces of water from a Type D structure as is obtained from 1 cc initial volume is not as simple as in the cases where no melting occurs.

"*Effect of Residual Organic Solvents.* As has already been indicated the length of drying cycle is mainly dependent upon the type of structure which forms during drying; therefore, any modifications in bottle design will have little effect on the overall cycle. It has been noted that the rate of vaporization in the early stages of drying was influenced somewhat by bottle design; however, the overall time of drying is influenced little. With thin-walled containers, such as the standard ampoule, the initial rate of heat transfer was found to be so great that melting occurred at the bottom of the plug; consequently, plate temperatures as high as 100°C could not be used until an insulating plug of dry penicillin had formed around the residual plug of ice.

"*Effect of Plate Design.* A few runs were made with the bottle surrounded by a loosely fitting copper sleeve soldered to the plate. In such cases the time required to dry to 1 per cent moisture was from 10 to 25 per cent less than for cases without the sleeve.

"*Effect of Temperature on Pressure Readings.* According to the work of Knudsen* at low pressure a temperature difference between the two ends of a small-diameter tube will cause a pressure gradient across the tube, even in the absence of flow, the higher pressure being at the high-temperature end of the tube. The magnitude of this pressure difference is a function of tube diameter, the temperature difference, and the absolute pressure, and with small diameter tubes at pressures encountered in this work the pressure gradient through the tube can be appreciable. In other words, it is necessary in measuring a true pressure that the temperature of the McLeod gauge be equal to that of the gas being measured. For example, if the McLeod gauge at room temperature is connected to the refrigerated condenser through a small tube, the gauge will indicate a pressure higher than the true pressure in the condenser. In many of the industrial installations utilizing low-temperature condensers it has been noted that the condenser pressure as measured is higher than the drier pressure. It would thus appear that the error in pressure measurement is greater than the pressure drop between the two points of pressure measurement, since it is to be expected that the drier pressure should be the higher."

---

* *Ann. Physik,* **31,** 205 (1910).

APPENDIX III

Data Tables

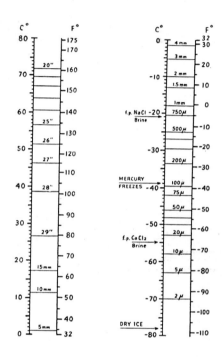

TABLE

PRESSURE EQUIVALENTS HG

Unit	in.	mm	μ
1 in. (inch)	1	25.4	25400
1 mm (millimeter)	.0394	1	1000
1 μ (micron)	3.9×10^{-5}	10^{-3}	1

APPENDIX IV
Embedding with Acrylic Plastic

Preservation of soft tissues in gross anatomy and pathology has normally presented a problem. The customary procedure has been to fix organs or slices of organs in various fluids, such as one containing formalin, with the addition of other materials to reduce loss of color and shrinkage to a minimum. These specimens are kept in the well-known covered round or square glass jars of laboratories of anatomy and pathology. However, the preservation of tissue color is not good and becomes worse upon storage. Moreover, the preserved specimen does not represent the original in size and shape because of shrinkage.

A recent departure (Max M. Strumia and J. Ivan Hershey, *J. Lab. and Clin. Med.*, 33, 1311–1321, 1948) in place of the customary procedure mentioned above makes use of freeze-drying followed by impregnation with "Plexiglas." This work was carried on at Bryn Mawr Hospital, Bryn Mawr, Pennsylvania, with the co-operation of Rohm & Haas Company. The process permits the preservation of the color and form of specimens of both human and animal origin, including organs either whole or in section. Excellent results have been reported (*loc. cit.*) with tumors, entire adult hearts, lungs and brains. Upon illumination, transparent blocks of "Plexiglas" containing organs or portions of organs present a life-like aspect. The specimens can be handled readily without danger of breakage, which contrasts with the customary formalin preservation in fragile jars.

The following is a decription of the steps to be taken.

FREEZING OF THE SPECIMEN

Preliminary to freezing, the fresh specimen should be trimmed and all excees fat removed. Two different techniques are used for freezing depending on the size of the specimen. For *small organs or slices of tissues* of any size and up to about 1 to 1½ cm

thick use the following procedure: Prepare a base of ice by freezing in a metal pan of suitable size and shape a layer of water
about 1 cm deep. Place the specimen, thoroughly wet, on the
base of ice and freeze by placing in a low-temperature cabinet
(-20 to $-25°$ C). Instantaneous freezing does not improve the
specimen and slow freezing should also be avoided. When the
specimen is frozen, add ice-water to form a layer about 1 cm
thick, and freeze successive layers of water, until the specimen is
completely covered with about 1 cm of ice.

For *larger specimens,* such as human heart, the procedure is as
follows: Prepare the base of ice as outlined above. Place the wet
organ on the ice and allow it to freeze. When the specimen is
thoroughly frozen and fixed to the base, spray it with water several
times, using an atomizer, to thoroughly glaze it with a thin layer of
ice. A layer of one or two millimeters in thickness is enough to
protect the surface of the organ from drying and subsequent loss
of color or shrinkage. The specimen is then completely embedded
in ice by freezing successive one-cm layers of cold water. Carefully avoid pouring the water on the organ itself, in order not to
melt the glaze of ice.

Before placing the block of ice in the drying apparatus, chip
off as much excess ice as possible to reduce the period of drying.
This operation is not essential except as a time saver. The ice
blocks must be thoroughly chilled to $-20°$ C or less before they
are transferred to the drying apparatus.

FREEZE-DRYING OF SPECIMENS

Any apparatus designed for the drying of biologicals from the
frozen state and of proper capacity can be used for this purpose.
It must be capable of maintaining a temperature of $-12°$ to
$-15°$ C in the specimen itself while the water is being removed by
sublimation. A chamber type of apparatus is preferable because
drying on manifolds presents a problem where the containers must
have openings large enough to accommodate large specimens.
When drying with heat, high final temperature should be avoided
because of fat in the specimens and a maximum of about $37°$ C
is advisable.

It is desirable to place the blocks of ice containing the specimens to be dried in a loosely tied bag made of a single layer of gauze (12 mesh). The wrapped specimens are placed in wire baskets or on mesh wire supports and so arranged as to allow a free flow of the water vapor.

For medium-sized specimens (approximately 5 to 7 cm in thickness but of any width fitting the drying chamber) and with the apparatus mentioned, 5 to 7 days are sufficient for complete drying. Very large organs, such as an entire brain, require 15 days for complete drying.

This method, when properly carried out, causes no distortion of the specimen as a result of drying except in cases where air may be trapped such as in the gastro-intestinal tract of a fetus or entire animal. In such specimens some contraction has been observed.

TRIMMING AND PRESERVATION OF DRIED SPECIMEN

Once the specimen is dried, it should be carefully maintained by placing in a glass desiccator containing a suitable dehydrating agent such as "Drierite." Before embedding, specimens may be kept in the dried state for several weeks or even months without deterioration. For best results, however, the dried specimen should be embedded as soon as convenient. With a very sharp knife, the specimen can now be trimmed, to remove all loose portions and to improve the specimen. It has been noted that retrimming of a specimen after drying, to obtain a very smooth surface, allows a much better view of the intimate structure of the organ. Excessive fat can be readily removed at this time, avoiding damage to the specimen. With a brush, very carefully remove dust from the surface of the organ.

SATURATION WITH THE LIQUID ACRYLIC MONOMER

The dried specimens will appear to have lost their color and texture, but these are immediately restored upon immersion into the liquid monomer at room temperature. It is most essential to obtain a very thorough saturation of the specimen with the liquid acrylic monomer, which must entirely replace all spaces previously occupied by water. This is accomplished by placing the specimen in a jar containing sufficient acrylic monomer to cover it completely. Preparation of this reagent is discussed below. The jar is then put in a vacuum desiccator and the vapor is alternately pumped out and air let in until the sample sinks in the monomer and no more bubbles issue from it. At this stage the specimen is ready for embedding in thickened monomer. Sometimes it is desirable to prolong the immersion in the monomer for the purpose of removing excessive amounts of pigment, a procedure which should be applied to such organs as a liver. With specimens of liver or organs containing other diffusable pigments or fat, the liquid monomer should be changed a number of times during the process of saturation.

PRELIMINARY POLYMERIZATION OF THE MONOMER

Reagents:

(1) *Inhibited ethyl methacrylate monomer.* Ethyl methacrylate monomer is supplied by the Rohm & Haas Company, Philadelphia 5, Penna., with inhibitor added to prevent spontaneous polymerization. For embedding work the monomer should be distilled to separate it from the inhibitor. Although separation by distillation is preferred, it has also been accomplished by a wash with a concentrated caustic solution. Add 2 per cent by weight of 50 per cent sodium hydroxide (or 1 per cent by weight of water and 1 per cent by weight of flake sodium hydroxide) to the inhibited ethyl methacrylate monomer. Shake the container vigorously (or stir so that the sodium hydroxide is constantly broken up) for at least ten minutes. At the end of this period, the sodium hydroxide will have become discolored. Allow small particles in the monomer to settle and siphon or decant the monomer out of the container, filtering it through a coarse filter paper.

(2) *Benzoyl peroxide* (a catalyst). The benzoyl peroxide catalyst is a 1:1 mixture of benzoyl peroxide with stabilizer, avail-

able from Cadet Chemical Corp., Buffalo 5, N. Y. or Lucidol Division, Novadel-Agene Corp., Buffalo 5, N. Y.

(3) *Stearic acid* (a mold lubricant).

Equipment:

(1) 1,000 cc Florence or Erlenmeyer flask.

(2) Hot plate with insulated or closed switches.

(3) Water or steam bath.

(4) Chemical hood with explosion-proof motor and switch.

Procedure:

The vapors of ethyl methacrylate are highly inflammable and must be kept from all open flames. Further, all switches, motors and other electrical equipment in the room must be of the explosion-proof type.

In those cases where the shape of the mold or some other consideration leads the operator to suspect that he may encounter difficulty in removing the finished casting from the mold, the addition of about 1 per cent stearic acid has been found to offer some advantage. It does not guarantee ready separation of the mold but at least it helps.

For a preparation on an approximately one-quart scale, proceed as follows: Dissolve 7 grams of stearic acid (omit in those cases where no mold removal problem is expected) and 100 milligrams of benzoyl peroxide catalyst in 500 cc of inhibitor-free monomer by shaking.

Filter the resulting solution. Place the solution in a 1000-cc flask and heat on a hot water or steam bath. *Do not heat over an open flame!* Bring the mixture to a boil, shaking frequently, and continue boiling for 2 to 3 minutes. Remove the flask from the bath. The reaction is highly exothermic and the mixture will continue to boil after removal from the heat source. Allow the mixture to boil spontaneously for 2 to 3 minutes; then cool under running water, swirling slowly, until boiling stops.

The process should be observed continually, since the reaction, unless checked, proceeds spontaneously to complete hardening of the mass. Continue cooling for approximately 10 minutes. The consistency at room temperature should be that of heavy molasses.

Store the mixture in a refrigerator at approximately 40° F until ready for use.

EMBEDDING OF SPECIMENS IN "PLEXIGLAS"

It is desirable to use glass containers for the final embedding. Metallic containers have not proven as satisfactory. Ordinary square "icebox" dishes or baking dishes as well as glass photographic trays have proven very satisfactory. It is desirable to prepare the receptacles by making a solid acrylic plastic base on which to rest the specimen. This hard base is made by pouring a layer of about 2 cm of the partially polymerized monomer into a clean dish of suitable size and depth. For this purpose a very thick medium can be used. Cover the dish with two or three layers of tightly fitted cellophane and allow to stand in the refrigerator until the layer is absolutely free of air bubbles. Then harden the thickened monomer by heating at 45° C. The base is now ready to receive the specimen.

Two slightly different techniques are used for embedding, depending on the general type of specimen. Procedure A is recommended for samples up to 2 cm thick, such as slices of various organs, flattened specimens of intestines, gall bladder, or halved kidneys, tumors, etc. Procedure B is suggested for large irregular organs, such as the heart, lungs, uterus, brain, whole liver, etc.

Procedure A—for smaller specimens.

Pour a small amount of the liquid monomer over the preformed hard base and thoroughly wet the base and the sides of the dish. Pour the liquid off and drain rapidly. Pour over the hard base a layer of the thickened monomer calculated to be just enough to cover the specimen. If bubbles have formed, cover with cellophane and place in the icebox until they have all disappeared. Do not allow the poured, thickened medium to stand for any period of time without a cover, particularly at room temperature or in the oven, because a tough film forms which renders subsequent operations difficult. When the medium is free of air bubbles, remove the specimen from the monomeric medium and place it edge-wise in the thickened medium until it rests on the firm base. Allow it then to be immersed in the thickened medium by lowering it very gradually in such a manner as to avoid trapping of air bubbles. It may be necessary at this time to add some of the thickened medium to completely cover the specimen, but under no circumstances should the layer be thicker than 3 cm. Cover the dish with cellophane and if air bubbles have been formed, replace in the refrigerator until clear. Then set in the oven at 45° C for polymerization. As previously stated, polymerization of ethyl methacrylate occurs with considerable production of heat. If the layer is too thick, heat dissipates too slowly and gas forms from boiling monomer. The gas is trapped in the form of bubbles which spoil the block. It is convenient, when handling large specimens, to have an oven provided with an exhaust fan which operates automatically whenever the temperature of a specimen rises above 46° C. The thermometer regulating the relay for the fan control should be of the mercury type, and should be placed in direct contact with the specimen being embedded. The oven in which the specimens are polymerized should have non-sparking contacts and no open switches. Mercury-type contacts are satisfactory. A block 3 cm thick will harden in approximately one week at 45° C. Successive layers of 1–2 cm in thickness may be added to obtain a suitable block.

Procedure B—for large irregular organs.

Begin the operation by preparing a suitable base as in Procedure A. Wet the base and sides of the container with monomer as before. Pour a thin layer of thickened monomer over the organ which has been removed from the liquid monomer. The container with the specimen is then very carefully sealed, using many layers of cellophane or similar material. It is placed in the icebox so that it is thoroughly freed of bubbles and then in the oven at 45° C until the layer hardens. This process is repeated until the organ is covered with a 1½-cm layer. Great care must be exercised to cover the whole organ and to avoid trapping of air bubbles. When the organ is thus glazed and fixed to the base, proceed carefully to embed it by adding successive layers of thickened monomer not exceeding 1/2 cm in depth, in order not to soften the glaze on the organ excessively. Whereas the embedding of large slices of organ offers no difficulty, the embedding of the entire large organs challenges the skill and ingenuity of the operator. The results, however, are well worth the effort.

FINISHING OF THE SPECIMEN

When the specimen is completely solidified, the edges of the plastic are detached from the glass with a sharp knife. On cooling, the blocks easily detach themselves from the walls and it will easily fall off with gentle tapping. The finishing of the block is carried out as follows:

The solid block which closely resembles "Plexiglas" is first rough cut to the approximate size and shape of the final block desired with an ordinary band, circular or jigsaw. If a lathe is available it is well to turn the faces of the block down since this will insure an absolutely flat surface. Since "Plexiglas" has machining qualities similar to those of brass and copper you would use metal cutting tools of this type. A coolant (water, or soap and water) may be used, if desired. If no lathe is available the block may be faced to a smooth (not accurately flat) surface by fastening emery paper to a block of wood and hand sanding with a circular motion. It is advisable to start the sanding with a coarse-grade emery paper and finish with a fine grade. If a sander is available the work may be accomplished much more quickly but remember that the final sanding should be a wet one, which will give a soft satin finish that can be easily buffed. Best buffing results are obtained with a very soft open type of buffing wheel using an abrasive which is a combination of fine alumina with wax or grease binder, and a polishing tallow. The block when finished should have a high luster and be free from color and as transparent as the finest optical glass.

More detailed information concerning the handling of "Plexiglas" is obtainable from the manufacturer, Rohm & Haas Company, Philadelphia 5, Pa.

BIBLIOGRAPHY

OF SCIENTIFIC LITERATURE RELATED TO DRYING BY SUBLIMA-
TION NOT INCLUDED AS SPECIFIC TEXT REFERENCES
IN INDIVIDUAL CHAPTER BIBLIOGRAPHIES

Adair, G. S. and Robinson, M. E. 1931. A direct method for the measurement of the hydration of proteins. Proceedings of the Physiological
Society, Jour. Physiology, 72.

Aldrich, C. A. and Boyle, H. H. 1940. Concentrated human blood serum
as a diuretic in nephrosis. The Jour. of the Amer. Med. Asso., 114,
1062–1065.

Allchin, J. P. and Herbert, D. A. 1945. Technical aspects of blood
transfusion work. The Pharmaceutical Journal, February.

Alsever, J. B. 1944. Plasma reserves for civilian defense, their distribution, control, preparation and clinical use. Amer. Jour. of Public
Health, 34, 165.

Amberg, S. and Osterberg, A. E. 1940. The dehydration of blood. Proceedings of the Staff Meetings of the Mayo Clinic, 15, No. 17, 267.

Anker, H. S., Johnson, B. A., Goldberg, J. and Meleney, F. L. 1948.
Bacitracin: Methods of production, concentration, and partial purifi-
cation, with a summary of the chemical properties of crude bacitracin.
Jour. Bact., 55, 249.

Bernheim, F., Neurath, H. and Erickson, J. O. 1942. The denaturation
of proteins and its apparent reversal. IV. Enzymatic hydrolysis of
native, denatured, and apparently reversibly denatured proteins.
The Jour. of Biol. Chem., 144, 259.

Bick, M. 1943. Concentration and drying of serum for intravenous use.
Med. Jour. of Australia, Sydney, 2, 227.

Blood Transfusion Association. 1941. Report.

Bloxsom, A. 1945. Intradermal use of convalescent serum against
measles. The Jour. of Pediatrics, 26, 32–35.

Boyd, W. C. 1939. Production and preservation of specific antisera for
blood-group factors A, B, M, and N. The Jour. of Immunol., 37, 65.

Breedis, C., Barnes, W. A. and Furth, J. 1937. Effect of rate of freezing
on the transmitting agent of neoplasms of mice. Proceedings of the
Soc. for Exptl. Biol. and Med., 36, 220–224.

Breedis, C. and Furth, J. 1938. The feasibility of preserving neoplastic cells in the frozen state. Science, 88, 531–532.

Brown, H. N. 1945. Low temperatures at low cost. Jour. Frank. Inst., 240, 487.

Butt, H. R. and Keys, A. 1938. Osmometric study of gum acacia solutions used for intravenous injection. The Jour. of Physical Chem., 42, 21.

Campbell, D. H. and Pressman, D. 1944. Scientific apparatus and laboratory methods—a simplified lyophil apparatus. Science, 99, 285.

Chapman, G. H., Berens, C. and Stiles, M. H. 1941. The coagulation of plasma by staphylococci. Jour. of Bact., 41, 431.

Christensen, R. 1942. A simplified "Lyophile" desiccator for small laboratories. The Jour. of Lab. and Clin. Med., St. Louis, 27, 799–802.

Coburn, D. R. 1942. Concerning the nature of type C botulinus toxin fractions. Science, 95, 389.

Cohn, E. J. 1944. A preventive of measles. Science-Supplement, 99, 10.

Cohn, E. J. 1944. Immune serum globulin. Science, 100, 10.

Cook, D. H. 1942. A low temperature vacuum drying apparatus. Jour. of Chem. Education, 19, No. 9.

Cooke, R. A., Barnard, J. H., Hebald, S. and Stull, A. 1935. Serological evidence of immunity with coexisting sensitization in a type of human allergy (hay fever). The Jour. of Exptl. Med., 62, 733–750.

d'Arsonval and Bordas, F. 1906. The desiccation of sera, vaccines, or other biologicals—vacuum distillation and evaporation at low temperatures. Comptes-Rendus de l'Academie des Sciences, 143, 567.

Davis, H. A. and Blalock, J. F., Jr. 1939. Autologous and homologous transfusion of human ascitic fluid. The Jour. of Clin. Invest., 18, 219–224.

Davis, H. A. and Meneely, G. R. 1942. The probability of obtaining potentially dangerous pools of human serum or plasma. Science, 96, 468–470.

Denslow, R. R. 1937. The use of toluene with carbon dioxide in obtaining low temperatures. The Chemist Analyst, 26, No. 2, April.

DeRobertis, E. 1941. The intracellular colloid of the normal and activated thyroid gland of the rat studied by the freezing-drying method. The Amer. Jour. of Anatomy, 68, 317.

DeRobertis, E. 1941. El metodo de fijacion por congelacion de Altmann-

Gersh. Sus aplicaciones y resultados en la histologia e histoquimica. Anales de la Sociedad Cientifica Argentina, E. IV, T. CXXXII, pag. 151 y sig.

Dykstra, T. P. and Dubuy, H. B. 1942. Preserving plant viruses in vitro by means of a simplified lyophile apparatus. Science, 96, 189–190.

Ecker, E. E. and Pillemer, L. 1938. An inexpensive method for the dehydration and preservation of complement and other biological materials. Amer. Jour. of Pub. Health, 28, No. 10.

Editorial 1941. Dried plasma and serum. The Lancet, 241, 105.

Edwards, F. R., Kay, J. and Davie, T. B. 1940. The preparation and use of dried plasma for transfusion. British Med. Jour., i, 377.

Einhorn, N. H. 1938. The biological effects of thymus extract (Hanson) on thymectomized rats. Endocrinology, 22, 335–341.

Einhorn, N. H. and Rowntree, L. G. 1938. The biological effects on thymus implantation in normal rats. Endocrinology, 22, 342–350.

Fedorov, N. A. 1947. New blood albumin substitute. Amer. Rev. Sov. Med., 4, 243–249.

Ferry, J. D. and Morrison, P. R. 1946. Fibrin film and other products from human plasma. Industrial and Engineering Chemistry, 38, 1217–1221.

Flexner, L. B. and Gersh, I. 1937. The correlation of oxygen consumption, function and structure in the developing metanephros of the pig. Publication No. 479 of Carnegie Institution of Washington, pages 121–127.

Flosdorf, E. W. and Mudd, S. 1942. Large scale desiccation of blood substitutes from the frozen state: a comparison of currently available types of equipment. Blood Substitutes and Blood Transfusion, Charles C. Thomas, Publisher, page 87.

Flosdorf, E. W. 1945. Drying by sublimation. Food Industries, 17, 22.

Flosdorf, E. W. 1945. Drying penicillin by sublimation in the United States and Canada. British Med. Jour., i, 216.

Flosdorf, E. W. 1945. Water vapor and the McLeod type of vacuum gage. Analytical Edition, Industrial and Engineering Chemistry, 17, 198.

Flosdorf, E. W. 1945. Drying meat by sublimation. Meat Magazine, April.

Flosdorf, E. W. and Mudd, S. 1945. Drying penicillin. Amer. Jour. of the Med. Sciences, 209, 694–695.

Flosdorf, E. W. 1945. Drying by sublimation. American Exporter, Industrial Supplement, May–June.

Flosdorf, E. W. 1945. Drying by sublimation. In Spanish. American Exporter, Industrial Supplement, May–June.

Flosdorf, E. W. 1945. Drying by sublimation. The Drug and Cosmetic Industry, 57, 188.

Flosdorf, E. W. 1945. High vacuum measurement with the McLeod Gage. Chem. & Met. Eng., November.

Flosdorf, E. W. 1945. Sublimation . . . its packaging requirements. Modern Packaging Magazine, November.

Flosdorf, E. W. 1946. Drying by sublimation. The Yale Scientific Magazine, 20, 10.

Flosdorf, E. W. 1947. Freeze-drying as applied to penicillin, blood plasma and orange juice. Chem. Eng. Progress, 43, 343.

Flosdorf, E. W. 1948. Hetdrogen na bevriezing. In Dutch. Technisch Bulletin, Vermolen, Den Haag, December, p. 6–8.

Folsom, T. R. 1941. An effective technique for desiccating plasma in useful quantities. The sterile unit desiccator. War Medicine, 1, 342–351.

Fox, M. and Hardgrove, M. 1940. Scarlet fever therapy. A comparison of convalescent serum and sulphanilamide. Amer. Jour. of the Med. Sciences, 199, 495–498.

Francis, T., Jr. and Salk, J. E. 1942. A simplified procedure for the concentration and purification of influenza virus. Science, 96, 499–500.

French, C. S., Holt, A. S. and Powell, R. D. 1946. The evolution of oxygen from illuminated suspensions of frozen, dried, and homogenized chloroplasts. Science, 103, 505.

Friedgood, H. B., Haagen-Smit, A. J., Garst, J. B. and Steinitz, L. 1947. The concentration and preservation of urinary substances by lyophilization. Science, 105, 99.

Friedman, C. A. and Henry, B. S. 1938. Bound water content of vegetative and spore forms of bacteria. Jour. of Bact., 36, 99.

Friedman, S. J. 1946. Drying. Industrial and Engineering Chemistry, 38, 22.

Galos, G. 1941. Changes in an osmotic system during freezing. Biodynamica, 3, 209–216.

Gehenio, P. M. and Luyet, B. J. 1939. A study of the mechanism of death by cold in the plasmodium of the myxomycetes. Biodynamica, 55, December.

General Electric Co. 1943. Storage and transfusion of blood and plasma. A bibliography of articles and publications up to January, 1943.

Gersh, I. 1934. Histochemical studies on the mammalian kidney. II. The glomerular elimination of uric acid in the rabbit. Anat. Rec., 58, No. 4 and Supplement, Mar. 25.

Goodspeed, T. H. and Uber, F. M. 1934. Application of the Altmann freezing-drying technique to plant cytology. Proceedings of the National Academy of Sciences, 20, 495–501.

Greaves, R. I. N. and Adair, M. E. 1936. A simple method for the preservation of sera by desiccation in the frozen state without the use of refrigerants. The Jour. of Hygiene, 36, 507.

Green, R. G. 1939. The use of modified distemper virus in the immunization of foxes. American Fur Breeder, August.

Green, R. G. 1939. Modification of the distemper virus. Amer. Veterinary Med. Asso., 95, 465–466.

Green, R. G., Carlson, W. E. and Swale, F. S. 1940. Vaccination of dogs with a modified distemper virus. Veterinary Medicine, 35, No. 5, May.

Green, R. G. and Stulberg, C. S. 1946. Distemperoid virus interference in canine distemper. Science, 103, 497.

Gronwall, A. and Ingelman, B. 1945. Dextran as a substitute for plasma. Nature, 155, 45.

Hale, M. W. and Walker, R. V. L. 1946. Rinderpest XIII. The production of Rinderpest Vaccine from an attenuated strain of virus. Amer. Jour. Vet. Research, VII, 199–211.

Hall, W. K., Fader, D. E. and Decherd, G. M. 1940. A simple method of preparing dried serum proteins for therapeutic use. Proceedings of the Soc. for Experimental Biology and Medicine, 44, 390–392.

Hammond, W. A. 1941. Progress and prospects in industrial drying. Catalyst, 102nd National Meeting American Chem. Soc., Sept.

Hankins, O. G., Ernst, A. J. and Kauffman, W. R. 1946. Chemical composition of raw and dehydrated meat. Food Research, 11, 501–506.

Hardgrove, M. 1941–42. Recent advances in the use of human serum and plasma. Wisconsin Med. Jour., 42, 298–302.

Hargett, M. V., Burruss, H. W. and Donovan, A. 1943. Aqueous-base yellow fever vaccine. Public Health Reports, 58, 505.

Harper, S. B., Essex, H. E. and Osterberg, A. E. 1940. The preparation and experimental use of dried blood plasma. Proceedings of the Staff Meetings of the Mayo Clinic, 15, 689.

Hartley, P. 1935. International Biological Standards. The Pharmaceutical Jour., December 14.

Hartley, P. 1936. B. Report on the international biological standards maintained at the National Institute for Medical Research, Hampstead, London, on behalf of the Health Organization of the League of Nations. Quarterly Bulletin of the Health Organization of the League of Nations, 5, Extract No. 29.

Hartley, P. 1937. D. A simple laboratory method for the desiccation of serum and other protein solutions. Quarterly Bulletin of the Health Organization of the League of Nations, 5, Extract No. 31.

Hauge, S. M. and Zscheile, F. P. 1942. The effect of dehydration upon the vitamin A content of eggs. Science, 96, 536.

Havens, W. P., Jr. and Paul, J. R. 1945. Prevention of infectious hepatitis with gamma globulin. Jour. Amer. Med. Asso., 129, 270.

Hay, E. C. 1946. The adrenotrophic renotrophic and cardiotrophic activities of lyophilized anterior pituitary in thyroidectomized rats. Amer. Jour. of the Med. Sciences, 212, 535–537.

Hays, E. E. and Koch, F. C. 1942. An apparatus for vacuum drying in the frozen state. Science, 95, 633.

Henry, B. S. and Friedman, C. A. 1937. The water content of bacterial spores. Jour. of Bact., 33, 323.

Hill, J. M. 1940. The intravenous use of concentrated plasma prepared by the Adtevac process. Texas State Jour. of Med., 36, 223–225.

Hill, J. M. and Muirhead, E. E. 1942. Desiccated plasma for national defense. The Jour. of Lab. and Clin. Med., St. Louis, 27, 812–819.

Hirschmann, D. J. and Lightbody, H. D. 1947. Resazurin reduction test and microbiology of egg powders prepared by lyophilization. Food Research, 12, 372–380.

Hirschmann, D. J. and Lightbody, H. D. 1947. Effect of bacteria on quality of stored lyophilized egg powders. Food Research, 12, 381–392.

Hirst, G. K., Rickard, E. R. and Friedewald, W. F. 1944. Studies in human immunization against influenza. Duration of immunity induced by inactive virus. The Jour. of Exptl. Med., 80, 265–273.

Hoagland, R. and Snider, G. G. 1946. Nutritive value of protein in dehydrated meat. Food Research, 11, 494–500.

Hoerr, N. L. 1936. Cytological studies by the Altmann-Gersh freezing-drying method. II. The mechanism of secretion of hydrochloric acid in the gastric mucosa. Anat. Rec., 65, 417.

Hoffman, W. S., Kozoll, D. D., Mok, W. T., Meyer, K. A. and Poppei, H. 1948. The determination of the nitrogen balance index of a new lyophilized amino acid preparation in protein-deficient patients. The Jour. of Lab. and Clin. Med., 33, 280.

Hoyt, R. E. and Levine, M. 1943. An improved method for concentrating serum and plasma in cellophane casings. Amer. Jour. of Clin. Path., 13, 105.

Hunt, A. B. and Osterber, A. E. 1942. The persistence of gonadotropin in dried pregnancy serum of human beings. Proceedings of the Staff Meetings of the Mayo Clinic, 17, 401.

Husband, M. W. and Loy, D. T. 1937. Immunity to smallpox. The Jour. of the Amer. Med. Asso., 109, 1797–1798.

Hydén, H. 1947. The nucleoproteins in virus reproduction. Cold Spring Harbor Symposia Quant. Biol., 12, 104–114.

Hyland, C. M. 1937. The value of convalescent serum in the acute contagious diseases. The Nebraska State Med. Jour., 22, 342.

Hyland, C. M. and Anderson, L. R. 1937. Prophylactic and therapeutic use of scarlet fever convalescent serum. Amer. Jour. of Diseases of Children, 54, 504–519.

Irvin, J. L., Merker, H., Anderson, C. E. and Johnston, C. G. 1939. The comparison of desiccated and normal hog gall-bladder bile. The Jour. of Biol. Chem., 131, 439.

Johnson, B. and Lerrigo, A. F. 1947. Crystalline sodium penicillin G. Some observations on its stability in solution and on related matters. Analytical Dept., Glaxo Laboratories, Ltd., July 29.

Johnston, F. B. 1943. Rapid moisture determination in dehydrated foods. Canadian Chemistry and Process Industries, Feb.

Joslyn, M. A. and Marsh, G. L. 1933. Changes occurring during freezing storage and thawing of fruits and vegetables. University of California Agricultural Experiment Station, Bulletin 551.

Kark, R., White, F. W., Souter, A. W. and Deutsch, E. 1941. Blood prothrombin levels and hippuric acid excretion liver function test in liver disease. Proceedings of the Soc. for Exptl. Biol. and Med., 46, 424–426.

Kazal, L. A., Higashi, A., DeYoung, M., Brahinsky, R. and Barnes, R. H. 1946. Horse brain thromboplastin. IV. Stabilization of activity of dried brain preparations. Archives of Biochemistry, 10, 183–193.

Keinosuke, Isiguro. 1941. Preservation of complement by drying it from the frozen state. Japan J. Med. Sci. VI. Bact. Parasitol., 2, 9–25; C. A., 36, 5, 1382.

Kendrick, D. B., Jr. and Newhouser, L. R. 1942. Blood substitutes in the military service. Military Surgeon, *90*, 306–315.

Knox, R. 1939. Desiccation of filterable tumours and other biological materials. The Jour. of Path. and Bact., *49*, 467–481.

Knudsen, M. 1910. Annalen der Physik, *31*, 205.

Kraybill, H. R. 1943. The dehydration of meat. Proceedings of Institute of Food Technologists, pages 90–94.

Krejci, L. E. 1942. The effect of drying from the frozen state on the physicochemical properties of citrated human blood plasma. J. Franklin Inst., *234*, 596–605.

Kyes, P. and Potter, T. S. 1939. The resistance of avian tubercle bacilli to low temperatures with especial reference to multiple changes in temperature. Jour. of Infectious Diseases, *64*, 123–134.

Ladenburg, K. and Redniss, A. 1948. Modern drying techniques solve many processing problems. Chemical Industries, October, pp. 598–603.

LaLande, W. A., Jr., McCarter, W. S. W. and Sanborn, J. B. 1944. Bauxite as a drying adsorbent. Industrial and Engineering Chemistry, *36*, 99.

LaMer, V. K. 1937. The energy of activation of protein denaturations. Science, *86*, 614–616.

Landis, E. M., Jeffers, W. A. and Shiels, E. 1938–9. The pressor effects of heterologous injections of heated kidney extracts. Proceedings of the Physiol. Soc. of Phila., *14*, 16.

Landsteiner, K., Longsworth, L. G. and van der Scheer, J. 1938. Electrophoresis experiments with egg albumins and hemoglobins. Science, *88*, 83–85.

Langner, P. H., Jr. and Kern, R. A. 1940. Studies on extracts made from pollens ground in a ball mill. The Jour. of Allergy, *11*, 488–493.

Lerche, M. and Hepp, L. 1940. Preserving blood plasma. Z. Fleisch- u. Milchhyg. *50*, 183–187; Chem. Zentr., *2*, 701.

Lewis, E. G. 1944. Demonstration of the liquid processing and drying of human transfusion serum and discussion of some quantitative aspects of dosage. The Proceedings of the Transvaal Mine Medical Officers' Association, *23*, 120.

Longfellow, D. and Luippold, G. F. 1943. Immunization to typhoid and paratyphoid fevers. The Amer. Jour. of Hygiene, *38*, 139.

Lopez, R. C. 1946. Liofilizacion de la alexina previamente estabilizada. Thesis, Universidad Nacional Autonoma de Mexico, Escuela National de Ciencias Quimicas, Mexico, pp. 1–52.

Luetscher, J. A., Jr. 1944. The effect of a single injection of concentrated human serum albumin on circulating proteins and proteinuria in nephrosis. The Jour. of Clin. Invest., 23, 365–371.

Luyet, B. J. 1937. The vitrification of organic colloids and of protoplasm. Biodynamica, No. 29, December.

Luyet, B. J. and Hodapp, E. L. 1938. Revival of frog's spermatozoa vitrified in liquid air. Proceedings of the Soc. for Exptl. Biol. and Med., 39, 433–434.

Luyet, B. J. and Condon, H. M. 1938. Temperature relationships and ice-water proportions during death by freezing in plant tissues. Biodynamica, No. 37, May.

Luyet, B. J. and Hodapp, E. L. 1938. On the effect of mechanical shocks on the congelation of subcooled plant tissues. Protoplasma, 30, 254.

Luyet, B. et Thoennes, G. 1938. Demonstration des proprietes isotropiques de masses cellulaires vitrifiees a la temperature de l'air liquide. Comptes rendus des seances de l'Academie des Sciences, 206, 2002.

Luyet, B. J. and Thoennes, G. 1938. The survival of plant cells immersed in liquid air. Science, 88, 284.

Luyet, B. J. and Gehenio, P. M. 1938. The survival of moss vitrified in liquid air and its relation to water content. Biodynamica, No. 42, November.

Luyet, B. et Thoennes, G. 1938. La reviviscence de fibres musculaires vitrifiees dans l'air liquide. Comptes rendus des seances de l'Academie des Sciences, 207, 1256.

Luyet, B. J. 1939. The devitrification temperatures of solutions of a carbohydrate series. The Jour. of Physical Chem., 43, 881.

Luyet, B. J. 1939. Vitrification of water. The Physical Review, 46, No. 12, 1244.

Luyet, B. J. and Galos, G. 1940. The effect of the rate of cooling on the freezing point of living tissues. Biodynamica, 3, 157.

Macchiavello, A. 1943. Concentrated convalescent serum in the treatment of exanthematic typhus, mumps, measles and chickenpox. Revista de la Facultad de Medicina, Bogota, 11, 567–630.

Mears, W. H. 1938. The oxygen exchange reaction of glycine hydrochloride and water. The Jour. of Chem. Physics, 6, No. 5, May.

Mears, W. H. and Sobotka, H. 1939. Heavy oxygen exchange reactions of proteins and amino acids. Jour. of the Amer. Chem. Soc., 61, 880.

McGuinness, A. C., Stokes, J., Jr. and Mudd, S. 1937. The clinical uses of human serums preserved by the lyophile process. The Jour. of Clin. Invest., *16*, 185.

Mohammed, A. H. 1944. Notes on the toxins of Egyptian scorpions. Biochem. J., Lond., *38*, 284.

Moore, E. and Thalhimer, W. 1939. Immunologic properties of scarlatina convalescent serum. Amer. Jour. of Diseases of Children, *58*, 1039.

Morell, S. and Shwartzman, G. 1937. The use of dialysis in the preparation and purification of immunologically active bacterial products. Science, *86*, 130.

Morley, A. H. 1945. Attenuation of measles. Brit. M. J., *1*, 923.

Morrison, D. B. and Hisey, A. 1937. The preparation of hemoglobin in a dry and active state. The Jour. of Biol. Chem., *117*, 693.

Morse, R. S. 1948. High vacuum dehydration and distillation. Chemistry and Industry Supplement, October 9, P. S-13.

Morton, A. A., Mahoney, J. F. and Richardson, G. 1939. Vacuum sublimation and molecular distillation apparatus. Analytical Edition, Industrial and Engineering Chem., *11*, 460.

Morton, H. E. and Pulaski, E. J. 1938. The preservation of bacterial cultures. I. Jour. Bact., *35*, No. 2, 163.

Morton, H. E. 1938. The preservation of bacterial cultures. II. Summary of methods. Amer. Jour. of Clin. Path., *8*, 243.

Mudd, S., Shaw, C. H., Czarnetsky, E. J. and Flosdorf, E. W. 1937. A low temperature ball-mill for the liberation of labile cellular products. The Jour. of Immunol., *32*, 483.

Mudd, S. and Flosdorf, E. W. 1941. Blood and blood substitutes in the treatment of hemorrhage, secondary shock and burns. New England Jour. of Medicine, *225*, 868–870.

Mukherjee, J. N. and Majumdar, B. R. 1943. Standard state of desiccation of dried blood plasma and the advantages of desiccation in the region of molecular flow. Indian J. Phys., *17*, No. 4, August.

Nymon, M. C., Gunsalus, I. C. and Gortner, W. A. 1945. An application of the lyophile process to the maintenance of cultures for microbiological assay. Science, *102*, 125.

Olive, T. R. 1943. Introduction to high vacuum in chemical industries. Chem. & Met. Eng., October, page 102.

Orent-Keiles, E., Hewston, E. M. and Butler, L. 1946. Effects of different methods of dehydration on vitamin and mineral value of meats. Food Research, *11*, 486–493.

Pauling, L. 1946. Analogies between antibodies and simpler chemical substances. Chemical and Engineering News, 24, 1064.

Perlmann, G. E. and Kaufman, D. 1945. The effect of ionic strength and protein concentration in the electrophoretic analysis of human plasma. Jour. of the Amer. Chem. Soc., 67, 638.

Pettit, H., Mudd, S. and Pepper, D. S. 1936. The Philadelphia and Alaska strains of influenza virus. The Jour. of the Amer. Med. Asso., 106, 890–892.

Pettit, H. and Stokes, J., Jr. 1937. The present status of the prevention and treatment of influenza. Amer. Jour. of the Med. Sciences, 193, 423.

Pfeiffer, D. C. 1943. An engineering discussion of the desiccation of human blood plasma. Mechanical Engineering, September.

Pillemer, L. and Ecker, E. E. 1938. A preliminary report on the specificity of keratins. Science, 88, 16–17.

Polding, J. B. 1943. A simple method of preserving bacteria dried in vacuo. The Jour. of Path. and Bact., 55, 502, 503.

Pomes, A. F. and Irving, G. W., Jr. 1945. Lyophilization apparatus. Science, 101, 22.

Prescott, S. C. and Tanner, F. W. 1938. Microbiology in relation to food preservation. Food Research, 3, 189.

Rahn, O. 1945. Physical methods of sterilization of micro-organisms. Bacteriological Reviews, 9, 1–47.

Railton, I. R., Cunningham, B. and Kirk, P. L. 1941. The preparation of sterile proteins in the "lyophiled" state. Science, 94, 469–470.

Raper, K. B. and Alexander, D. F. 1945. Frozen dehydration preserves mold cultures. Drug Trade News, Mfg. Sect., July 16, p. 52.

Rayner, A. G. 1943. A simple method for the preservation of cultures and sera by drying. The Jour. of Path. and Bact., 55, 373, 375.

Roberts, E. C., Cain, C. K., Muir, R. D., Reithel, F. J., Gaby, W. L., VanBruggen, J. T., Homan, D. M., Katzman, P. A., Jones, L. R. and Doisy, E. A. 1943. Penicillin B, an antibacterial substance from penicillium notatum. The Jour. of Biol. Chem., 147, 47.

Rowntree, L. G., Clark, J. H., Hanson, A. M. and Steinberg, A. 1935. Biologic effects of thymus extract (Hanson). Archives of Internal Medicine, 56, 1–29.

Rowntree, L. G. 1935. Further studies on the thymus and pineal glands. Proceedings, Inter-State Postgraduate Medical Assembly of North America.

Rudolph, J. A. 1943. Serum reactions: A working classification. Military Surgeon, 93, 473.

Schade, A. L. and Caroline, L. 1944. Raw hen egg white and the role of iron in growth inhibition of shigella dysenteriae, staphylococcus aureus, escherichia coli and saccharomyces cerevisiae. Science, 100, 14.

Schade, A. L. and Caroline, L. 1944. The preparation of a polyvalent dysentery bacteriophage in a dry and stable form. II. Factors affecting the stabilization of dysentery bacteriophage during lyophilization. Jour. of Bact., 48, 179.

Schade, A. L. and Caroline, L. 1944. The preparation of a polyvalent dysentery bacteriophage in a dry and stable form. III. Stability of the dried bacteriophage towards heat, humidity, age and acidity.

Schaffer, N. K., Ziegler, W. M. and Rowntree, L. G. 1938. Certain iodine-reducing substances of thymus extract. Endocrinology, 23, 593.

Scherp, H. W. and Hughes, T. P. 1939. A simple and inexpensive apparatus for the desiccation of biological materials from the frozen state. The Jour. of Immunol., 36, 29.

Seegers, W. H. 1945. Arrangement for drying proteins from the frozen state. Science, 101, 284.

Seibert, F. 1943. Protein chemistry in tuberculosis. The Catalyst, January, p. 4.

Shaughnessy, H. J. and Zichis, J. 1943. Prevention of experimental rabies. The Jour. of the Amer. Med. Asso., 123, 528.

Siedentopf, H. and Levine, M. 1942. An apparatus for continuous filtration in blood and plasma transfusions. Science, 96, 303.

Smith, C. A. 1942. Human milk technology. Jour. of Pediatrics, 20, 616.

Smith, D. E., Czarnetzky, E. J. and Mudd, S. 1936. The mechanism of inactivation of mercurial antiseptics by serum, and its implications regarding the possibility of intravenous antisepsis. Amer. Jour. of the Med. Sciences, 192, 790.

Smith, G. F. 1930. Drying agents. A comparison of their values as a function of physical and chemical properties. Published by J. T. Baker Chemical Co., Phillipsburg, N. J.

Solomon, E. M. 1944. Human serum treatment of atypical pneumonia. Jour. of Lab. and Clin. Med., 29, 493.

Stahl, A. L. 1944. Citrus fruit juice concentration. Science Supplement, 99, 10.

Steinberg, A. 1938. A modified and improved method for the preparation of thymus extract. Endocrinology, 23, 581.

Stevens, D. S. 1938. A low-temperature evaporator. The Jour. of Lab. and Clin. Med., 23, 978–979.

Stokes, J., Jr., McGuinness, A. C., Langner, P. H., Jr. and Shaw, D. R. 1937. Vaccination against epidemic influenza with active virus of human influenza. Amer. Jour. of the Med. Sciences, 194, 757.

Strickler, H. S. and Shaffer, C. B. 1948. On the use of the Campbell-Pressman lyophilizing apparatus for urinary extractives. Science, January 16, p. 71.

Strumia, M. M. and McGraw, John J. 1942. Blood plasma. Jour. of the Amer. Med. Asso., 118, 427.

Strumia, M. M. 1942. Preservation of prothrombin in dried plasma. The Jour. of the Amer. Med. Asso., 119, 710.

Strumia, M. M. 1942. The role of low temperature in the preservation of plasma. Refrigerating Engineering, September, page 154.

Strumia, M. M. and McGraw, J. J. 1942–3. A method and apparatus for shell freezing and rapid drying of plasma and other products from the frozen state by low temperature water vapor condensation in vacuo. Jour. Lab. and Clin. Med., 28, 1140–1155.

Stull, A., Glidden, M. and Loveless, M. 1936. Protein content of human serums. The Jour. of Allergy, 7, 333.

Swift, H. F. 1922. The preservation of stock cultures of bacteria by freezing and drying. Int. Asso. of Medical Museums, Bull. 8, 128–132.

Swift, H. F. 1937. A simple method for preserving bacterial cultures by freezing and drying. The Jour. of Bact., 33, 411.

Taylor, A. C. 1944. Apparatus for the freezing-drying of tissues for storage. The Jour. of Lab. and Clin. Med., 29, 657.

Taylor, A. C. 1945. The rates of freezing, drying and rehydration of nerves. J. Cell. and Comp. Physiol., 25, 161.

Taylor, A. R. and Beard, J. W. 1940. An inexpensive apparatus for drying from the frozen state. Science, 92, 611.

Thalhimer, W. 1938. A simple inexpensive method for concentrating serum under sterile conditions. Proceedings of the Soc. for Exptl. Biol. and Med., 37, 639.

Thalhimer, W. and Stillerman, M. 1939. Prevention and modification of measles with concentrated pooled ascites fluid and with its globulin fraction. Proceedings of the Soc. for Exptl. Biol. and Med., 42, 683.

Thalhimer, W. 1943. Blood typing and criteria for blood-typing serums. Jour. of Pediatrics, 23, 714.

Thoennes, G. 1940. Properties of muscle fibers subjected to vitrification by extremely rapid cooling. Biodynamica, 3, 145.

Thompson, W. D., Ravdin, I. S. and Frank, I. L. 1938. Effect of hypoproteinemia on wound disruption. Archives of Surgery, 36, 500.

Thompson, W. D., Ravdin, I. S., Rhoads, J. E. and Frank, I. L. 1938. Use of lyophile plasma in correction of hypoproteinemia and prevention of wound disruption. Archives of Surgery, 36, 509.

Toomey, J. A., Lewis, N., Averill, E., Drury, W. and Takacs, W. S. 1944. Active and passive immunity in experimental hemophilus pertussis infection in mice. The Jour. of Lab. and Clin. Med., 29, 21.

Tui, C. and Wright, A. M. 1942. The preparation of nonpyrogenic infusion and other intravenous fluids by adsorptive filtration. Annals of Surgery, 116, 412.

Tui, C. 1944. Practical aspects of pyrogen problems. Jour. of the Amer. Pharmaceutical Association, Practical Pharmacy Edition, 5, 60.

Turner, T. B. 1938. The preservation of virulent treponema pallidum and treponema pertenue in the frozen state; with a note on the preservation of filtrable viruses. The Jour. of Exptl. Med., 67, 61.

VanBruggen, J. T., Reithel, F. J., Cain, C. K., Katzman, P. A. and Doisy, E. A. 1943. Penicillin B: Preparation, purification, and mode of action. The Jour. of Biol. Chem., 148, 365.

VanBruggen, J. T. 1946. A rapid method for drying oxalate solutions. Astoria Extension Research Lab. Dept. of Biochemistry, University of Oregon Medical School.

Walder, H. J. and Gradis, H. E. 1944. An improved method for collecting, centrifuging and pooling blood plasma. Annals of Surgery, 120, 785.

Watts, P. S. 1945. The effect of humidity on the survival of dried cultures of streptococcus agalactiae. The Jour. of Path. and Bact., 57, 191.

Weiser, R. S. and Osterud, C. M. 1945. Studies on the death of bacteria at low temperatures. I. The influence of the intensity of the freezing temperature, repeated fluctuations of temperature, and the period of exposure to freezing temperatures on the mortality of Escherichia coli. Jour. of Bact., 50, 413–439.

Weiser, R. S. and Hargiss, C. O. 1946. Studies on the death of bacteria at low temperatures. II. The comparative effects of crystallization, vitromelting, and devitrification on the mortality of Escherichia coli. Jour. of Bact., 52, 71–79.

Weiss, P. 1944. Frozen-dried nerve grafts. The Jour. Amer. Med. Asso., *124*, 1063.

Wertman, K. and Plotz, H. 1944. Presence of typhus antibodies in commercial frozen and dried complement. Proceedings of the Soc. for Exptl. Biol. and Med., *55*, 29.

Whitmore, R. A., Seligson, D., Kraybill, H. R. and Webb, B. H. 1948. Packaging dehydrated meat. Food Research. January–February.

Williard and Smith, G. F. 1922. Anhydrous magnesium perchlorate. J. Amer. Chem. Soc., *44*, 2255.

Woodard, W. A. 1947. Crystalline sodium penicillin G in pharmaceutical preparations. Research Division, Glaxo Laboratories, Ltd.

Wyckoff, R. W. G. 1945. Some biophysical problems of viruses. Science, *101*, 129.

Zittle, C. A., Devlin, H. B., Rodney, G. and Welcke, M. 1945. Removal of bacterial pyrogens from protein hydrolysates. The Jour. of Lab. and Clin. Med., *30*, 75.

AUTHOR INDEX

SUBJECT INDEX